D1060531

STUDIES IN HISTORY, ECONOMICS AND
PUBLIC LAW

Edited by the

FACULTY OF POLITICAL SCIENCE
OF COLUMBIA UNIVERSITY

———

NUMBER 402

COSMOGONIES OF OUR FATHERS

SOME THEORIES OF THE SEVENTEENTH AND THE
EIGHTEENTH CENTURIES

BY

KATHARINE BROWNELL COLLIER

COSMOGONIES
OF
OUR FATHERS

Some Theories of the Seventeenth and the
Eighteenth Centuries

by

KATHARINE BROWNELL COLLIER

1968
OCTAGON BOOKS, INC.
New York

To my Mother

TABLE OF CONTENTS

PART I

GENERAL SURVEY

CHAPTER I

THE CONFLICT OF SYSTEMS

THE history of thought is in large part the attempt to interpret old knowledge and dogma by the light of new discoveries. Frequently such exposition has taken the form of an effort to reconcile the doctrines of ancient religious teachers with the more recent conclusions of science. The seventeenth and the eighteenth centuries present clearly a typical example of such a controversy with the customary bitter words, aspersions upon character and even persecutions directed against the champions of innovation. Almost universal hostility to the heliocentric astronomy of Copernicus, Kepler and Newton and to the enlarged view of Wright and Kant, which subordinated the solar system to a greater whole, was aroused by the belief that such theories conflicted with revealed statements in the Bible implying a geocentric, or perhaps homocentric, universe, created by God from nothing in six days. Gradually, as proofs accumulated, the hostility was replaced by marvelous hypotheses explaining the Biblical text in terms of the new truths, and finally by acceptance as axiomatic of the scientific principles involved.

The painful readjustment necessitated by so radical a change in scientific and religious beliefs produces four types of reaction, probably due to differences in the temperaments and the previous ideas of the individuals concerned. The first type is a vigorous rejection of all new thought that does not square with the old; the second, a discarding of all the old because of its apparent disagreement with the new; the third, a peculiar arrangement of the mind in thought-tight

13

compartments to prevent any influence from one set of doctrines upon another; and the fourth, an attempt to harmonize the new with the old thought. The third reaction is unquestionably the least disturbing and has in all ages been the resort of countless men in the semi-scientific professions, such as medicine, while the fourth is both the most interesting and the most prolific in controversial literature. The seventeenth and the eighteenth centuries present examples of all these methods for treating new facts; but I shall deal chiefly with illustrations of the fourth group, the authors of which produced the greatest volume of commentary. I shall discuss various attempts at harmonization of the new scientific theories with the Biblical statements concerning the nature of the universe, especially with reference to the account of creation in the first two chapters of Genesis. Since several authors associated with their hypotheses of creation and the nature of the universe the Scriptural accounts of the deluge, the final conflagration and the fate of the world, these topics will also be touched upon. Unless the deluge and the final conflagration were denied or attributed to miraculous interventions by God, involving, presumably, the unpopular doctrine that matter could be newly created and later annihilated, these two catastrophes had to be explained by secondary causes consistent with the theory of creation advanced. Therefore the theory had to take them into consideration. Even though the secondary causes were believed to be set in motion by God, or, as was sometimes asserted, though their action was suspended by Him, nevertheless, the constitution of the earth had to be so conceived that the results were plausible.

In the seventeenth and the eighteenth centuries authors clearly perceived this necessity, and the most logical tended to explain the original creation of the earth and its re-formation after the flood as due to the same causes and proceeding by the same steps until the development of plants and animals was reached. Many writers asserted that the forces which produced the deluge reduced the earth to its original chaotic condition. The two groups of topics were so intricately entwined that the account of creation cannot be separated from the account of the deluge without distortion. Therefore, I shall treat of the reciprocal effects of scientific and Scriptural doctrines as illustrated in the account of the deluge as well as in that of creation. Although numerous books discuss the main stream of discovery and thought, such backwaters and eddies as were caused by the attempt to reconcile the new and the old beliefs, while important in their day, are seldom mentioned in our day. A recapitulation of these forgotten hypotheses, which deflected multitudes from the main course of their centuries' intellectual progress, is perhaps useful as an illustration of the way in which misleading paths are followed when new truths reveal themselves.

Although Copernicus published his book *De Revolutionibus* in 1543, it was not until the advertisement of the theory by Bruno fifty years later and its even more effective exposition by Galileo during the first decades of the seventeenth century that the theory attracted much attention. The earliest readers seem not to have perceived its implications. During the seventeenth and the eighteenth centuries, however, the corollaries to the theory with their applications to dogmas derived from the Bible were no longer obscure. They stirred Europe to its intellectual foundations and produced repercussions across the Atlantic. The triumph of the doctrines enunciated by Copernicus, Kepler and Newton may be considered complete when the Roman Catholic Church tacitly sanctioned them in 1835 by removing Copernicus's works and those composed by other supporters of the new astronomy from the *Index Librorum Prohibi-*

torum.   Naturally the attempts to harmonize the heliocentric theory with Genesis had a shorter history, which fell well within the two centuries and reached its period of greatest importance close to 1700.   One method still in vogue was the narrative of the events during the six days of creation with a commentary upon the Biblical terminology.   These Hexaemerons are direct descendants of those written by so many of the Church Fathers.   A work of this nature by two Catholic abbés went through several editions even so late as 1740.[1]

The best material on the harmonization of new scientific theses with the Bible is in English, the work of clergymen or doctors.   Evidently the ministers were interested as theologians, and the physicians as scientists.   Perhaps the condemnation of Galileo prevented in Catholic countries the promulgation or even the conception of elaborate theories contrary to the accepted doctrines of the Church.   Descartes set forth such a theory; but he felt it necessary to publish his *Principles* in Holland, and did not escape severe reprobation in spite of his explanation that he was merely showing how the world might have been created, and that according to his theory the earth did not move since it still remained in the same relative position to the surrounding particles of the solar vortex.[2]

Somewhat earlier Marin Mersenne (1588-1648), a Franciscan with considerable knowledge of mathematics and of music, who wrote a commentary on Genesis, discussed many such topics.   Though alive to new scientific discoveries, such as the Jovial satellites, the phases of Venus and of Mercury, the supra lunar position of comets and the use of telescopes,

[1] Duguet and d'Asfeld, *Explication de l'ouvrage des six jours* (Paris, 1740).

[2] Descartes, *Oeuvres* (Paris, 1824), vol. iii, *Les principes de la philosophie*, especially parts iii and iv (1st ed., Amsterdam, 1644).

and interested in such reports as the *Sidereus Nuncius* of Galileo and Kepler's discussion of the Martian orbit, Mersenne presented no unified picture of the cosmos, and at the same time concealed his own views modestly and efficiently behind the doctrines of his predecessors. However, he did make some definite statements. Although he said that the astronomical mathematics he presented was true for all three of the current world systems, those promulgated by Ptolemy, by Tycho Brahe and by Copernicus and Kepler, he repeatedly declared that the earth remained motionless at the center of the universe. The arguments with which he attempted to prove this thesis were largely Scriptural. Nevertheless, he left a loop-hole for changed views, for he mentioned that the Church had not yet assembled a Council to discuss and affirm or reject the mobility of the earth. He believed that the firmament or stellar heaven was a solid sphere, though probably he thought that the lower heavens were liquid. To this stellar sphere he ascribed a distance from the earth equal to 14,000 semi-diameters of the earth, in accordance with the calculations by Tycho Brahe. Beyond it he located the waters which were raised at creation. Not only at the outmost bounds of the universe was a store of water, but also at the center. Below the surface of the earth it formed an abyss, clearly the source of all springs. From both came the waters which submerged the earth in the days of Noah.[3]

---

[3] Mersenne, *Novarvm Observationvm Physico-mathematicarvm Tomvs III. Qvibvs accessit Aristarchvs Samivs De Mvndi Systemate* (Paris, 1647); Mersenne, *Vniversae Geometriae, Mixtaeqve Mathematicae Synopsis* (Paris, 1644), p. 258; Mersenne, *Les prelvdes de l'harmonie vniverselle, ov qvestions cvrievses* (Paris, 1634), pp. 1-135, 210-228; Mersenne, *Qvaestiones Celeberrimae in Genesim* (Paris, 1623), pt. i, cols. 79, 80, 112, 799-804, 807-826, 831-849, 869, 872, 879-920, 1007, 1013, 1075b, 1076b, 1513-1572, 1607-1712, pt. ii, col. 111.

Riccioli, a Jesuit to whom the order entrusted the defense of its position, devoted nearly one-third of his astronomy to a summary of the Ptolemaic, the Tychonic and the Copernican systems, together with his own, which resembled the Tychonic. He gave a most equitable statement of the arguments on each side.[4] In fact, his arguments for the theory which he named Copernican are so strong that evidently the only influence that deterred him from its acceptance was the decision of the Church. He even admitted that the scientific evidence favored the mobility of the earth, but asserted that the Bible and the Fathers obviously declared for the motion of the sun and the central position of the earth. Nevertheless, he seemed not wholly convinced of terrestrial immobility and location at the center of the universe. In the discussion of Joshua's miracle he stated that all agreed in regarding it as a real cessation in motion of the solar body, or of the earth, if the Copernicans were correct.[5] Gassendi's *Institutio,* a favorite textbook on astronomy during the period of uncertainty, wavered between the Tychonic and the Copernican hypotheses.[6]

Even so late as 1769, at the demand of the Sorbonne, which called his theories contrary to the accepted dogmas of the Church, Buffon recanted the ideas about the formation of the earth that he had enunciated in an earlier edition.[7] Most

[4] Riccioli, *Almagestvm Novvm Astronomiam Veterem Novamqve Complectens* (Bologna, 1651), vol. i, pp. 49-52, 505-631; vol. ii, pp. 247-500.

[5] *Ibid.,* vol. ii, pp. 478-482, 485, 486.

[6] Gassendi, *Institutio Astronomica Juxta Hypotheses tam Veterum quam Copernici & Tychonis* (Amsterdam, 1680). (Revised by the author and published posthumously.)

[7] Jéhan, *Dictionnaire de cosmogonie et de paléontologie* (Paris, 1854), art. "Géologie (Histoire de la)", cols. 635, 636. The date of the letter from the Sorbonne was January, 1751. Both the original theses and the recantation were in the *Histoire naturelle,* which was published at intervals. The controversial matter was printed as early as 1749, chiefly in the

Catholic scientists expressed themselves cautiously or did not treat of controversial subjects. The result of this tendency is a poverty of material from Catholic sources. In the Protestant countries on the continent the influence of Luther, Melanchthon and Calvin, who opposed or at best ignored Copernicus,[8] was more potent than in England. The great emphasis placed by Protestants upon the Bible naturally produced a conservative attitude toward scientific discoveries that seemed to contradict it. Nevertheless, the diversity of sects among the Protestants and perhaps the emphasis, inherent in their rebellion, upon the validity of individual Scriptural interpretation reacted upon later church leaders. Whatever the cause, it is unquestionably true that the volume of scientific hypotheses relating to topics treated in the Bible from Protestant sources, and even their quality, is superior to that emanating from Catholics, at least during the seventeenth and the eighteenth centuries.

Another influence in England that may have aided the profuse production of printed matter, from pamphlets to folios, was the secular tone of the English clergy from the Restoration to the French Revolution. Goldsmith pictured the ideal clergyman in the middle of the eighteenth century as passing his days in hunting, playing backgammon, writing tracts and listening to his daughters' singing. If his was a poor country parish, he added to his occupations manual agricultural labor on a rented farm. His chief clerical duties other than reading the service and preaching short sermons on Sunday seemed to be dispensing hospitality to all and urging his parishioners to marry young and to avoid ale

Théorie de la terre; the recantation, in an edition printed in Paris in 1769, vol. v.

[8] Stimson, *The Gradual Acceptance of the Copernican Theory of the Universe* (Hanover, N. H., 1917), pp. 39-41.

houses.[9]   Even in the more serious presentation of clerical
life in *The Deserted Village* [10] Goldsmith mentioned only
cursorily visitation of the sick and the dying and guidance
of his parishioners into paths of righteousness.   Ambitious
clergymen apparently sought to recommend themselves to
their superiors by publishing in ponderous volumes hypotheses that harmonized religion and science.   Addison gave
a humorous account of the greater honor paid to the authors
of larger books.   The author of a folio set himself above
him who had produced merely a quarto, and he in turn
lorded it over the writer of a smaller volume.   At the lowest end of the scale in both his own estimation and that of
the public was the author of ephemeral pamphlets and single
sheets.   On the other hand, one might improve his position
by the production of many works.   Addison calculated that
the publication of six octavos was equal to that of one
quarto, and congratulated himself on the imminent appearance of a new volume that contained the recent *Spectator*
papers.[11]

Most of the comment on the so-called Copernician theory
before 1650 was unfavorable.   The Humanists, who had in
general captured the universities, were even more attached
to the Ptolemaic theory than their predecessors.   Late in
the sixteenth century Tycho Brahe had advocated the belief
that the earth was the center of the universe, around which
revolved the sun, the moon and the eighth sphere, while the
sun was the center for the orbits of the other planets.   In
1644, when Descartes published his theory, he said that the
Tychonic doctrine was generally received by those who

[9] Goldsmith, *The Vicar of Wakefield* (1st ed., London, 1766), especially chap. ii.

[10] 1st edition, London, 1770.

[11] *The Spectator* (London and New York, 1898), no. 529, Nov. 6,
1712, vol. vii, pp. 270, 271.

rejected Copernicus.[12] Especially on the continent and among Catholics the Tychonic compromise and the adaptations of it by such men as Riccioli, as well as Descartes's own system, served as stepping stones to the full acceptance of the heliocentric belief as developed by Copernicus, Kepler and Newton. In the period before Descartes an overwhelming preponderance of opinion appeared for the Ptolemaic system; in the twenty years 1650-1670 the advantage of the Tychonic or semi-Tychonic over the earlier belief, at least in the importance of its advocates, was evident; but before the close of the century the heliocentric system had advanced from support by the well-nigh solitary figures of Kepler, Descartes and Hobbes to practically universal acceptance. In the eighteenth century almost no one opposed the main trend "except rustics, laborers, and women, all of them illiterate." [13]

Before and even after the publication in 1687 of Newton's theory on the universality of gravitation,—an event that seems to have struck the decisive blow on behalf of the heliocentric system,—one popular method of discussion was the presentation of all three accounts, sometimes without decision as to the most probable. Francis Bacon said: " The same phenomena, the same calculations, are compatible with

---

[12] Descartes, op. cit., Les principes de la philosophie, pt. iii, sec. 38.

[13] Heyn, Specimen Cometologiae Sacrae (Leipzig, 1742), p. 10, " excipio tamen rusticôs, opifices, mulierculas, expertes litterarum omnes." Though this remark was made by one of Heyn's pupils, Heyn accepted responsibility for the ideas expressed in the book. At the time he was rector in the university in Brandenburg. Similar assertions were made in England by Cudworth, The True Intellectual System of the Universe (London, 1743) (1st ed., 1678), preface, p. xxix; in France in the Lettre de M. de Castelet à Monsieur Mallement de Messange sur les deux nouveaux systhémes qu'ils ont inventez (Paris?, 1679?), p. 6; in Holland by Huygens, Nouveau traité de la pluralité des mondes (Amsterdam, 1718) (1st published, 1698), pp. ix, xii, 1, 2; and in Germany by Wolf, Cosmologia Generalis (Frankfurt and Leipzig, 1737) (2nd? edition), p. 61.

the astronomical principles both of Ptolemy and Copernicus ",[14] but in the same book he declared the diurnal motion of the earth most false.[15]

The more or less impartial presentation of the Ptolemaic, heliocentric and Tychonian theories, sometimes with subvarieties of the last-named, continued throughout the seventeenth century. Blancanus showed an example of this benevolent neutrality.[16] Gaspar Schott, a famous Jesuit, who finally accepted the Tychonic theory,[17] attempted to give such an impartial summary of all systems. Christian Wolf, who later called the earth a planet, mentioned the three systems as if they were equally valid.[18] Hakewill declared that the sun moved at such an incredible speed that " not a few . . . good Mathematicians " believed the earth moved and the sun was stationary.[19] Robert Burton, like Bacon, spoke in favor of both the geocentric and the heliocentric doctrines, but ended by the declaration that the Ptolemaic was probably correct.[20] Half a century later Joseph Glanvill would not commit himself to an opinion but declared that the general belief favored the Ptolemaic system.[21] Colbert, Louis XIV's great minister, in 1668, when he had almost reached

[14] Bacon, *Works* (Boston, ?), vol. viii, *De Augmentis Scientiarum* (1st ed., 1623), bk. iii, ch. iv, p. 502.

[15] *Ibid.*, p. 488.

[16] Blancanus, *Sphaera Mvndi* (Bologna, 1620). His name was really Giusseppe Biancani.

[17] Schott, notes in Kircher, *Iter Extaticum Coeleste* (Würzburg, 1660), pp. 36-39.

[18] Wolf, *op. cit.*, pp. 58, 61, 75, 76.

[19] Hakewill, *An Apologie or Declaration of the Power and Providence of God in the Gouernment of the World* (Oxford, 1635) (3d ed.), pt. ii, p. 173.

[20] Burton, *The Anatomy of Melancholy* (London, 1920) (1st ed., 1621), vol. ii, pp. 57-67; vol. iii, p. 15.

[21] Glanvill, *Scepsis Scientifica* (London, 1665), p. 58.

the zenith of his power, found time to compose and to publish, in the same volume with a disquisition on military archi-
tecture, a tractate summarizing no less than eight systems
including his own. His ideas resembled Tycho Brahe's
although he rejected his predecessor's assumption that the
heaven of the fixed stars was fluid and declared that the
planets Mars, Jupiter and Saturn were moved by their own
solid orbs.[22]   Mallet, also, in a popular textbook on geography and history compared the various systems, and,
though not enunciating his opinion, seemed to prefer the
Cartesian variation of the commonly designated Copernican
theory.[23]

The most famous and influential instance of either
assumed or actual impartiality in treating astronomical
theories was, of course, that which brought upon Galileo the
rigors of an inquest by the Inquisition.   In 1632 he published in Florence the *Dialogo dei due massimi sistemi del
mondo,* a work immediately popular throughout Europe.
The four dialogues of which it consisted purported to give
arguments in favor of both the heliocentric and the geocentric theories without arriving at a conclusion, but the vigorous support of the new doctrine showed so clearly the
author's sympathies that in spite of his age he was summoned
to Rome for recantation.[24]

In the ensuing chapters the aim has been to consider the
views of a sufficiently large selection of authors to illustrate

[22] Colbert, *Regi Armis Omnia Expugnanti Architecturam Militarem
Sapientia Omnia Constituenti Totius Mundi Constitutionem Belli Pacisque
Arbitro Bellatricem Pacificamque Mathesin* (?, 1668), pp. 5-13, especially
p. 13.

[23] Mallet, *Description de l'univers* (Paris, 1683).

[24] The official documents were revealed to the public in the last half
of the nineteenth century. Galileo and his achievements have been discussed by many authors, among whom may be mentioned Fahie, *Galileo
His Life and Work* (New York, 1903).

the effort at reconciliation of the Biblical cosmology with the advance of science rather than to attempt any exhaustive summary of the cosmogonies of two centuries.   More works have been examined than have been here analyzed; and those writers who seemed best and most fully to illustrate the theme have been presented, while others who touched on it less systematically or less directly have been passed over.   Many a scientist like Rohault, many a geographer and cosmographer like Gottfried, many a historian like Lambert and Condorcet has been omitted; but it is hoped that the thought of the time on our theme has been adequately reflected.

CHAPTER II

Fludd, an Early Conciliator of Science and Genesis

A CHARACTERISTIC development of the period, culminating in the last decade of the seventeenth century with its brisk interchange of *Defences, Reflections, Remarks* and *Vindications,* was the attempt to explain the Biblical narrative of creation by the observed facts of science, or sometimes to reverse the process.

Among the earliest of the harmonizers was a physician, Dr. Robert Fludd (1574-1637), who in 1617 published a folio entitled *Utriusque Cosmi Maioris scilicet et Minoris Metaphysica, Physica atque Technica Historia.* In the first part [1] he presented his ideas as to the method of creation. His frontispiece showed the earth, a globe divided between land and sea, surrounded by the circle of air. This was enveloped by that of fire, by the circles of the seven planets including the sun, by the heaven of the fixed stars and finally by three more circles separated by flames. The inmost of these three outer bands contained figures of twenty-four men [2] with crowns on their heads or in their hands; the second and the third pictured angels of different types. Outside all, at the top, was a cloud from which extended a hand holding a chain. The other end of the chain was attached to the wrist of a woman. She represented Nature and was superimposed upon those circles so that the solar orb lay at her heart and breast, its true region, and

---

[1] Fludd, *Utriusque Cosmi Maioris scilicet et Minoris Metaphysica, Physica atque Technica Historia* (Oppenheim, 1617), pp. 13-206.

[2] Are these the elders? Rev. 4: 4, 10; 5: 5-14.

the orb of the moon near her stomach. One foot rested on the sea, and the other on the land of the central globe.[3]

According to Fludd, Moses and St. Peter declared the primitive matter to have been water.[4] The only additional principle required for the production of the universe was light or fire,[5] by the action of which [6] on the formless abyss, hyle or water [7] the universe was created. The primitive darkness was more than mere privation of light and existed before light.[8] The spirit of God, this light or fire,[9] moving on the face of the waters, formed from them the three other elements, earth, air and fire, which differed in density.[10] From the purest parts of all four elements were shaped the different varieties of angels. Both good and bad angels were created on the first day in and with the spiritual heaven or empyreum.[11] The empyreum was made by the spirit of God, which cut out of the formless abyss a spherical universe by circling around it and forced to the center the shadows or *tenebrae,* so that it left the highest heaven, the empyreum, free from shadows. This passage around the universe of

[3] Fludd, *op. cit.,* pp. 7, 8, where an explanation of the diagram was given. Without the explanation an observer would be inclined to the opinion that the planetary orbs near her heart and stomach were respectively those of Mars and Venus.

[4] *Ibid.,* pp. 14, 24, 25.

[5] Like many others, Fludd considered light and fire different manifestations of the same thing.

[6] *Ibid.,* pp. 28-32, 39, 150, 169.

[7] Abyss, hyle and water were three names for the same mass of matter.

[8] *Ibid.,* pp. 26, 27.

[9] Later Fludd distinguished between the spirit of God and light, saying that the Holy Spirit acted first, and immediately afterward light was created and probably travelled the same path that the Holy Spirit had just traversed. *Ibid.,* pp. 151, 152.

[10] *Ibid.,* pp. 35, 38, 69, 70, 169. Fludd both identified and differentiated fire and light.

[11] *Ibid.,* pp. 38, 39, 109, 110, 114, 117.

the Spirit or of the primeval light in its wake probably constituted the first day.[12]

The same light, following the same course on the second
day, drove the shadows still farther toward the center, and
freed the middle regions. Between the empyreum and the
middle heaven was located the crystalline sphere, to which
the light raised watery particles from the thicker central
section when the inchoate mass reflected the rays. As these
same rays were re-reflected from the developing crystalline
sphere, they left its lower surface so cold that the water
became ice, and thus tempered the middle heaven's heat,
which was due to the motion of the eight planetary and
stellar orbs. The matter of the middle heaven or firmament
consisted of ether. In the upper part of the lowest heaven,
which was the heaven of air, the rotation of the orbs upon
one another created the invisible substance of flame, which
reinforced the natural warmth and light of the sun.[13]

On the third day the original light again encircled the
universe. It cleared the lowest heaven from shadows and
forced them still farther into the center of the universe.
Thus was formed the hard and cold ball of the terrestrial
globe.[14] There was, however, still a continual struggle
between the light or fire and the cold or shadows. Some
of the light penetrated too far, became entangled and, as it
were, captured by the shadows. From the combination
were produced stars, planets, plants, animals, minerals,
metals and even the bodies of men. Thence came also the
great central fire in the earth, which formed the place of
the devil and hell. Such different results as these were due
to the difference in the original locations of the *tenebrae*

---

[12] Fludd, *op. cit.*, pp. 47-52, 127, 128, 133, 151, 152, 169.

[13] *Ibid.*, pp. 53, 54, 56-58, 62, 63, 133, 135, 137.

[14] *Ibid.*, pp. 61, 62, 64, 65, 133.

from which the objects were developed.[15] The celestial
bodies had a similar genesis. Since light was itself invisible,
it could be seen only when reflected by some opaque body.
After some light had been enclosed in matter, the force of
other rays, together with the impulse inherent in the imprisoned light, raised the mass till it reached the crystalline
sphere, to which it became attached by freezing. The opacity of this spot of shadow enclosing a modicum of light then
reflected all future light and appeared to mankind as a star.
Probably the stars were shaped on the second day. The
Milky Way was an opaque band of the same matter, fastened
to the concave surface of the crystalline heaven between it
and the stars. Comets were sparks of various planets,
especially of Mars, which on their earthward journey became
enclosed in the thick matter of the upper air and for a time
continued to attract to themselves solid matter. They found
a position of equilibrium in the upper air and reflected the
rays of sun and stars. They grew until the heat, generated
by the reflected rays, caused the whole to break open,
especially when the influence of Mars was diminished, as
by the approach of some planet with different qualities.
The imprisoned spark then escaped and the opaque matter
was redissolved into air.[16]

The history of the sun differed from that of the stars,
although it was a similar mass of matter enclosing light or
forma. The combination of matter and light was forced to
the center of the universe, the earth, there to deposit its
corruptibility, and was afterwards raised to the middle

[15] Fludd, *op. cit.*, pp. 65, 67, 70, 71, 76, 105, 133, 135, 170, 172.

[16] *Ibid.*, pp. 125-131, 148, 180, 184-187, 197. Fludd here rejected
the Aristotelian thesis as to the origin of comets. Aristotle attributed them to terrestrial exhalations only, and believed that they were all
close to the earth, since the heavens always remained unaltered. His
doctrine held sway through the fourteenth and the fifteenth centuries and
even into the seventeenth.

heaven. Since matter eagerly attracts form to perfect itself,
the mass of the sun drew to itself the rays of light dispersed
through the middle heaven. Even yet it continued the
process. By this theory Fludd explained the delay till the
fourth day in the creation of the sun. God wished to take
its mass from the earth. Its history was also a symbol of
the death and the resurrection of Christ. The supercelestial
light descending was buried three days in the earth, and
then, rising glorified by the assistance of the rays from
above, ascended into the ethereal heaven with a body purified
from corruption. There it was given a crown and a scepter;
and thence it poured out life, form and virtue upon all
plants. The light that preceded sunlight had not been so
effective because it had been dispersed through a greater
quantity of matter. Since scattered force is weaker, its heat
was not so successful in the rarefaction and the dissipation
of the condensed matter in the heavens; and therefore the
first three days were much darker than later days. On the
other hand, any fire is stronger or weaker in proportion to
the strength or the weakness of the resistance afforded by
the matter with which it is combined. Thus the fire of the
empyreum, where matter was greatly rarefied, emitted
merely a pleasant warmth and had the highest degree of
perfection. In the middle heaven, where the consistency of
matter was greater, the fire was more intense but not harm-
ful. It conserved and multiplied inferior creatures by its
temperate warmth. The farther towards the center the fire
travelled, the more its rays were constricted by the increasing density of matter, so that the fires of hell, the lowest
of all, were destructive beyond imagination, and tortured
eternally. Nevertheless, the more remote from the empyreum it was, the more it was mixed with shadows and the
weaker was its power over them. In this respect the light
of the middle heaven was less efficient than the unadulterated

light of the empyreum; and that of the lowest heaven, which was produced on the third day and which Fludd called tertiary, was even less effective.[17]

The sun had equal parts of matter and form. After its creation it repulsed the thicker constituents of the middle heaven towards the earth. Meantime a reaction against the sun's influence raised vapors from the ether near the outer surface of the sphere of fire, which formed the highest part of the aerial heaven. At the point where the forces of repulsion and reaction balanced, the combination of vapors and *tenebrae* was moved by a double circular motion, from west to east according to the impulse of matter and from east to west according to the progress of light. By these conflicting stimuli the dense substance, which was suspended at that height, was compressed into a globe, as two opposing winds create an airy cloud. Thus was shaped the planet Mercury. Then vapors rising from Mercury met midway exhalations from the sun, and Venus was born. In a similar manner arose all the other planets.[18]

For the movement of these planets Intelligences or angels were not needed. Nevertheless, each of the heavens and of the stars had a spirit to preside over it.[19] The empyrean heaven was moved, however, by the presence and the power of the Holy Spirit. To prove both the naturally circular motion of the heavens and the fundamental mistake in Copernicus's heliocentric doctrine, Fludd adduced many of the traditional arguments: that circular motion is more noble than any other type of motion; that the earth, being cold, gross and heavy, should be at the center of the universe; that the heavens consisted of light and therefore were filled with

[17] Fludd, *op. cit.*, pp. 122, 124, 125, 132-144, 163, 164, 169, 180.

[18] *Ibid.*, pp. 131, 143-146.

[19] *Ibid.*, pp. 150, 151, 158-162. Possibly Fludd meant planets, not stars, since he named the angels presiding over the seven planets.

desire and strength for motion and also contained a multitude of spirits which aided the movement; and that buildings and people would be unable to stand if the earth moved. He added Biblical references to prove the immobility of the earth, including Joshua's invocation to the sun and the moon and the recession of the shadow on Hezekiah's sun-dial.[20]

Minerals were formed by mixtures of sulphur and mercury, cooked in the earth by heavenly, earthy and watery heat. They were affected also by stellar influences other than heat. Some differences were due to the relative proportions of sulphur and mercury. Moreover, the freer from shadows the sulphur and the mercury were, the purer, more perfect and more precious was the mineral produced. Minerals and plants were both created on the third day from sparks of the weakest light enclosed in the *tenebrae* of the lowest heaven and from sparks of the secondary light enclosed in the shadows of the middle heaven. The light, which formed the *anima* of the plant, sought naturally to rise; and the rays of light from heaven and the heavenly bodies assisted it. They penetrated the earth's surface and with their heat opened the pores constricted by cold so that they furnished a path for the plant. Therefore plants grew upward. For the creation of animals with senses more celestial heat was needed; hence, though of the same elements as plants, they were not created till after the sun. Man had in addition a portion of spiritual light, the especial gift of God.[21]

From this brief summary it is clear that Fludd jumbled Aristotle and the neo-Platonists, Paracelsus and Moses into a confused tangle. On the other hand, he was not wholly untouched by modern influences. He inserted data, even with illustrations, for some two dozen " experiments ",

[20] Fludd, *op. cit.*, pp. 151-158.

[21] *Ibid.*, pp. 133, 135, 137, 173-179, 205.

which were intended to prove his doctrines by analogy. That he was seldom quoted by later theorists on cosmogenesis and apparently had little influence on their ideas is not surprising when one considers the obscurity of his style, the unending repetitions and the contradictions in which he indulged.

CHAPTER III

DESCARTES, THE RIVAL OF ARISTOTLE

DESCARTES is said to have composed his account of the creation before the condemnation of Galileo, but to have been so alarmed by that event that he refrained from publishing his theory for nearly a dozen years and translated it into Latin before he finally printed it.[1] The explanation of creation formed most of the third and the fourth parts of his *Principles of Philosophy,* which was published in Amsterdam in 1644 and was immediately condemned by the Sorbonne notwithstanding his assertion that it was a pure hypothesis to aid in apprehending the works of God, and that he believed without reservation in the Mosaic account,[2] and in spite of his submission of all his opinions to the authority of the Church.[3]

After the lip service of his preliminary remarks that, of course, his topic was not how God created the world but how He might have accomplished the same results by the use of secondary causes [4] had He so desired, Descartes wholly ignored the Mosaic account. It seems necessary to give a summary of at least some of his ideas because they won the allegiance of contemporary thinkers, and even of semi-thinkers in the fashionable salons, so that for many Carte-

[1] Stimson, *The Gradual Acceptance of the Copernican Theory of the Universe* (Hanover, N. H., 1917), p. 85.

[2] Descartes, *Oeuvres* (Paris, 1824), vol. iii, *Les principes de la philosophie,* pt. iii, secs. 44, 45.

[3] *Ibid.,* pt. iv, sec. 207.

[4] The authors of the period were greatly impressed by the distinction between the immediate acts of God and those which He performed by the agency of secondary causes or nature and its laws.

sianism replaced Aristotelianism as a philosophical and scientific explanation of the universe [5]; and the later harmonizers of theology and science tried to unite the conceptions of Moses and Descartes. In England, however, perhaps because of insular jealousy and later because of pride in its own Newton, Cartesianism seems not to have been dominant.[6]

Descartes endeavored to appease theological scruples by the assertion that, while the earth travelled around the sun, it could not be said to move, since movement is really a continuing new relationship between an object and its surroundings, whereas the earth was merely carried around by the matter in which it floated and was always surrounded by the same particles.[7]

God was the first cause of both matter and motion, the quantity of each of which in the universe was unvarying. All properties of matter depended upon the movements of its parts.[8] Descartes held it more in accord with a noble and philosophic conception of God to consider Him the author of order than of chaos. Therefore all matter was at first alike and divided into approximately equal parts, each of which revolved around its own center. These subdivisions of matter were grouped into at least as many large congeries as there are now stars, planets and comets; and each congeries was driven circularly, so that it formed a whirlpool or vortex. In the primordial whirls the particles not originally

---

[5] The university of Louvain, for example, 1651-1691, was "practically composed of Cartesians". Stimson, *op. cit.*, p. 86. Though Newton's opinions finally conquered those of Descartes on the continent, the struggle was protracted; and even so late as 1734 the influential Swedenborg upheld the Cartesian tenets. *Cf. infra*, pp. 109, 183, 184.

[6] John Keill at Oxford, who gave the first course on Newtonian philosophy, refuted Descartes's vortices in 1699. Stimson, *op. cit.*, p. 90. *Cf.* also *infra*, pp. 109, 110.

[7] Descartes, *op. cit.*, pt. iii, secs. 17-19, 24-29, 38, 39.

[8] *Ibid.*, pt. ii, secs. 23, 24, 36.

round would become so as the corners were rubbed off.[8]   To avoid a vacuum [10] Descartes affirmed that the spaces between and around the larger particles became filled with infinitesimal parts of the same matter, the bits just removed, which travelled much more swiftly since they were compelled to pass through paths more narrow and winding.   In addition, matter sometimes assumed another shape.   These particles, which were larger than the dust or infinitesimal bits and not so easily moved as the rounded balls first mentioned, constituted what Descartes called the third element.   It was opaque and reflected light; and from it the earth, the planets and the comets were made.   The dust, which was luminous because of speed, he named the first element.   It was the source of sun and stars, while the round balls of the second element were transparent, formed the vortices and obviously had the greatest volume.   The first element increased by erosion at the expense of the other two elements till there was more than enough to fill the spaces around the balls. Meantime, centrifugal force drove the balls to the outer edge of the revolving mass and forced the first element to the cen-

[9] Descartes, *op. cit.*, pt. iii, secs. 46-48.

[10] Much of Descartes's theory was based on the doctrine upheld by Aristotle that a vacuum in nature was impossible, for example, *ibid.*, pt. iii, sec. 79.   Descartes based the belief on *a priori* reasoning.   *Ibid.*, pt. ii, secs. 16-19.   From this axiom he concluded that motion in the universe was circular since each particle must take the place previously occupied by another and must be immediately replaced.   He did not see that in an absolutely full universe all motion, at least all which resulted in readjustments of position, was impossible; and his *plenum* contained enough minute interstices among the particles that were due to their constant motion and their peculiarities of shape to permit particles to exchange neighbors as well as to move in a mass.   As a result of his belief he asserted the existence of material particles extremely swift in motion and capable of subdivision into an infinity of smaller particles to accommodate the irregularities of other motions without the production of a vacuum.   *Ibid.*, pt. iii, sec. 51.

ter, since its particles were the smallest.   Having lost their
protuberances, the balls of the second element took up less
room than at first and left a spherical space for the reception
of the first element.   Thus a star arose from the first element
at the heart of each vortex.   Light was the pressure by the
particles of the first and the second elements upon one another as they continually strove to escape from the center.[11]
The vortices differed in size and touched one another at all
possible tangents.   The poles of two vortices were the only
parts that could never touch, since, if the poles coincided
and the whirls rotated in the same direction, they would
coalesce, while, if their rotation was in opposite directions,
they would neutralize each other.   Because of their pressure
on one another the forms of the vortices were elliptical rather
than circular.   A natural result of the centrifugal force in
each vortex was that the particles of the first element on the
plane of the equator, where the force was greatest, were continually emerging from the central ball and even leaving the
vortex to enter an adjoining vortex at or near its poles, where
the pressure was least.   The balls of the second element
would follow except that they were impeded by their lack
of radial speed, by their greater size, which prevented their
passage through the minute intervals among the particles of
the second element in the new vortex, and by their original
circular motion, which carried them too quickly past the pole
of the other vortex, while the atoms of the first element
emerged from the central sphere with a more nearly straight
motion.   Normally the loss and the gain of any whirl balanced.   If more matter entered from one side of a vortex
than from the other, the location of the central body would
not be the geometrical center, though its shape would not be
affected by that of the vortex but would always be spherical.

[11] Descartes, *op. cit.*, pt. iii, secs. 49-64, 77.

It, as well as the matter of the surrounding vortex, had as a whole a rotary motion. Although the particles of the first element were all small, there was an infinite gradation of sizes among them. Some of the less minute became attached by their angles and lost a portion of their speed through its transfer to smaller, less irregular particles. Despite the fact that the motion natural to the particles of the first element was straight, the course of the compounds just mentioned, which were generally in transit from the pole to the center of the vortex, was deflected into a spiral by the motion of the vortices; and they were still further twisted by the necessity for seeking a path through the tiny and constantly shifting triangular spaces among the balls. Thus were formed from the first element bodies twisted like conch-shells. To them Descartes attributed the phenomena of magnetism.[12]

The particles of the second element, which formed the heavens, were not alike in size and speed. Even if they were originally equal, some were more reduced by friction. Those nearest the sun were smallest and swiftest. They moved faster because they were pushed by the solar particles, which were continually seeking to enter at the poles of the sun and to leave at the ecliptic. If it were not for their inferior size, their superior speed would allow their escape farther from the center. The balls of the second element in the solar vortex increased in size and decreased in speed as their location approached the orbit of Saturn, where they took perhaps thirty years to travel around the sun instead of approximately that number of days. Beyond that locality the speed again increased to the edge of the vortex. This change was due to the elliptical shape of the vortex, which forced the balls to travel in a narrower path in parts of their orbit. In order to move, one ball must pass the others that had been beside it and therefore must go faster. Because

[12] Descartes, *op. cit.*, pt. iii, secs. 65-78, 84, 88-93.

of its increased force and speed the ball proceeded a greater
distance in a straight line, so that the faster it moved, the
farther from the center it finally travelled.[13]

Since the vicinity of the axis in each vortex was less
agitated by motion than the rest, some of the slower particles
were forced thither and became attached to one another by
their angles. A number of these, which have been already
mentioned as the cause of magnetism, were pushed inward
to the surface of the central body or sun, swam there and
grew by accretion into continually larger conglomerations.
Like scum, they obstructed the light, and formed what is
known as sun-spots.[14] They did not move so fast as the
particles of the first element, on the surface of which they
floated, and therefore did not press so hard upon the balls
of the second. Therefore light, the result of pressure upon
these balls, was lessened by the growth of such masses.
They formed the comparatively inert third element. Sun-
spots were easily dissolved when bits were torn off by the
underlying swiftly-moving matter, or when it broke through
and submerged them. Sometimes, however, the spot was
enlarged until it covered the whole sun. It caused the solar
sphere to look pale or to disappear. After the whole had
been darkened, often the matter within broke out and covered
the surface with a thin layer of the first element in particularly violent agitation so that the sun became visible once

[13] Descartes, *op. cit.*, pt. iii, secs. 82-85.

[14] In discussing sun-spots Descartes treated a subject that had become
amazingly popular after the invention of the telescope at the beginning
of the century had revealed to mankind these flaws in the solar effulgence.
Galileo, who, if not the first to observe them, was almost the earliest to
discuss them, had deduced from them two theories, which speedily gained
acceptance, one that the sun revolved on its axis in a little less than a
month, and the other that heavenly bodies were corruptible. He based
a plausible proof of the earth's annual course on their path across the
sun's face, which varied from straight to curved lines according as the
earth was in the plane of the sun's equator or not. *Cf. infra*, pp. 320-324.

more and was even more brilliant than at first. The spot might be dissolved if it was thin and soft, or might remain as a solid crust below the surface. In time a new sun-spot might be formed over both the first crust and its covering of fire. By this process Descartes explained the phenomena of new and variable stars. At first all spots were soft and not dense; but, if they remained, they were hardened by the pressure of the solar matter beneath.[15]

Such alterations resulted in variations in the relative sizes of the vortices. The balance was disturbed by the change in pressure as the central sphere was more or less obscured. When the central star was entirely covered, the pressure that it had exerted to prevent the matter of another vortex from engulfing its own was removed; and its vortex was surely, though sometimes slowly, swallowed by one of the surrounding vortices or absorbed piecemeal by several. Finally the star, by this time hard and opaque, was swept away by the largest neighboring vortex and became a comet or a planet. It was carried around by the matter of its new vortex, towards the center of which it sank because its substance was less mobile than were the particles near the outer margin of the vortex. If it was so solid that it had acquired as much agitation as the balls around it before it had descended to the slowest level, that is, in the solar vortex before it had reached the path of Saturn, it would return to the circumference and travel to another vortex. Thus it would become a comet, and shine by light reflected from the central body of each vortex in turn. But if its solidity was less, it would continue to descend toward the center of the vortex till it reached a position of equilibrium, and would become a planet. Solidity meant the quantity of the third element in the spots or crust and in the air that surrounded the planet

---

[15] Descartes, *op. cit.*, pt. iii, secs. 87-98, 101-104, 110-114.

as compared with its surface area and its volume. The air was formed from the disruption of earlier spots into particles of irregular shape.[16]

We saw the light of the stars though they were in other vortices because the pressure of the particles of the first element upon the balls of the second was transferred to the balls of the neighboring vortex. Probably the firmament was the surface of the vortex that contained the earth. Because of refraction stars were perhaps not in their apparent location, or one star might appear to be two.[17]

The satellites of the planets were originally stars. They became covered with spots, lost their own vortices and were carried away by the vortices of the planets. Later the planets underwent similar experiences. For example, some five or six thousand years ago the earth, carrying the moon along, descended into the vortex of the sun. The planets were distant from the sun in a ratio corresponding to their solidity, with the least solid the nearest. Since the moon and the earth were of the same solidity or density, they sought the same orbit; but, because the moon was the smaller, it travelled more swiftly. With the surrounding air and some particles of sky from their former vortex, they had made some resistance at the time of their absorption into the the solar whirl and created in the vicinity of the earth a weak, supplementary vortex, which had ever since carried the moon around. Together with the original motion of the earth when it was a star, this smaller whirlpool was the cause of our planet's rotation on its axis. The direction of inclination for the poles of the earth remained the same as when it had its own vortex, but the amount of inclination had gradually lessened.[18]

16 Descartes, op. cit., pt. iii, secs. 100, 111, 114-121, 130, 140.

17 Ibid., pt. iii, secs. 130, 131.

18 Ibid., pt. iii, secs. 144, 146, 147, 149, 150, 155, 156; pt. iv, sec. 2.

In the Fourth Part Descartes explained from the principles previously enunciated the formation and the qualities of
the earth and all that was therein, including magnetism, electricity, telepathy and what he called sympathy and antipathy.
He even expounded the natural cause for the bleeding of a
dead man's wounds at the approach of his murderer.[19] The
terrestrial globe developed into its present condition in the
following way. Some branching and very irregular particles
of the third element, which touched but did not press upon
one another, formed the air. The pressure of the celestial
second element, heat, light and various other motions divided
the rest of the third element into earth particles, which were
very irregular in shape, and water particles, which were
largely in the form of little rods lying upon one another,
supple and easily sliding. Their transparency resulted from
their small size and such an arrangement that they were surrounded by straight passages through which the balls of the
second element or their effects might be transmitted and
light produced. The layer of liquid was formed below a
hard crust of earth. Finally the cracks in the crust, through
which the particles of air had been passing up and down according to the temperature, were so enlarged by the process
and by the corresponding passage by particles of the first
and the second elements that the crust broke and subsided
upon an inner globe, which had been forming below the air
and the water. Since the crust was larger in circumference
than the inner sphere, it was piled by its fall into all sorts
of irregular shapes. The highest points were, of course,
mountains; the flat places, plains; the hollows, valleys or sea
beds. Below some of the mountains were cavities containing air and water.[20] Descartes showed how the same proc-

[19] Descartes, *op. cit.*, pt. iv, secs. 2-78, 133-187.
[20] *Ibid.*, pt. iv, secs. 16, 32-48.

esses that developed the four elements and the present shape of the earth formed mercury, salt and sulphur, and produced metals, raising them till they were within the reach of man. He was apparently a believer in the central fire, though he did not understand wholly its continued existence without fuel.[21]

Although Descartes's system is most notable because it is purely mechanical and explains all phenomena as resulting from the motion of a uniform matter, from which both celestial and terrestrial objects evolved by the erosion and the cohesion of their particles, it is also noteworthy because he appealed to no authorities.[22] He developed all the complex harmonies of the world from a few simple and clearly conceived general principles by a process of *a priori* reasoning with occasional references to the data of experience. Nevertheless, he accepted from the past, probably without realizing his debt, his fundamental ideas. He copied many features of his theory from Democritus and other atomists, but never credited them with the suggestions. When he declared his intention to reject all authorities, it apparently did not occur to him that the validity of the Paracelsian salt-sulphur-mercury formula or of such Aristotelian concepts as the four elements could be doubted. He bent his endeavors

[21] Descartes, *op. cit.*, pt. iii, sec. 150, pt. iv, secs. 3, 44, 57-75. Gadroys, who followed Descartes almost slavishly while purporting to be unprejudiced, was inclined to accept his method of forming the earth and the mountains, but suggested another way because of this difficulty concerning fuel for the central fire. In the vortex there were originally such quantities of the third element as to smother the star at its center. The result was the formation of a sphere that contained the third element and that by the loss of its vortex and its migration into the solar vortex became the earth. The fire at its heart had been completely extinguished. Gadroys, *Le systeme du monde* (Paris, 1675), pp. 313-347.

[22] He was so independent that he had no wish to visit Galileo though he was in Florence during the height of the Italian astronomer's fame, and refrained from meeting Kepler when he was in Germany. Fahie, *Galileo His Life and Work* (New York, 1903), pp. 390, 391.

to an explanation by his theory of their production, and then considered the problem solved.

On the other hand, his exposition was remarkably free from verbosity and repetition and was arranged in a thoroughly logical order. One could not say of him, as was written of Fludd, " The obscurity of the style is only equalled by the absurdity of the matter." [23] The enthusiasm with which Descartes's ideas were welcomed may have been partly due to his clarity. His doctrine of vortices and his insistence on the impossibility of a vacuum were repeated as almost axiomatic for more than a century. Many theorists accepted his system bodily. Even Burnet was influenced by Descartes's idea that the crust of the earth broke and subsided upon an interior sphere. At least, their explanations concerning the origin of mountains and other phenomena were strikingly similar. His interpretation of sun-spots, of variable and new stars, and of planets and comets as dead suns was also widely accepted.[24]

[23] Manuscript note in a copy of Fludd, *Utriusque Cosmi Maioris* (Oppenheim, 1617), presented to Columbia University by Gen. John Watts de Peyster.

[24] Burnet, *The Sacred Theory of the Earth* (London, 1722) (1st ed., 1684-1689), vol. i, especially pp. 181-205; vol. ii, pp. 141, 317; Burnet, *Doctrina Antiqua de Rerum Originibus* (London, 1729, 1736), *Archaeologiae Philosophicae*, pt. i, critique, pp. 36, 37, 51. The agreement of other authors with Descartes will appear in later chapters. Even Riccioli listed him among the authorities on comets whom he had presumably consulted, though Riccioli was the clerical spokesman for the opposition to the so-called Copernican doctrines, and though the works of Descartes had been banned by the Church, as soon as they were published. Riccioli, *Almagestvm Novvm Astronomiam Veterem Novamqve Complectens* (Bologna, 1651), vol. ii, p. 2. In a book translated from French into Latin and later into English, Jacques Rohault (1620-1675) gave Descartes's theories a wide circulation without emphasizing their source. Rohault, *System of Natural Philosophy* (London, 1723).

CHAPTER IV

THE PEDAGOGUE'S APPROACH TO THE PROBLEM OF MOSES'S SCIENTIFIC ACCURACY

DURING the centuries between 1600 and 1800 educators were not indifferent to the relationship between the facts of experience and the Mosaic philosophy and history. Even in the seventeenth century their reliance upon authorities other than the Bible, as well as the reliance of their contemporaries, was less than that of their predecessors. That the study of science was encouraged by the more advanced teachers can be inferred from Milton's encomiums in the *Tractate on Education.*[1] The new discoveries and theories were incorporated in textbooks by practical teachers. They often invented hypotheses of their own to prove that the Mosaic testimony agreed with the other two criteria of truth in the physical universe, the first of which was reason and the second experience or the testimony of the senses. A correct interpretation of the three necessarily gave the same results. Comenius said that all three should be used,—first sense, then reason and lastly the Scripture, which taught nothing contrary to reason though often that which was beyond and above reason.[2] The general opinion of educators, like that of other authors during the era, was that the words of Moses were a touchstone by which all must be examined. We must " assent to God speaking to us through

[1] Milton, *Tractate on Education* (Cambridge, 1890) (1st ed., 1644), pp. 11-13.

[2] Comenius, *Naturall Philosophie Reformed by Divine Light* (London, 1651), preface and pp. 3-8. The book was originally entitled *Synopsis physicae ad lumen divinum reformatae.*

Moses." [3]   The common explanation for such statements of
the great lawgiver as were obviously contrary to fact was
the thesis that he spoke in accordance with the capacity of
the vulgar or used colloquial idioms.[4]

Comenius's book shows that by 1651 a leader in education felt it necessary to produce a treatise on physics for
school use.   His teacher, John Henry Alsted (1588-1638),
a German Protestant,[5] had some years earlier presented an
account of physical theory in four parts.   He treated of the
Mosaic philosophy, the Hebrew (that is, the rabbinical and
"cabbalistic "), the Peripatetic and the Chemical, with no
clear statement of his own views.   He apparently, however,
accepted God as the only efficient cause for the creation of
the universe.   The primary matter, created from nothing on
the first day, did not include the heaven of the blessed.
Matter was divided into two varieties: the first, light or
celestial; the second, earth and water or terrestrial.   Terrestrial matter was opaque instead of bright.   The Spiritus
that moved upon the waters, as a bird incubates her young,
was the Holy Spirit, neither a wind nor any of the other
frequently suggested natural agents; and this process gave
form to matter.   Earth, water and fire were created on the
first day.   The creation of light implied the production of
a lucid, globular body.   The primal light included both elementary fire and the heaven with the matter of the future
celestial spheres.   They were differentiated by the degree
of its purity.[6]   On the second day appeared the expanse of

[3] Alsted, *Physica Harmonica* (Herborn, 1642), pp. 4-6. " Nostrum
est, assentiri Deo nobis per Mosen loquenti," p. 5. Comenius called
Moses God's secretary, Comenius, *op. cit.*, p. 10.

[4] Alsted, *op. cit.*, p. 13 and innumerable other places.

[5] Author of an encyclopedia, Alsted, *Cursus philosophici encyclopaedia
libris xxvii complectens universae philosophiae methodum serie praeceptorum regularum* (Herborn, 1620).

[6] Alsted, *Physica Harmonica* (Herborn, 1642), pp. 15, 17-21, 25-28.

air and ether, which separated the waters. Those above the
firmament were sustained less by the force of fire than by
that of the celestial bodies and their own mobility. Alsted
mentioned the ancient belief as still current that from the
waters above the firmament birds were formed, as fish were
from the inferior waters, though he neither affirmed nor
denied its truth.[7] With more self-confidence he asserted
that the superior waters were the clouds.[8] All bodies were
produced from light, water or earth. Unformed light constituted the matter of heaven and of fire; and formed light,
the stellar and the empyrean heavens and the bodies of the
stars, which were the denser parts of their orbs. Water was
the material basis of air as well as of fish and of birds, while
other animals, plants and minerals were produced from
earth.[9] This volume suggested what Alsted had previously
asserted definitely in a treatise on mathematics,—the immobility of the earth at the center of the universe and the
revolution of sun, stars and planets around it.[10] In the
earlier book he treated of astrology as seriously as of astronomy, and even showed how to make prognostications.[11]

Alsted's greater pupil, John Amos Comenius (1592-
1671), agreed with him in placing the earth at the center
of the universe, while the heavens travelled around it,[12] but
seemed to incline to the Tychonian theory since he made
Venus and Mercury revolve around the sun.[13] His account

[7] Alsted, op. cit., pp. 29, 32, 33, 36.

[8] Ibid., pp. 38, 39.

[9] Ibid., pp. 34, 36, 38, 39.

[10] Alsted, Methodus Admirandorum Mathematicorum Novem libris
exhibens universam Mathesin (3rd ed.) (Herborn, 1641), bk. v on
Astronomy (or Astrology), pp. 170, 204-208, 214-216, where he spoke
of Copernicus as refuted, and bk. vi on Geography, pp. 254-256.

[11] Ibid., pp. 220, 229, 244-247.

[12] Comenius, op. cit., pp. 81, 89, 90, 96, 108, 116, 117, 119, 120, 127.

[13] Ibid., p. 122.

of creation was much more complete than his master's. Genesis 1:1 meant to him the creation of the heaven of heavens with angels,[14] and of matter in the form of a chaos somewhat like smoke. It consisted of atoms which had no coherence. They so filled the world as to prevent a vacuum. Matter was the first principle of the visible world.[15] The second principle was the spirit of God, breath or the spirit of life.[16] It was diffused throughout the universe, ruled matter and produced all creatures by introducing into each the appropriate form. In the beginning it instilled into the dark and confused matter of chaos a strength by means of which the mass began to stir. To aid this spirit God produced light, the third principle, which was purely active. It made matter visible, divided it into forms and perfected all. It was separated into two parts, one of which was left in the sky and later formed the heavenly globes, while the other was sunk into the earth for various uses including the production of minerals.[17] By its threefold virtue " of illuminating, moving it selfe, and heating " [18] and by its circuit around the world, the light began to heat

[14] Comenius, *op. cit.*, pp. 10, 18, 19. By saying that the earth was void, Moses implied that the heaven was not empty ; hence that there were angels, *ibid.*, p. 230. " Thus the structure of the Universe ought to proceed, so as to begin with the most simple creature, and end in that which is most compound but both of them rationall ; that it might appear, that God created these onely for himself, but all the intermediate for these." *Ibid.*, p. 16, also p. 18. Job 38: 4, 7 spoke of the angels as spectators of creation ; therefore both they and their dwellings must have been created at the very beginning, and both in a moment, *ibid.*, p. 19. Angels were created out of the Spirit of the world, which was in existence before the earth. Part of the Spirit was left in heaven for that purpose, while part was sent down into the material world. *Ibid.*, pp. 230, 231.

[15] *Ibid.*, pp. 10, 28-32.

[16] Probably Comenius meant the spirit of the world by these terms.

[17] *Ibid.*, pp. 10, 11, 20-28, 30, 32-37, 46, 231, 239.

[18] *Ibid.*, p. 11.

and thus to rarefy and to divide matter and to cause the difference between day and night. As the light or firmament rarefied matter, it drove the denser part both to the outer limit of the visible world and to the thick dregs that formed the earth at the center of the universe. In the form of water the denser part settled at both extremities.[19] On the third day the four elements were separate,—air, water, earth and ether, the last of which was the firmament or heavens.[20] The highest element and the purest part of matter was not fire but the heaven furnished with fiery light.[21]

In the beginning the earth had no mountains, for " the grosser parts of the matter flowing about poised themselves equally about the center," [22] and the waters covered the whole; but then the sea retreated, probably because mountains had been raised by an earthquake. (Psalm 104 spoke of the noise on that occasion.) This earthquake had been caused " by the fire sunk into the earth; which giving battle to the cold there conglobated, shook the earth, and either caused it to swell variously or rent it asunder," producing valleys and mountains with hollow caves.[23] Earthquakes continued to form mountains.[24]

Comenius believed in the contemporaneous creation of herbs and animals, even without seeds, from humid and putrefied matter by the diffused soul of the world, with the assistance of heat.[25] Hence the production of plants on the third day by the spirit of the world from " fat vapours on

[19] Comenius, *op. cit.*, pp. 11, 12, 36, 37, 46, 79, 81, 88.

[20] *Ibid.*, p. 13.

[21] *Ibid.*, pp. 79, 80.

[22] *Ibid.*, p. 94.

[23] *Ibid.*, p. 93.

[24] *Ibid.*, p. 94.

[25] *Ibid.*, pp. 22, 23, 72, 73, 130, 154, 200, 210.

the earth " caused by " the heat of Coelestiall light " [26]
seemed to him quite natural. In like manner he readily
accepted the formation of " *reptiles, as earthwormes* ",[27] the
rudiment of nature, and of " *fishes and birds, animals of a
more light compaction* " from water as the softer element,
when the heat increased after the formation of the sun and
stars, and the creation of other animals from clay.[28]   Like
Alsted, he believed that a vacuum in the universe was impossible.   This impossibility he attributed to the action of
the spirit or soul of the world, which moved through the
whole of matter to preserve it and made the air or the water
close again behind a cut.[29]   He considered that the sympathy
and the antipathy of animals toward one another resulted
from their original creation and from the design of God,
and said " every creature beareth its signature about it ",
so that from the appearance of animals and plants their use
might be deduced.   This was because the spirit formed a
body in accord with its own nature.   The spirit was originally divided by God's command into many dissimilar portions, one for each species.   Thereafter it preserved the
peculiarities of its type.[30]   His belief in the occult sympathies and antipathies of objects, in their substantial qualities,
by which he meant their salt, sulphur and mercury, in their
tendency to seek their like which caused the rising of fire and
the falling of heavy bodies to their natural place,[31] his comparison of the macrocosm and the microcosm, his statement
concerning the transmutation of the four elements by heat,

[26] Comenius, *op. cit.*, p. 13, also p. 130.

[27] *Ibid.*, p. 14.

[28] *Ibid.*, pp. 14, 15.

[29] *Ibid.*, pp. 31-34, 43, 44, 46, 91.

[30] *Ibid.*, pp. 34, 35.

[31] He associated the tendency of bodies to seek their natural places
with the tendency to seek like objects.

his location of the waters above the firmament outside the ever-rolling frame to cool it, his theory that thunder-bolts or stone axes were formed in the clouds by the ascension of stony vapors and that small animals such as frogs were sometimes shaped in the same place, his elaborated analogies, his leaning toward astrology, his doctrine that comets were vapors reflecting the sun, his belief in the subterranean deep of waters connected with an unfathomable Ocean, the importance he attributed to the number seven,—all these show that Comenius was more modern in his pedagogy than in his science.[32]

[32] Comenius, *op. cit.*, pp. 16, 42, 43, 46, 47, 50-55, 58, 62, 64, 68, 69, 81, 82, 89, 95, 97-99, 100, 108, 116, 121, 126-128, 130, 140, 141, 206-209, 226, 227, 239-242.

CHAPTER V

KIRCHER, THE CATHOLIC SCIENTIST

AMONG the most quoted authors of the mid-seventeenth century was a Jesuit, Athanasius Kircher, a friend of Riccioli and of Christopher Scheiner, and a man of encyclopedic information. In 1656, at the prompting of a dream,[1] he wrote the account of a journey under angelic guidance through the universe. Most of the information was delivered in the form of a dialogue between the angel Cosmiel and Theodidactus. A large proportion of the knowledge was accurate, for he discussed the liquidity and the corruptibility of the heavens, the revolutions of Mercury and Venus around the sun, the invisibility of the earth from the stars, their composition of the same matter as the earth, their varying distances and the existence of nebulae still more remote;[2] but he combined with these correct doctrines belief in the four elements and descriptions of the planets and their guiding intelligences appropriate to the influences attributed to them by astrologers.[3] He acquiesced in the ancient astrological dogmas, concerning the effects of different planets and stars on the earth. For example, in his opinion Mars moved the choleric humor, inciting men to wrath and bloodshed, affected

[1] According to his friend, Gaspar Schott, who had been urging him to write such a book. Kircher, *Iter Extaticum Coeleste* (Würzburg, 1660), p. 4.

[2] Kircher, *Itinerarivm Exstaticvm* (Rome, 1656), pp. 9, 12, 20, 26, 55, 259, 260, 266, 286. This title was altered in the 1660 edition to *Iter Extaticum Coeleste*.

[3] *Ibid.*, pp. 50-88, 90-94, 96-119, 121-150, 181-197, 203-218, 227, 228, 231-242, 254, 255.

the liver and the brain and caused maniacal fury and vertigo. Jupiter, on the other hand, caused pleasant and healthful serenity in the air, gave peace, fertility and abundance and presided over sweet-smelling plants.   It inclined men to prudence, gravity and difficult deeds of lofty character.   The planets affected those plants, animals and men whose natures were attuned to them; and, of course, the results varied according to the various combinations of the celestial bodies.[4] In addition, Kircher revived the ideas and the vocabulary of the great scholastics and their predecessors.   For instance, he attributed the phenomena of the world to the interaction of form and matter, the active and the passive principles, the warm and the humid radical.

Finally Cosmiel taught Theodidactus the history of the creation of the world.[5]   By the sole power of His will God created heaven and earth in a state of chaos.   This was the abyss of darkness with no form or shape.   Light was the first *forma* of the world [6] and was necessary for its existence. Placed in all objects of the universe, light was the warm radical, " by which alone they are formed and preserved; . . . the active principle of all nature." [7]   Mixed with the humid radical,—that is, the waters or the passive principle, light produced all things.   Then God separated chaos into portions, from which planets and stars might be produced. Each of the celestial globes consisted of all four elements, water, earth, air and fire; [8] and the matter of each sphere was given a tendency to its own center so that a particle re-

[4] Kircher, *op. cit.*, pp. 110-115, 155-158, 193-197, 210-215, 237-242.

[5] *Ibid.*, pp. 291-307.

[6] *Ibid.*, p. 292.

[7] " Quo solo formantur & sustentantur ; . . . totius naturae actiuum." *Ibid.*, p. 293.

[8] *Ibid.*, pp. 9, 24, 51-54, 90-92, 101-103, 190-192, 218, 219, 293, 305-307, 447 and elsewhere.

moved from one body to another would return to its own globe as soon as it was released. At the center of the whole universe was the immobile earth for the sake of which all things were made. It was placed there in order to receive more easily and more completely than it could elsewhere influences from the rest of the universe.[9] After all the globes of the universe had been severally consolidated, since they were still covered with water, God commanded the liquid to be gathered into one place,—i. e., into furrows, *alveos,* on each globe, and the dry land to appear. The earth was a prototype of the other spheres. Part of the water was, however, relegated to the farthest limits of the universe beyond the firmament,—that is, beyond the expanse filled by the globes of the universe. Part was converted into ether, in which the stars ran their courses.[10]

Inasmuch as all the globes had their own centers, which light bodies fled and heavy bodies sought, the humid constituents of each breathed out a vapor or effluvium, which became its atmosphere.[11] Part of the solar effluvium formed the sun-spots, which were a kind of clouds.[12] The various atmospheres, which were carried around by the revolutions of their globes, formed the vortices. Since the globes differed, the vortices differed also and could not mix. Therefore there was no danger of the globes' deserting their assigned positions.[13] The vehemence and the efficacy of the sun were

[9] Kircher, *op. cit.*, pp. 50, 76-78, 101, 192, 193, 270, 277, 278, 293, 317-322, 447.

[10] *Ibid.*, pp. 294-300.

[11] *Ibid.*, pp. 53, 59, 172-175, 179, 180, 191, 218, 270, 277, 278, 302, 303, 317, 318, 447.

[12] *Cf. infra*, pp. 320-324.

[13] *Ibid.*, pp. 167, 175-177. The introduction of vortices suggests how quickly the ideas of Descartes had spread even to his enemies, the Jesuits. Kircher apparently felt it necessary to incorporate them into his system. In fact, he listed Descartes's *Fundamenta nouae Philosophiae* among the sources of his material, *ibid.*, p. 464.

so great that it poured out an enormous quantity of effluvia, largely smoky and bituminous, though rarefied.   Sometimes the force of the eruption by which the vapors were cast forth was so tremendous that they were thrown to a very great height and gained liberty.   They were agitated by the motion of the ether and spread out into inestimable magnitude. Their reflection of the sun's rays to the earth occasioned the appearance of a comet, " dirum mortalibus omen." [14]   As the earth was periodically afflicted with earthquakes, floods and volcanic eruptions, " either by the malignant aspect of the stars, or by a gathering like that of an ulcer swelling with malignant humors, or of some feverish matter ripe for breaking out, after certain periods of years," [15] so the sun from time to time suffered paroxysms or attacks of chronic diseases.   These produced a vast increase in sun-spots, which pushed one another away and piled up until they broke loose as a comet.   The comet was carried farther from the sun because of its resistance to the swift motion of the ether in that vicinity.   Then, however, the frigidity of the ether or the nature of its new location dissolved the comet; and the sun reclaimed its own part, while the rest returned to the chaos whence it was produced.   Not only the sun, but also other heavenly bodies and even the earth could pour out sufficient effluvia to make comets or what appeared to be new stars, though these were not necessarily visible from the earth.[16]

[14] Kircher, op. cit., p. 167.

[15] " Siue maligno siderum aspectu, siue coaceruatione veluti vlceris malignis humoribus tumentis, aut febrilis cuiusdam materiae ad erumpendum maturae, post certas annorum periodos," ibid., p. 168.

[16] Ibid., pp. 159-175, 177, 178, 180, 278-282. Kircher did not attempt to reconcile the two methods that he suggested for the formation of comets, though by his statement that the effluvium might be terrestrial he apparently wished to harmonize his doctrine with the Aristotelian belief, which had attributed to the earth the vapors that were the source of

Since God was said to have made everything in number, weight and measure, [17] there must be symmetry and proportion in the universe. Without them, celestial and terrestrial objects would not have the proper reciprocal effects. The locations chosen for the various orbs and their relative sizes were necessary that they might temper one another. Even the maleficent planets, Mars and Saturn, like snakes and toads, were valuable to carry off the corruption and the poison that accumulated through the universe, though of course their influence had to be modified by that of the benign celestial bodies. All the heavenly spheres rotated on their axes and circled around the earth so that they might pour down influences from every part of their surfaces upon each section of the inferior world, for the sake of which they had been created. Besides their effects upon the earth, they were placed near enough to one another to permit mutual reactions. [18]

Eight years later Kircher published a book, conceived in a less popular vein, on the subterranean world. The first part was developed in the form of geometrical proofs and corollaries. In this ponderous folio he presented the same picture of a central, motionless earth, the end of the whole creation, and of light and heavy bodies, which generated subterranean objects by mingling as their innate impulses caused them respectively to seek or to fly from the center. Again he averred the swift motion of the firmament, the rotation of planets and stars and the planetary revolutions about the sun.

comets. Kircher perhaps had it in mind to imply that his view was a mere enlargement of the older one, though in fact it contradicted one of the most cherished doctrines of the Greek philosopher, the incorruptibility of the heavenly spheres.

[17] Kircher, *op. cit.*, p. 323.

[18] *Ibid.*, pp. 61, 100, 101, 109-114, 187, 229, 230, 232, 235-242, 323-331, 337, 346-349.

Again he enlarged upon the influence of the heavenly bodies on the universe as a whole, on one another and on the earth. They all had axes parallel to that of the earth to prevent vertigo and confused motion and to make them more perfectly adapted to influence sublunar objects. He even listed among the necessary qualifications of a mine supervisor a knowledge of astronomy in order that from consideration of the celestial regions he might discover extensions of the metallic or mineral veins.[19] Nevertheless, the rays of sun and stars did not penetrate below the surface of the earth but were reflected; and therefore their virtue, which, though occult, was carried only by light and heat, could not directly make metals. However, it aided in the task by influencing the air, which in turn affected the water. Air through the pores of the earth and water through subterranean channels were diffused throughout our globe and assisted in the formation of stones, metals and plants. Metals and minerals were the result of the mutual attraction of similar sulphurous-salt-mercurial vapors driven through the earth. By evaporation they were turned into appropriate gems, stones or metals.[20]

Kircher, like other scientists of the seventeenth century, was inclined to use magnetism as a *deus ex machina* to explain many results. For example, he declared that the magnetic force of the earth helped these planetary influences by attracting them, and that it kept the earth steady and prevented the full effects of alterations in the center of gravity due to eruptions, earthquakes and variations in the position of sea and land.[21]

[19] Kircher, *Mundus Subterraneus* (Amsterdam, 1664, 1665), t. i, pp. 1-4, 14, 16, 19, 20, 37, 38, 47, 48, 55-65, 103-106, 109, 129-136, 153, 168, 192, 200-202, 223, 226, 324, 333; t. ii, pp. 7, 171, 381.

[20] *Ibid.*, t. ii, pp. 162-167, 237, 238, 251, 253, 257, 269, 270.

[21] *Ibid.*, t. i, pp. 103, 106, 107. Other mentions of magnetism occurred as follows: t. i, p. 3, t. ii, pp. 238, 253, 328 and elsewhere.

As a pious son of the Church, Kircher said that creation occurred almost six thousand years ago, when God out of nothing created everything at once. Into every part of this undistinguishable matter he infused a quality or "sulphureo-salino-mercurialis " spirit, endowed with " plastic and magnetic virtue; the first of which gave the separate species form, figure, color; the other force attracting like particles." He created everything else except the human soul by means of this *panspermia*.[22] God created then and had since created nothing *de novo* except the human soul, as is clear from the account in Genesis.[23] Creation was preceded by a plan or idea in the mind of God, a visualization of the universe in all its details. The world was made for man in order that he might come to know God. Neither God nor the angels had any need of it. Hence whatever in any locality was admirable must be present also in the earth, which was a sort of epitome of the universe. As man was a microcosmos, representing in little the whole universe, so the earth was a geocosmos. This resemblance of both man and the earth to the universe of course produced analogies between parts of man's body and the earth. The bones that prevented man's frame from being dissolved corresponded to the mountain chains that, according to Kircher, extended from pole to pole and from east to west. For this reason, as well as because of their other advantages and the Scriptural mention of mountains during the flood, the primitive earth must have had such eminences. As through innumerable canals the four

[22] Kircher, *op. cit.*, t. i, p. 64, t. ii, pp. 327, 328, 378. " Virtus plastica & magnetica ; quarum prior singulis speciebus formam, figuram, colorem; altera similium vim attractivam contulit." *Ibid.*, t. ii, p. 328.

[23] Kircher, *Arca Noë* (Amsterdam, 1675), p. 94. Kircher here as in other places called this the sacred oracles of Moses, "quae meritò omni humanae cognitionis certitudini multis parasangis anteferre debemus." Kircher, *Mundus Subterraneus* (Amsterdam, 1664-5), t. ii, p. 327.

humors were carried to the members of man's body and air was thus transported for breathing and for tempering the *"aestus"* of the heart and the blood, so through subterranean channels were carried water, fire, air, vapors and exhalations of all kinds.   Both in man and in the earth the humors were increased by the moon as it waxed.[24]

As was said in Genesis, the earth before the creation of light was covered with water.   Then the dry land, struck with the voice of God, appeared, while the waters were drawn off into hollows.   Apparently Kircher meant that some of the surface was raised and the rest depressed.   The land was hardened into stone by the subterranean fire and by the salt placed therein at the beginning.   The original mountain chains came into being in this way.   But not all mountains were made at creation.   Even after the flood mountains of sand or mud were raised.   By a kind of petrifying sap they became stone.[25]   Not until after the primitive separation of land and sea did the seeds of all things, though in the earth from the first, become active.   Immediately after the mention of the first plants Moses narrated the formation of the sun, moon and stars, by whose influences earth joined the active principle to the passive, and engendered plants.   Then the Bible straightway narrated the production of aquatic and flying animals by the three principles of salt, sulphur and mercury.[26]

[24] Kircher, *op. cit.*, t. i, pp. 55, 56, 67-75, 97, 108-111, 129-136, 153, 158, 168, 175, 182, 240, 273, 324, 329, 333, t. ii, pp. 5, 336, 381, 390, 391. Kircher, *Turris Babel* (Amsterdam, 1679), pp. 133, 134. *Cf. infra*, p. 329.

[25] Kircher, *Mundus Subterraneus* (Amsterdam, 1664-5), t. i, pp. 162, 163, 327, 333, t. ii, p. 5.

[26] *Ibid.*, t. i, p. 109, t. ii, pp. 330-336, 378. Kircher was not altogether clear as to how plants were created before the celestial bodies. He slurred over the problem, but may have felt that the primeval light served the purpose of the sun before the fourth day. Or he may have thought that the creation of the sun and the stars antedated the Mosaic narrative. The planets were clearly coeval with the earth.

When the mountains were raised, cavities were left in the earth. Since nature abhors a vacuum,[27] these cavities were filled with earth containing seminal principles, air, water or fire. They were called respectively Geophylacia, Aërophylacia, Hydrophylacia and Pyrophylacia.[28] The combination of subterranean water and fire was necessary for the preservation of the earth; and therefore God placed within our globe these reservoirs, with an elaborate system of branching channels. By the interactions of the four elements contained therein the whole system was kept in circulation and in health. All seas and lakes were joined by streams above or below ground. Sometimes these channels were connected with volcanoes, which served as spiracles or chimneys, furnished air to nourish the pyrophylacia and purged the fire of superfluous smoke and flames. The base of the ocean was like a sieve and let the water down by innumerable channels to nourish the central fire. This in turn raised the water to the hydrophylacia high in the mountains, whence it poured forth as rivers and returned to the sea. The reservoirs of air not only nourished the fire, but also sometimes acted upon the water to force it up to the tops of mountains and other high places.[29]

The largest of the pyrophylacia, which was at the center of the earth, served as hell to punish the wicked. Their souls were removed by the weight of their sins as far as possible from God. The fire of hell was in reality the element but it was raised by supernatural power to greater efficacy. It gave no light. Probably purgatory was located in another pyrophylacium. The central fire served an additional pur-

[27] Kircher, op. cit., t. i, pp. 56, 110, 184, 235, 236 and elsewhere.

[28] Ibid., t. i, pp. 111-120 and elsewhere.

[29] Ibid., t. i, pp. 16, 17, 19, 70-72, 74-76, 86-89, 99-103, 111-120, 137, 145-151, 158, 163, 164, 168, 179-190, 193, 201, 219-223, 226-243, 256-260, 270, 329, t. ii, pp. 7, 157, 162, 167, 237, 238, 467.

pose.   The ascent of its particles in every direction affected all production of metals, minerals and plants.   It sent its influence both to all the other pyrophylacia and to the surface of the earth.[30]

Not only did the water of the ocean circulate through small subterranean channels to the mountain tops and thence by rivers back again into the sea; but it also poured itself in cataracts through the earth, being engulfed in a great whirlpool at the north pole and escaping again at the south. During its passage through the earth, it met subterranean fires and was, as it were, cooked, so that it furnished nourishment necessary for the production of earthly bodies, such as minerals, metals and plants.   This circulation served in addition to prevent the putrefaction of the water and the noxious exhalations that would result from immobility on its part.   All these theses Kircher proved from " reason, experience, authorities," and illustrated by maps.[31]

Although the earth was created with all its present features, Kircher was modern in his realization of its constant physiographic changes.   He mentioned the rise and the destruction of mountains caused by earthquakes and eruptions as well as their gradual attrition by time.   The advance and the retreat of the sea, generally as caused by earth tremors, seem to have impressed him.   Islands, such as Sicily and Atlantis, had been separated from or joined to the mainland or had been swallowed up by the sea; and Asia, united to North America even after the deluge, had been sundered. Rivers had formed deltas by bringing earth down into the sea.[32]

[30] Kircher, op. cit., t. i, pp. 17, 19, 113, 114.

[31] Ibid., t. i, pp. 158-161.   " Tum ratione, tum experientia, authoribusque," ibid., t. i, p. 158.

[32] Ibid., t. i, pp. 76-84, 99, 181 ; Kircher, Arca Noë (Amsterdam, 1675), pp. 4, 188-196.

A most interesting feature in the *Mundus Subterraneus* was the innumerable illustrations. Perhaps the most fascinating of these were the maps or plans of the hydrophylacia and the pyrophylacia [33] and the map of the sun. The solar map with its description was so vivid that Swinden selected the sun as the obvious location of hell and was delighted to correlate the recently adopted doctrine that the solar sphere was the center of the universe with the ancient theory that hell must be as far as possible from heaven.[34]

Kircher wrote several other books, from the pages of which we may glean some additional facts about creation. For example, God then created a definite number of animal species, the progeny of which increased until they filled the earth. By the influence of different climes, or of the heavenly bodies, or of their parents' imaginations and by cross-breeding, they were so changed as to seem new species; but of course it was necessary to take into the ark only the representatives of the original species.[35] It was also obviously unnecessary for Noah to preserve those reptiles, including insects, that were born of decaying matter.[36] Paradise was planted on the third day of creation in northern Mesopotamia. Until the flood all the patriarchs lived in that district.[37]

Kircher's work was popular and was constantly mentioned with respect by both Catholics and Protestants. Even before publication the first edition of the *Itinerarivm Exstaticvm* was almost sold out, and copies were exported from

[33] Kircher, *Mundus Subterraneus* (Amsterdam, 1664-5), t. i, between pp. 174 and 175 and pp. 180 and 181.

[34] *Ibid.*, t. i, pp. 57-62. The picture is between pp. 60 and 61. Swinden, *An Enquiry into the Nature and Place of Hell* (London, 1727).

[35] Kircher, *Arca Noë* (Amsterdam, 1675), pp. 49-51, 75, 76, 94-97.

[36] *Ibid.*, pp. 48, 49, 51-54.

[37] *Ibid.*, pp. 197-203.

Rome to France and to Germany.[38] In 1660 another edition was published north of the Alps at Würzburg by a friend and fellow Jesuit, Gaspar Schott, with voluminous notes and defenses. To this was added an account of Kircher's *Mundus Subterraneus*.[39] Like Kircher, Schott accepted the Tychonian system, after giving a summary of the three conflicting systems, and rejected the heliocentric on theological grounds.[40] He agreed with Kircher, Scheiner [41] and others that the heavens were fluid throughout,[42] while Riccioli believed that the lower or planetary portion was liquid and the upper or stellar heaven, adjacent to the supercelestial waters, was solid.[43] Schott as well as Kircher believed that the stars were moved by Intelligences, denied inhabitants of the moon and " other stars " on Biblical grounds, asserted that the heavenly globes carried their vortices or atmospheres filled with their effluvia around with them instead of being carried by these vortices and accepted the effects generally attributed by astrology to the planets. He disagreed with his friend about the distances of the fixed stars, for he conceived them all to be about the same distance from the earth.[44]

38 Kircher, *Iter Extaticum Coeleste* (Würzburg, 1660), p. 1.

39 *Ibid.*, pp. 9, 10.

40 *Ibid.*, pp. 36-39.

41 Scheiner, who died in 1650, was another Jesuit, who wrote a book entitled *Rosa Ursina*, quoted by Schott and others. The book was written in opposition to Galileo.

42 Kircher, *op. cit.*, p. 35.

43 Riccioli, *Almagestvm Novvm Astronomiam Veterem Novamqve Complectens* (Bologna, 1651), vol. ii, pp. 224, 225, 238-244, 289.

44 Kircher, *Iter Extaticum Coeleste* (Würzburg, 1660), pp. 35, 60, 94, 152-154, 233, 241, 243, 244, 283-289, 312-315, 342, 343. Schott attributed to Kircher the belief that the stars were moved by Intelligences. Kircher was convinced that they inhabited and acted upon the celestial spheres, but was vague as to their exact purpose. The duties of the planetary angels were discussed by Kircher also in Kircher, *Itinerarivm Exstaticvm* (Rome, 1656), pp. 97, 98, 117, 182, 183, 203, 227, 228, 254, 255. *Cf.* also *supra*, p. 51.

CHAPTER VI

Two Theologians of the Seventeenth Century

THE seventeenth century was a period when theologians flourished. Those of the Roman Catholic Church, like Kircher and Bossuet,[1] accepted the Church's interpretation of the Mosaic narrative. Because of their orthodoxy many of the clerical effusions possess little originality, but the weighty quartos of Protestant scholars and theologians present scattered data of some interest. Two of the most frequently quoted divines were Samuel Bochart (1599-1667), a French scholar born in Rouen and for many years pastor in Caen; and Edward Stillingfleet (1635-1699), who took an important share in the English controversies of the century and was made Bishop of Worcester. Both were men of noble character and of profound erudition.

Bochart's chief works were a *Geographia Sacra* (1646 and 1651), which was largely an account of the places where the descendants of Noah settled after the dispersion, and the *Hierozoicon* (1663).[2] For this account of the animals mentioned in Scripture he gathered material from Pliny and Aristotle even more freely than from the sacred pages. At his death Bochart left notes for a treatise on the location of the Garden of Eden. They were edited by a friend. He had also located Eden on a map and solved the difficulty of the four rivers in the garden by having the Tigris and Euphrates join in the northern part of Paradise, form a single stream for some distance and then separate. He declared it not

[1] Bossuet, *Discours sur l'histoire universelle* (Paris, 1850).

[2] Bochart, *Opera Omnia* (Leyden, 1712), 3 vols.

unusual for the same river to have different names at various
parts of its course.[3]   As was natural in view of his interest
in animals, Bochart treated in several places of their presentation before Adam for names.   The frontispiece of the first
volume pictured the processional approach of all the beasts,
including the unicorn, while a dog sat at Adam's feet.
All creatures except the aquatic and hybrid were led to
him by angels or by a secret impulse from God, as they
were later brought to the ark.   Bochart gave many reasons
for the episode, among which was the Lord's purpose that
animals might feel man's dominion.   Adam's great wisdom
was shown in the appropriateness of the appellations he invented.   He was able to impose them on other men because
they were his descendants.   This incident also proved that
Hebrew was the primitive tongue, since the suitability of
these and other early names vanished in other tongues.
Language was given by God to Adam and Eve immediately
upon their creation that they might understand him and
enjoy each other's conversation.[4]   Bochart agreed with
those who said that God created everything through Christ.
The birds as well as the beasts were made from earth, not
from water.   He almost casually denied the possibility of
Pre-Adamites on the ground that Moses distinctly rejected
such inhabitants of the earth.   Nevertheless, he seemed to
accept the Talmudic suggestion that ten things were created
after creation, including the rainbow, manna and the Pit.[5]
Even in Paradise Adam cultivated the land, but without toil;
similarly, the serpent's method of progression was not
changed after man's fall but was merely made laborious.[6]

[3] Bochart, *op. cit.*, vol. i, map opposite p. 9.   Also pp. 9-30.

[4] *Ibid.*, vol. i, columns 50-52, 699-704; vol. ii, preface, cols. 2, 20-21,
53-72, 77.

[5] *Ibid.*, vol. ii, cols. 55, 193, 955; vol. iii, col. 350.

[6] *Ibid.*, vol. i, cols. 843, 844.

Stillingfleet's *Origines Sacrae, a Rational Account of the Grounds of Natural and Reveal'd Religion,* first published in 1622, had reached its eighth edition when it was included in a posthumous edition of his works in 1709. Its appearance was followed immediately by a series of rapid promotions which placed the author in the episcopal see of Worcester. Like Bochart, he denied the existence of Pre-Adamites, and called the belief a frivolous suggestion. He declared that the events of the first ages were preserved in memory, though in corrupt form, by heathen tradition, which by its agreement reinforced the Mosaic account. Moses had unusual ability and training, and was therefore able to discern and to reject things contrary to reason or untrue. Since he would not intentionally lie because of his belief in his inspiration by God, what he wrote was true. In addition, the miracles which he performed confirmed Moses's word by the authority of the Lord.[7] " The great gullery of the world hath been, taking philosophical Dictates for the standard of Reason, and unprov'd *Hypotheses* for certain Foundations for our discourse to rely upon. And the seeking to reconcile the Mysteries of our Faith to these, hath been that which hath almost destroy'd it, and turn'd our Religion into a mere philosophical Speculation."[8] On this ground he rejected the atomic theory of creation and " whirlpools " with especial reference to Descartes, whose system he summarized. He declared that the Cartesian hypothesis was not, however, atheistic, since, as the French philosopher himself said, it required an antecedent creation of matter by God. This thesis coincided with Stillingfleet's doctrine that matter was not eternal, though he differed from Descartes by saying that its creation was contemporaneous

[7] Stillingfleet, *Origines Sacrae* (London, 1709), pt. i, preface and pp. 9-43, 66-90, 216, 221, 226, 231, 265, 267-270, 334-336.

[8] *Ibid.*, pt. i, p. 81.

with its formation into the visible universe.   The universe, which was made of nothing by God, was not formed solely for the sake of men.[9]

In his discussion of the flood Stillingfleet adopted the hypothesis that a great reservoir of waters underlay the earth's crust and was connected with the sea.   To supply springs moist vapors rose from it through the earth even to the tops of mountains as blood rises in the veins from the liver.[10]   He agreed with those who rejected the universality of the deluge, and preferred to leave America unsubmerged. Of course all human beings outside the ark perished.   As to the survival of animals Stillingfleet remained in doubt, but affirmed the probability of a wider distribution for them than for mankind, since the method of their creation was different and implied large scale production in all parts of the earth.   The species of animals were so defined and limited in the beginning that no new ones had since appeared. God's declaration that the work was good proved that they and men were fully perfect in the qualities characteristic of their species.   Therefore Adam before his fall possessed great intellectual powers.   He did not know everything; but his reason was perfect; and he had the intrinsic power of recognizing truth and falsehood, as he showed by his ability to bestow appropriate names on animals.[11]

The writings of Bochart and Stillingfleet are characteristic of the best Scriptural commentaries and sermons during the seventeenth century so far as they touch upon scientific subjects.   Their ponderous erudition is more evident than any startlingly novel doctrine based upon recent scientific hypotheses.   When clergymen wished to promulgate un-

[9] Stillingfleet, *op. cit.*, pt. i, pp. 237-239, 244, 263, 265, 266, 270, 277, 278, 280-296, pt. ii, pp. 18-20, 23-25, 30, 93, 101-116.

[10] *Ibid.*, pt. i, pp. 340-344.

[11] *Ibid.*, pt. i, pp. 1-3, 337-339, pt. ii, p. 9.

orthodox theses, they generally published their opinions anonymously, as did John Wilkins (1614?-1672), Bishop of Chester, who about 1638 published two popular books on lunar inhabitants and on the planetary nature of the earth.[12]

[12] Wilkins, *The Mathematical and Philosophical Works* (London, 1707-1708).

CHAPTER VII

Burnet, the Stimulator of Controversy

With Thomas Burnet (1635-1715) and his successors from 1681 to 1700 we reach a new phase. The new astronomy was accepted whole-heartedly, but so was the Mosaic account. Aristotle, however, was in less repute. Although there were still quotations from authorities, they seem to have been inserted rather from a desire to make the new doctrines plausible and palatable to the general public than from any belief in their importance. Burnet, for example, who quoted more learnedly than most of his contemporaries from every possible author, said in his *Archaeologiae Philosophicae* that he had meant to write his *Theory of the Earth* without reference to the Bible or the ancients. As the work developed, he constantly gained new light on his beliefs from both sources; and the theory illumined more clearly both the Bible and the classics. As an appendix or commentary on the *Theory* he collected an imposing list of quotations that he ascribed to poets and philosophers of China, Assyria, India, Persia, Arabia, Phoenicia and Egypt as well as to the more familiar Greeks and Romans, and published them, with other material, in Latin under the title *Archaeologiae Philosophicae,* probably in 1692.[1]

---

[1] Burnet, *Doctrina Antiqua de Rerum Originibus* (London, 1729, 1736), *Archaeologiae Philosophicae*, pp. 1, 2. The dedication to King William was dated 1692, though the date of publication was given as 1676 by Greenslet, *Joseph Glanvill* (New York, 1900), p. 126. Burnet's book, dated London, 1692, was favorably reviewed in the Royal Society of London, *Philosophical Transactions* (London, 1665-1933), no. 201, 1693, pp. 796 *et seq.*

Both intellectually and chronologically Burnet was a scientist and a scholar before he was a theologian. Before he became clergyman and bishop, he had been physician to Charles II. In 1680 or 1681 [2] he published in Latin a quarto entitled *Telluris Theoria Sacra*.[3] Its resemblances to Descartes's beliefs, as well as its differences, suggest that he was inspired to his task by the work of the French philosopher. The book evidently pleased Charles II, for he encouraged the author to produce an English version.[4] The result was *The Sacred Theory of the Earth,* which was published during the period 1684-1689 and immediately became popular. The first two books were dedicated to King Charles and the others to Queen Mary. The fifth edition in 1722 inserted an ode to the author by Addison, and Steele in the *Spectator* mentioned the theory several times with enthusiasm.[5] Burnet retained royal favor after the Revolution of 1688, since he was chaplain to William III in 1692, when his publication in Latin of the *Archaeologiae Philosophicae* caused a great scandal because he rashly rejected, especially in *Part I, A Critique on the Mosaic Creation,* a large part of the literal narrative in Genesis, and suggested that Moses in his account of the creation spoke in accordance with the common opinion of his contemporaries or perhaps

[2] The date assigned in the *Dictionary of National Biography* is not the same as that in the life of Burnet included in the *Doctrina Antiqua* (p. 4). Other events in his life, together with accounts of his writings and of his opponents, were given in his biography in the *Doctrina Antiqua,* especially pp. 3, 5-14, 17.

[3] Reprinted, Burnet, *Telluris Theoria Sacra, Originem & Mutationes Generales Orbis Nostri, . . . Accedunt Archaeologiae Philosophicae, Sive Doctrina Antiqua de Rerum Originibus* (Amsterdam, 1694).

[4] Jéhan, *Dictionnaire de cosmogonie et de paléontologie* (Paris, 1854), art. " Géologie (Histoire de la)," col. 626.

[5] For example, *The Spectator* (London, 1898), no. 143, August 14, 1711, no. 146, August 17, 1711.

in parables.[6] Burnet made the task of interpretation still easier by the assertion that the account pertained only to the formation of our earth about six thousand years before, while the universe was much older.[7] Everything, including elemental matter and angelic and celestial substance, was created at one time out of nothing.[8] Burnet had intended to write on the whole of creation, but had become too old.[9]

The stars were fiery; and the planets, among which he placed the earth, opaque. The other planets were probably formed out of separate collections of matter, each in the condition of a chaos, in a manner similar to the production of the earth. Even after creation the history of the earth

[6] Burnet, *Doctrina Antiqua de Rerum Originibus* (London, 1729, 1736), *The Life of Dr. Thomas Burnet*, pp. 13, 14 *etc., Letter to Bookseller by C. B.*, p. ii, also *Archaeologiae Philosophicae*, 1st pt., p. 174, *Part I, A Critique on the Mosaic Creation*, pp. 3, 29, 41, 46, 47, 51-59, 67-89; Burnet, *The Sacred Theory of the Earth* (London, 1722), vol. ii, pp. 387-390, *A Review Of the Sacred Theory of the Earth, And of its Proofs: Especially in Reference to Scripture.* Greenslet, *op. cit.*, p. 126, declared that Burnet's purpose was to express grave doubts of the historical and the scientific truth of the Pentateuch. The *Archaeologiae Philosophicae* was translated into English only after Burnet's death, in 1729 or 1736, for both dates are given, and published under the title *Doctrina Antiqua de Rerum Originibus*, together with a collection of other papers. Chief among them was a series of *Remarks* by the editors or the translator, who felt compelled to defend the Biblical version and to suggest that Burnet's statements should not be accepted at their face value. To this was added a biography of the author, an *Essay on the Use of Reason in Religion, An Appendix Concerning the Modern Brachmans in the Indies* by Burnet and the translation of a small French tract by M. De la Jonchere entitled *The Immobility of the Earth Demonstrated.*

[7] Burnet, *The Sacred Theory of the Earth* (London, 1722), vol. i, pp. 2, 3, 47; Burnet, *Doctrina Antiqua de Rerum Originibus* (London, 1729, 1736), *Archaeologiae Philosophicae*, 1st pt., p. 162, 2d pt., p. 4, *part i critique*, pp. 11, 29-38, 45-51.

[8] *Ibid., Archaeologiae Philosophicae, part i critique*, pp. 34, 35, 45, 50.

[9] *Ibid., Archaeologiae Philosophicae*, pp. vi-viii.

was a prototype of theirs. Venus had a flood like ours about the same time, as was proved by Varro's account of its appearance in the days of Ogyges or Noah; the broken and disordered surfaces of Mars and of the moon evinced a series of events that resembled the terrestrial; on Saturn apparently the polar caps fell into the abyss and left the equatorial belt as a ring; Mercury was too near the sun for its constitution to be discernible; Jupiter, except in a single spot, retained its outer crust. Twice Burnet spoke as though each star might pass through the stage of a chaos and become a planet, and added that planets might break their crusts and be restored to their stellar glory.[10]

Burnet showed his scientific bent by devising such an explanation of creation as would elucidate the causes and the manner of the earth's greater subsequent vicissitudes. His theory accounted for the flood and the final conflagration, for the millennial world and our globe's state after the Last Judgment, as well as for its creation; but most of the

---

[10] Burnet, *op. cit., Archaeologiae Philosophicae*, 1st pt., pp. 180, 181, 2d pt., p. 74, *part i critique*, pp. 35-37, 51; Burnet, *The Sacred Theory of the Earth* (London, 1722), bk. i, pp. 229-233. Sir Walter Raleigh had explained the traditional peculiar appearance of Venus by mist in the air from our flood, together with the fact, for which he quoted Galileo and his "perspective glasses," that Venus occasionally appeared horned. Raleigh, *The History of the World* (Edinburgh, 1820) (1st ed., 1614), vol. i, pp. 209, 210. It was explained as due to the moisture in the air by Warren, *Geologia* (London, 1690), pp. 160, 161. Warren as well as Raleigh, Burnet and Beaumont said that St. Augustine had quoted Varro, who attributed to Castor the statement that during the time of Ogyges the planet Venus changed color, shape, size and course. Since this was perhaps the first Ogyges, who was Noah, the changes were probably due to the moisture in the air at the time of the deluge. This vapor would make the planet seem larger, with various excrescences and altered color, and would make its course seem to fluctuate. Beaumont agreed and added that Venus was really horned from time to time. Beaumont, *Considerations On a Book, Entituled The Theory of the Earth* (London, 1692-3), pp. 66-68. *Cf.* also *infra*, p. 313.

criticism he aroused dealt with his hypotheses concerning
the creation and the deluge.[11]

The original chaos, well authenticated by both the Bible
and pagan authors, consisted of particles of differing density.
The strife of the whole mass, which was due to the mixture
of dissimilar parts, was followed by the separation of the
jarring elements. They formed concentric orbs [12] because
the particles settled to the center of the chaos in accordance
with their specific gravity. Since the primitive mixture had
neither excrescences nor cavities, the earth produced from it
was smooth, regular and uniform, without mountains or
sea. At the center was a solid mass of heavier matter like
the yolk of an egg.[13] This solid core, or part of it, even
preceded the precipitation of the various constituents in the
chaos. It was, or possibly enclosed, the central fire,[4]
Around it lay in spherical form the liquid particles, and in a
still larger sphere, the gaseous or airy. The oily or greasy
portions of the liquid gradually separated from the watery
and floated on the surface. The fine particles of solid matter
that had been suspended in the air settled upon the oleaginous superficial layer, and, since they were unable to penetrate it, became mixed with it into a gummy mass. The

[11] Book i of the *Theory* dealt with the creation, book ii with the
primeval world and the flood, book iii with the final conflagration and
book iv with the millennium and the fate of our planet after the Judgment.

[12] Burnet, *Doctrina Antiqua de Rerum Originibus* (London, 1729, 1736),
Archaeologiae Philosophicae, 2nd part, pp. 12-15.

[13] Burnet, *The Sacred Theory of the Earth* (London, 1722), vol. i.
The Orphic theory of the mundane egg appealed to Burnet, who enlarged
on it in several places. *Ibid.*, vol. i, pp. 85, 86, 95, 96, 373, 374, 388;
Burnet, *Doctrina Antiqua de Rerum Originibus* (London, 1729, 1736),
Archaeologiae Philosophicae, 1st part, pp. 150, 164, 2nd part, p. 39;
Beaumont, *op. cit.*, pp. 143-148, who rejected and even ridiculed the
suggestion.

[14] Burnet, *The Sacred Theory of the Earth* (London, 1722), vol. i,
pp. 85, 374; vol. ii, pp. 68-72, 194.

compound hardened into a rich, fertile soil or crust of earth, that covered an abyss of waters as the shell of the egg covers and constricts the white. This crust, which was spherical, or rather ovoid with the longest diameter from pole to pole, was smooth, without rocks or oceans.[15] The idea that a chaos in settling would naturally produce a smooth-surfaced sphere was strengthened in Burnet's mind by the statement that God, seeing the earth, pronounced it good, and by the thesis that He would naturally make only a perfect world, without mountains, which were blemishes, the ruins of a frightful catastrophe.

These Mountains are plac'd in no Order one with another, that can either respect Use or Beauty; and if you consider them singly, they do not consist of any Proportion of Parts that is referable to any Design, or that hath the least Footsteps of Art or Counsel. There is nothing in Nature more shapeless and ill-figur'd than an old Rock or a Mountain, and all that Variety that is among them, is but the various Modes of Irregularity. . . . 'Tis true, they cannot look so ill now as they did at first; a Ruin that is fresh, looks much worse than afterwards, when the Earth grows discolour'd and skinn'd over. But I fancy, if we had seen the Mountains when they were new born and raw, when the Earth was fresh broken, and the Waters of the Deluge newly retir'd, the Fractions and Confusions of them would have appear'd very ghastly and frightful.[16]

[15] *Ibid.*, vol. i, especially bk. i, pp. 67-88. Burnet, *Doctrina Antiqua de Rerum Originibus* (London, 1729, 1736), 1st part, p. 176, and especially 2d part, pp. 16-96. Keill, *An Examination of Dr. Burnet's Theory of the Earth. Together with some remarks on Mr. Whiston's New Theory of the Earth* (Oxford, 1698), pp. 38-45, 48-51, 103, 104, 107-143, 172, proved, sometimes by elaborate mathematical calculations, all these doctrines impossible.

[16] Burnet, *The Sacred Theory of the Earth* (London, 1722), vol. i, bk. i, pp. 195, 196; *cf.* also p. 43. Also Burnet, *Doctrina Antiqua de Rerum Originibus* (London, 1729, 1736), *Archaeologiae Philosophicae, part i critique*, p. 45.

It seemed to the author impossible that the sea channel could have been scooped out and the excavated soil placed elsewhere in so short a space of time as a single day. The waters could not have flowed in that time from the center of the continents to the ocean bed. Moreover, any rivers thus formed would have been salt; and they could not have watered Paradise or the earth with their fugitive flow, which could not be replenished since springs were not yet born. No rain had fallen and water had not had time to run into the sea and to return by ways not yet opened far inland to the heads of rivers.[17] For this reason and other similar ones, chiefly the deficiency of time, Burnet rather boldly suggested the story of the Garden of Eden to be a parable.[18] He rejected also the account of the waters above the firmament, and explained the statement as an attempt of Moses, by the hypothesis of a receptacle for water from which the Almighty might let down rain, to favor the vulgar idea that rain was sent from heaven as a direct act of God, rather than the true doctrine that it was a condensation of vapors.[19] Burnet also rejected Moses's idea that light antedated the sun as impossible, and asserted that the sole reason for the proposition was to prevent the belief that God worked three days in the dark.[20] All these statements Burnet believed to have been inserted from political motives and because of the impossibility involved in explaining natural philosophy to vulgar capacities. He declared that the Israelites were especially gross and stupid. Had Moses told them

[17] Burnet, *op. cit.*, *Archaeologiae Philosophicae*, *part i critique*, pp. 15-17, 42-45. As is clear, Burnet in this place refused to decide between the rival theories as to the source of springs, whether from rain or from the sea by subterranean passages.

[18] *Ibid.*, *Archaeologiae Philosophicae*, *part i critique*, pp. 10-26.

[19] *Ibid.*, *Archaeologiae Philosophicae*, *part i critique*, pp. 38-41.

[20] *Ibid.*, *Archaeologiae Philosophicae*, *part i critique*, pp. 41, 42.

BURNET STIMULATOR OF CONTROVERSY 75

facts they could not understand, they would have ridiculed
and left him; and he could not have led them or instilled
moral truths by giving them doctrines which, though false,
were superior to those of neighboring peoples and would
lead them to the worship of God.[21]

Burnet's primeval earth displayed other peculiarities. It
was always equidistant from the sun; and, since its axis was
not oblique,[22] it enjoyed perpetual spring. The serenity of
the atmosphere and the stability of the heavens and of the
ether produced longevity not only in men but also in animals
and in plants. The same reasons, together with the richness
of the soil and the dews of heaven, caused the spontaneous
generation of plants, animals and men from the earth.
Even to the present time the earth produced insects and little
creeping things without parents.[23] There were no

violent Meteors there, nor any that proceeded from Extremity
of Cold; as Ice, Snow, or Hail; nor Thunder neither; for the
Clouds could not be of a Quality and Constancy fit for such an
Effect, either by falling one upon another, or by their Disruption. And as for Winds, they could not be either impetuous or
irregular in that Earth; seeing there were neither Mountains
nor any other Inequalities to obstruct the Course of the Vapours;
nor any unequal Seasons, or unequal Action of the Sun, nor any

[21] Burnet, *op. cit.*, *Archaeologiae Philosophicae*, *part i critique*, pp.
3, 29, 41-49, 51-59, 67-89.

[22] Burnet, *The Sacred Theory of the Earth* (London, 1722), vol. i, bk.
ii, especially pp. 371, 372. The change in axis came from the flood which
disturbed the center of gravity in the earth or perhaps·its magnetism.
Ibid., vol. ii, *An Answer to the Exceptions made by Mr. Erasmus Warren,
Against the Sacred Theory of the Earth* (London, 1722) (3rd ed.), p. 37.

[23] Burnet, *The Sacred Theory of the Earth* (London, 1722), vol. i,
bk. i and bk. ii, especially pp. 245-250, 254-262, 269-306, 335, 369; Burnet,
Doctrina Antiqua de Rerum Originibus (London, 1729, 1736), *Archaeologiae Philosophicae*, 2d part, pp. 63-96. Keill, *op. cit.*, pp. 62-83, 172,
173, denied both the truth and more particularly the desirability of such
a perpetual equinox.

contrary and struggling Motions of the Air: Nature was then a Stranger to all those Disorders. But as for watry Meteors, or those that rise from watry Vapours more immediately, as Dews and Rains, there could not but be Plenty of these in some Part or other of that Earth; for the Action of the Sun in raising Vapours was very strong and very constant, and the Earth was at first moist and soft, and according as it grew more dry, the Rays of the Sun would pierce more deep into it, and reach at length the great Abyss which lay underneath, and was an unexhausted Storehouse of new Vapours.[24]

Burnet then declared that the vapors would be forced towards the poles where they would be condensed into continuous rains, since the evaporation at the equator was continuous, and would form lakes encircling the planet not far from each pole. These would overflow into rivers, which would make their way towards the equator because the oviform shape of the earth made the equator nearer the center of our globe than were the poles. Since the rivers would traverse only rainless territory, they would gradually evaporate and divide into ever smaller streams till, after having watered the earth, they lost themselves in the hot sand belt of the torrid zone.[25] Because of heat and drought, this narrow equatorial belt was impassable. Burnet suggested that the site of Paradise was probably in the southern hemisphere, and that the torrid zone was perhaps the flaming sword that protected it from invasion.[26]

Gradually the heat of the sun dried the earth's crust so that it " chapped " and became weakened. No winter in-

[24] Burnet, The Sacred Theory of the Earth (London, 1722), vol. i, bk. ii, pp. 308, 309.

[25] Ibid., vol. i, bk. ii, pp. 310-319. Keill, op. cit., pp. 84-107, 145-157, 173, 174, 334, 335, asserted that no rivers could be thus formed, and that they would not sufficiently water the earth if they did exist.

[26] Burnet, op. cit., vol. i, bk. ii, pp. 319, 332-334, 346-363.

tervened to close the cracks. Meanwhile the solar warmth heated and volatilized the water in the abyss below so that it exerted a constantly increasing pressure. At the foreordained time, 1656 years after the creation, when man had become corrupt, this continual summer broke the earth crust. It was divided into several masses, one for each continent or large island, and fell into the abyss. For example, the crust was fractured from pole to pole through the present Atlantic and Pacific Oceans. The edges fell faster than the centers of the masses. Because they crumpled under, because the inner earth had less surface area than the crust and because water and air were imprisoned underneath the middle parts of the continental masses, the central portions remained elevated. The crash produced mountains and irregularities of the strata, and left many caverns filled with air, fire and subterranean waters. Most mountains were hollow and filled with these three elements. The subsidence of the outer crust caused the deluge, for the waters dashed to the tops of the high mountains just formed, and some months were required for their gradual collection into those portions of the abyss left uncovered for their reception,— i. e., the ocean beds. Even years passed before the surface of the earth was freed by human industry from some of the innumerable lakes and bogs left by the flood. Noah's ark was probably stabilized by guardian angels during the rough weather. It floated more easily because the catastrophe began with a rain, the earliest in the history of the world. At least none earlier was mentioned.[27]

[27] Burnet, *op. cit.*, vol. i, bk. i, pp. 63-66, 68, 69, 90-114, 118-145, 149-153, 196, 199-201, 211, 244, 328. The last statement seems to contradict his method of producing rivers. He explained the discrepancy by the later statement that this was the first rain in the temperate zone. He solved the difficulty of repeopling America by the suggestion that probably some antediluvian men and animals in that hemisphere were saved like Noah. *Ibid.*, vol. i, bk. ii, pp. 374-376; Burnet, *Doctrina Antiqua*

Burnet was not satisfied to produce merely an elucidation of the causes for the present condition of the earth and a poetical rhapsody concerning its primeval state. He sought to prophesy the future fate of the globe. According to him, the exterior portions of the earth as deep as the bed of the sea would be dissolved by fire and reduced anew to chaos. The fire would be preceded by a terrible drought, which would diminish or totally remove most streams and bodies of water and would so desiccate all vegetation that it as well as the surface and subterranean stores of bitumen, sulphur, coal, pitch and oil would serve as fuel. Possibly fresh fuel would be supernaturally added. The entire catastrophe would be partly natural, partly miraculous. Presumably God would act by the agency of angelic hands. The air-filled caverns and cracks would be increased in number and in size by earthquakes. Eruptions on land and sea would commence in Italy; and Rome, like Sodom, would be swallowed up by a lake of fire and brimstone. Such water as remained in the oceans would be evaporated by the streams of burning lava, which would pour into the sea bed, or would be drawn into subterranean cavities to replace that which by its transformation into a vapor had aided or caused the production of earthquakes and of eruptions. At the

de Rerum Originibus (London, 1729, 1736), Archaeologiae Philosophicae, 2d part, pp. 40-63. This explanation of the flood was denied by Keill, who called it "an Ingenious Romance," largely on the ground of insufficient water. Keill, op. cit., pp. 146-149, 157-170, 175, 176. De Luc quoted the Abbé Pluche, Spectacle de la nature, tome iii, 2de partie, as believing in a primeval earth having a perpetual equinox. It was founded upon a great abyss of water, into which, broken by an earthquake and a change in the axis, it sank at the deluge. The tipping of the axis produced great variations of temperature in the two hemispheres. This caused violent winds, which so beat upon the waters of the sky that they were condensed and poured down upon the earth. De Luc, Lettres physiques et morales sur l'histoire de la terre et de l'homme (The Hague and Paris, 1779, 1780), vol. i, pp. 338-342.

same time, the axis of the earth would return to its original position. Eventually the core of earth would be surrounded by an undifferentiated molten mass. Outside the whole would be a chaos of air, water vapor and earth particles, which would form an opaque cloud of darkness. Gradually the heavier particles would settle upon the earth core as they had at creation, and would form anew a fertile crust without sea or mountains, like that which rejoiced the inhabitants of the primeval earth. This millennial world would be inhabited in peace and joy by the righteous until the Day of Judgment. After that time the earth would probably be turned into a mass of ethereal matter like a sun or a star, and would be removed to some other part of the universe. Thus our planet would reassume its original stellar status.[28]

Whoever reads Burnet will be impressed by the vagueness of his proofs. He quoted freely from ancient authors and from the Church Fathers, even in the *Theory,* but like all his contemporaries seldom mentioned the specific title of a book and even more infrequently the exact chapter. His references to the Bible were more precise; but like many other commentators he did not realize the poetic quality of the Psalms, and for scientific data quoted as readily from them and from the book of Job as from the Pentateuch, which was accepted as historical by practically everybody. A basic text for his theory was 2 Peter 3:5-7 with its implication that the present world differed materially from the antediluvial and the millennial, both of which were upon the waters. Another weakness was Burnet's illogical tendency to slip from a possibility to a certainty in stating a proof, as may be seen in the following quotations. In the first book of the *Theory,* he said, " For if we admit for the *Yolk* a

---

[28] Burnet, *The Sacred Theory of the Earth* (London, 1722), vol. ii, bk. iii, pp. 63, 64, 74, 75, 77, 78, 88, 90, 91, 93-103, 106-129, 133, 136, 137, 157, 158, bk. iv, pp. 192-197, 204, 215, 232-236, 260-265, 289-304, 308, 316-320.

Central Fire (which tho' very reasonable, we had no occasion to take Notice of in our Theory of the Chaos) "; and followed it in the second book with this, "We have show'd there (*Book* I. *c.* 5) that the Figure of it, when finish'd, was Oval, and the inward Form of it was a Frame of four Regions, encompassing one another, where that of Fire lay in the Middle like the Yolk, and a Shell of Earth inclos'd them all ".[29] Burnet mentioned the fact that Descartes explained the irregular shape of the present earth by an hypothesis similar to his, but considered that the Frenchman had been guilty of great oversights, especially in his omission of the deluge and in his neglect of the centuries during which the primitive crust lasted as a habitable globe. It seems doubtful that Burnet ever realized how greatly he was indebted to his predecessor.[30]

[29] Burnet, *op. cit.*, vol. i, bk. i, p. 85, bk. ii, p. 374.

[30] Burnet, *op. cit.*, vol. i, bk. i, pp. 153, 154; Burnet, *Telluris Theoria Sacra* (Amsterdam, 1694), pp. 34, 91, 92.

CHAPTER VIII

The Zealous Debaters

Burnet's theory evoked a response. There was a plethora of answers. The year after the appearance of the complete English translation, Erasmus Warren, rector of Worlington in Suffolk, published a volume, part of whose title read *Geologia: or, a Discourse Concerning the Earth before the Deluge. Wherein The Form and Properties ascribed to it, In a Book intituled The Theory of the Earth, Are Excepted against.* He rejected most of Burnet's views and suggested some of his own. This called forth an *Answer* from his opponent, and Warren responded in 1691 with a *Defence* of his exceptions. The next year, in reply to Burnet's *Short Consideration of the Defence,* he printed another article named *Some Reflections upon the Short Consideration Of the Defence of the Exceptions against the Theory of the Earth.* In the same winter John Beaumont produced *Considerations On a Book, Entituled The Theory of the Earth.* In 1698 John Keill wrote *An Examination of Dr. Burnet's Theory of the Earth. Together with some remarks on Mr. Whiston's New Theory of the Earth,* to which both those attacked published replies. In addition, a series of longer works, which appeared during the last decade of the seventeenth century, were clearly inspired by Burnet. Woodward published his *Essay toward a Natural History of the Earth,* John Ray his *Three Physico-Theological Discourses* and his *Wisdom of God Manifested in the Works of the Creation* and William Whiston his *New Theory of the Earth.* John Harris defended Woodward with *Remarks On*

*some Late Papers, Relating to the Universal Deluge: And
to the Natural History of the Earth.*

Warren's work was rather incoherent. He declared that
to affirm the dissolution of the earth as the cause of the flood
would prove Moses's description of the rivers of Paradise
false, since they could not be in both the prediluvial and the
postdiluvial world. Such a rejection of the description
" would be horrid Blasphemy, it [the description] being
dictated by the Holy Ghost." [1]   In another passage he said,
" Should God deceive . . . in *one* case, he might do it in
more," or in all; and so good and wise a man as Moses must
have written truly. [2]   Nevertheless, like Burnet and many another, he interpreted Biblical passages literally or liberally to
suit his need. [3]   An objection he raised to Burnet's theory was
based on the time involved. Each day of creation consisted
of twenty-four hours; and the formation of the outer crust
by Burnet's method would take too long, even if the dust in
the air drifted down as fast as snow. [4]   Another objection
he offered to Burnet's earth crust was that it could not have
formed on a foundation of water and oil, which must have
been continually fluctuating because of the earth's rotation
and the tides caused by the moon. In spite of Burnet, the
moon was certainly in existence at the time, as Moses declared. In addition, the hypotheses concerning the division
of the chaotic matter into concentric spheres and the formation of the earth's crust were scientifically unsound, since

[1] Warren, *Geologia* (London, 1690), p. 286.

[2] Warren, *A Defence of the Discourse Concerning the Earth Before
the Flood* (London, 1691), pp. 2, 3.

[3] *Ibid.*, pp. 46-60, 165-197 for example.

[4] God with His own finger wrote the Decalogue containing the statement that creation took six natural days. Hence the time is clear. *Ibid.*,
pp. 8-12, 18-22. Warren, *Geologia* (London, 1690), pp. 48-71, especially
pp. 54, 55, 62.

water, oil, air and earthy particles would not act in the manner described by Burnet.

Warren denied many other dicta of Burnet. The creation discussed in Genesis was of the entire universe, including the sun and the moon. Burnet proved the weakness of his own theory by omitting part thereof in the second edition, —that is, the statement that the sun and the moon were not created on the fourth day but were only revealed by the dissipation of the chaos.[5] If inconsistency is proof of an imperfect theory, Warren himself was at fault. He explained light before the perfect sun as in accord with "the Cartesian Principles,"[6] since light was a pressure of celestial matter away from the center of the vortex, and said that this pressure perhaps commenced on the first day and increased with the increase of solar matter at the center until the fourth day. Then he drew back and declared that the sun and the stars were created perfect. He added that perhaps the first three days were not divided or distinguished save by God's acts, as is now the case at the poles, but merely were three epochs of twenty-four hours each.[7] He denied that the earth was originally a chaos, and said it was merely "an incultivate and uninhabited lump,"[8] made directly by God out of nothing.[9] Burnet's statement that the ovoidal form of the terrestrial globe was caused by the greater pressure of the air at the

[5] Warren, *op. cit.*, pp. 73-80; Warren, *A Defense of the Discourse Concerning the Earth Before the Flood* (London, 1691), pp. 12-14, 18-22, 30-34; Warren, *Some Reflections upon the Short Consideration Of the Defence of the Exceptions against the Theory of the Earth* (London, 1692), pp. 42, 43, 50. A similar objection to the limitation of the Mosaic account of creation to the earth was made by Beaumont, *Considerations On a Book, Entituled The Theory of the Earth* (London, 1692-1693), pp. 148, 149.

[6] Warren, *Geologia* (London, 1690), p. 52.

[7] *Ibid.*, pp. 51-54.

[8] *Ibid.*, p. 90.   [9] *Ibid.*, pp. 89-91, 97.

equator, which forced the waters to the poles, was contro-
verted by the fact that the air over the torrid zone would have
been more rarefied by heat and therefore the pressure in that
area would have been reduced. Warren presented several
other reasons for rejecting the hypothesis of an ovoid earth
or for showing that it would not have had the qualities attributed to it.[10]   Burnet's earth would lack waters. It would
take too long for the solar rays to evaporate water from the
abyss through so thick a crust, which was dry since it had
been formed of dust and oil. Before the vapors could be
driven to the poles to return as rivers, the atmosphere must
be saturated; and much water evaporated by day would fall
again at night in the same spot. Because the land was level,
the water would not have been able to excavate channels for
itself and would have formed marshes till channels were dug
for it, probably by man. But the Bible mentioned rivers as
soon as man was created, even before it rained. Moreover,
there must have been a receptacle for fish, because these were
created by God on the fifth day. He acted immediately,
without recourse to natural means; the waters merely furnished suitable matter. The appearance of fish demanded
clearly the existence of oceans as well as of streams, since
not all varieties lived in fresh water. Such an abyss as Burnet described could have furnished an abiding place for no
animals. Adam was given dominion over the fish of the
sea, which in another passage were bidden to increase and fill
the waters in the seas.[11]   Warren declared that both moun-

---

[10] Warren, *op. cit.*, pp. 73-77, 114-120, 189-200; Warren, *Some Reflections upon the Short Consideration Of the Defence of the Exceptions against the Theory of the Earth* (London, 1692), pp. 22-26; Warren, *A Defence of the Discourse Concerning the Earth Before the Flood* (London, 1691), pp. 35-38, 82-94; Beaumont, *op. cit.*, pp. 100-112, also denied this ovoid earth and the qualities Burnet suggested.

[11] Warren, *op. cit.*, pp. 109-119; Warren, *Geologia* (London, 1690), pp. 107-120, 218-230.

tains and seas made the world more beautiful and useful;
hence both existed from the beginning.[12]   Besides, the Bible

[12] Warren, *op. cit.*, pp. 143-149; Warren, *A Defence of the Discourse
Concerning the Earth Before the Flood* (London, 1691), pp. 118, 143;
Warren, *Some Reflections upon the Short Consideration Of the Defence
of the Exceptions against the Theory of the Earth* (London, 1692), p. 52.
The value of mountains is a point on which most of Burnet's critics were
agreed.   In a much-quoted passage Ray gave some sixteen advantages of
mountains, including their usefulness as boundaries and defence against
attacks and " for the exercise and delight of such ingenious persons as are
addicted to search out and collect those Rarities [plants], to contemplate
and consider their Forms and Natures, and to admire and celebrate the
Wisdom of their Creator." Ray, *Three Physico-Theological Discourses*
(London, 1693), pp. 35-45 and Ray, *The Wisdom of God Manifested in the
Works of the Creation* (London, 1759), pp. 215-220 (1st editions respectively 1692 and 1691).   Ray was quoted to this effect by Foxton in his *Remarks*, pp. 247-249, in Burnet, *Doctrina Antiqua de Rerum Originibus*
(London, 1729, 1736).   Similar statements were made by Beaumont,
op. cit., pp. 55-60, 69, and by Bentley, *The Folly and Unreasonableness of
Atheism Demonstrated* (London, 1699), pp. 273-276 (1st delivered 1692).
Keill, *An Examination of Dr. Burnet's Theory of the Earth.   Together
with some remarks on Mr. Whiston's New Theory of the Earth* (Oxford,
1698), pp. 47-61, 93, showed that the lack of mountains and sea was both
impossible and undesirable.   Much later Scheidt criticized Burnet on this
ground, Leibnitz, *Opera Omnia* (Geneva, 1768), vol. ii, *Protogaea*, preface
by Scheidt (1749), pp. 183, 184.   Others who felt the value of mountains
were Hakewell, *An Apologie or Declaration of the Power and Providence
of God in the Gouernment of the World* (Oxford, 1635), pt. ii, pp. 60, 70;
Kircher, *Mundus Subterraneus* (Amsterdam, 1664-5), t. i, pp. 67-75, who
included among their values their addition to the beauty of the landscape;
Wilkins, *The Mathematical and Philosophical Works* (London, 1707-8),
bk. i, pp. 64, 65; Woodward, *An Essay toward a Natural History of the
Earth: and Terrestrial Bodies* (London, 1695), pp. 149-156; Derham,
Physico-Theology (London, 1742), p. 78; Buffon, *Oeuvres complètes*
(Paris, 1831, 1832), *Théorie de la terre* (1st ed., 1744), vol. ii, p. 57;
Cockburn, *An Enquiry into the Truth and Certainty of the Mosaic Deluge*
(London, 1750), pp. 238, 239.   On the other hand, Blancanus said that
the earth was once in a more nearly perfect state without mountains or
valleys, though he thought that at that time it was completely submerged
by water and that it was being reduced again to that state.   Blancanus,
Sphaera Mvndi (Bologna, 1620), pp. 81-85, 98, 99.   For Burnet's criticism
of mountains *cf. supra*, p. 73.

mentioned mountains. In addition, mountains could not have been produced as Burnet believed, since those of the moon, which Galileo said were higher than ours, though the moon was smaller, could not have been formed by the sinking of a planetary crust into a shallower abyss.[13] Burnet was mistaken in another matter since so important a change as that from a perpetual equinox in the primeval world to our four seasons would have been reported by tradition had it happened. Moreover, the Bible implied clearly that seasonal variations preceded the flood. Such a disruption of the earth's crust as Burnet affirmed for the cause of the deluge would have been impossible, as then the equatorial belt would have fallen first and become an ocean, whereas it was almost wholly dry land.[14]

Burnet's original difficulty with the flood narrative had been the deficiency of water. He said that the submergence of an earth like the present would require the equivalent of at least six or eight oceans.[15] Warren therefore suggested that the height of fifteen cubits above the mountains, to which the waters rose, meant perhaps only fifteen cubits above the higher inhabited plateaus. He tried to prove there was enough water in the caverns of the mountains to produce such a flood. Men and animals would have been unable to escape by scaling the peaks because of the darkness and because of the violence of the rains rushing down the slopes.[16] Both

[13] Warren, op. cit., p. 52; Warren, Geologia (London, 1690), pp. 201-206; Warren, A Defence of the Discourse Concerning the Earth Before the Flood (London, 1691), pp. 95-97.

[14] Warren, Geologia (London, 1690), pp. 160, 162-176, 289, 290.

[15] Burnet, The Sacred Theory of the Earth (London, 1722), vol. i, bk. i, especially pp. 13-40; Burnet, Doctrina Antiqua de Rerum Originibus (London, 1729, 1736), Archaeologiae Philosophicae, 2d part, p. 40. Cf. also infra, pp. 400, 401.

[16] Warren, op. cit., pp. 300-355; Warren, A Defence of the Discourse Concerning the Earth Before the Flood (London, 1691), pp. 165-169, 172-

Burnet and Warren agreed in rejecting a new creation of waters,[17] a descent of liquid from supercelestial regions [18] and a transmutation of air into the sister element.[19] Sub-terranean waters could not have emerged without some expulsive force within the earth, and none was named in Scripture.[20]

Warren suggested briefly as a possible hypothesis concerning the formation of the earth's contours that the hollow of the sea was caused by pressure from above by God. Thereupon the waters, with the additional assistance of the Holy Spirit, rushed into the depression. When the load was removed from the rest of the earth, the moisture within the ground was turned to vapor by the sun's heat, and raised the earth as yeast did dough, especially since the pores were closed so that the vapors had no vent until they exploded,[21] and

175, 190-197, 209; Warren, *Some Reflections upon the Short Consideration Of the Defence of the Exceptions against the Theory of the Earth* (London, 1692), pp. 11, 12.

[17] *Ibid.*, p. 38. Besides, creation was finished in six days. Warren, *Geologia* (London, 1690), p. 313; Burnet, *The Sacred Theory of the Earth* (London, 1722), vol. i, bk. i, pp. 25-28.

[18] If the heavens were fluid, they could not have supported such waters; if solid, the waters could not have bored their way through. If the reservoir was below the stars, even in the form of the finest mist, the waters would have concealed them; if above, the stars would have been deluged first. Since the earth was not the center of the universe, these waters could not have merely slid to it past the stars. In addition, these waters must appear and disappear during less than a year. Burnet, *op. cit.*, vol. i, bk. i, pp. 22, 23.

[19] *Ibid.*, vol. i, bk. i, pp. 28-30.

[20] *Ibid.*, vol. i, bk. i, pp. 19-23, 25-30; Burnet, *Doctrina Antiqua de Rerum Originibus* (London, 1729, 1736), *Archaeologiae Philosophicae,* 2d part, pp. 40-43, 51; Warren, *op. cit.*, pp. 313-318.

[21] Warren, *op. cit.*, pp. 209-211; Warren, *A Defence of the Discourse Concerning the Earth Before the Flood* (London, 1691), pp. 98-102; Warren, *Some Reflections upon the Short Consideration Of the Defence of the Exceptions against the Theory of the Earth* (London, 1692), pp. 5, 6.

since the primitive earth, being " soft, and light, and unctuous," [22] was yielding and more disposed to such effects.
Moreover, the downward pressure in the sea bed would force
up the land near by. As the hills dried and hardened into
stone, some parts broke off and left asperities. Weather,
the deluge, the currents of the waters at creation and in
rivers since then had still further altered the surface of the
earth.[23] At the period of creation the sun was more efficient.
Perhaps it had no " Maculaes." [24] Warren propounded an
interesting suggestion, that the disagreement as to the season
of the year at which the creation and the flood occurred indi-
cated that it was not the same season all over the earth. On
the other hand, Burnet saw a general agreement among
authorities as to the time of year and thought that this proved
a perpetual equinox.[25]

With regard to the major problem of the earth's position
in the universe, both Burnet and his critics seemed to take
the heliocentric theory, which they called Copernican, for
granted, though Burnet said that the enlightened and the
vulgar differed on the subject and " even at this Day . . .
the learned or unlearned Vulgar " could not " indure to hear
of the Sun's Rest, and the Motion of the Earth." [26] In the
same volume with the *Archaeologiae Philosophicae,* however,

[22] Warren, *Geologia* (London, 1690), p. 211.

[23] *Ibid.,* pp. 210-214; Warren, *A Defence of the Discourse Concerning
the Earth Before the Flood* (London, 1691), p. 101.

[24] Warren inserted into his English text this peculiar form of the
Latin word which was used for sun-spot. *Ibid.,* p. 98.

[25] *Ibid.,* pp. 67, 68; Burnet, *The Sacred Theory of the Earth* (London,
1722), vol. ii, *An Answer to the Exceptions made by Mr. Erasmus
Warren, Against the Sacred Theory of the Earth* (London, 1722) (3rd
ed.), p. 31.

[26] Burnet, *Doctrina Antiqua de Rerum Originibus* (London, 1729,
1736), *Archaeologiae Philosophicae,* 1st part, p. 183, and also *part i
critique,* pp. 28, 29.

Foxton, who was apparently both editor and translator of Burnet's work, printed in 1728 or 1729 a small tract by M. Jonchere, or Dela Jonchere, an engineer in his twenties, who resided in London, entitled *The Immobility of the Earth demonstrated,* together with the summary of a long work in Latin and French, *A New System of the Universe,* which the ambitious youth hoped to publish by subscription. It declared the magnitudes, distances, proportions and motions of celestial bodies in all previous systems contrary to nature, reason, physics, mechanics and geometry, and placed the earth at the center of the world and of all orbits followed by celestial bodies. It affirmed the opacity of the stars, which reflected the light of the sun. Weather, crops, mortalities and other public calamities might be foretold by the aspect of the heavens. This book was to prove a godsend to the general public, for it purported to contain the art of learning astronomy without a teacher. Perhaps M. De la Jonchere suspected a lack of enthusiasm for his theories on the part of the universities under Newtonian domination.

John Beaumont used some of the same arguments against Burnet as Warren had, but chiefly emphasized the great advantages of the present state of the world over that portrayed by his antagonist.[27] He asserted that since the knowledge of astronomy had come down from antediluvian times the universe must then have been similar. The attainment of this knowledge, together with that of the other arts and sciences, and the transmission of the tradition relating to the creation, the fall and the future redemption of man were the reasons for the longevity [28] " granted only to the *Patriarchs* and some few others by a particular Providence, and this through the means of a certain Panacaea, well known to the

---

[27] Beaumont, *op. cit.,* pp. 25b-48, 52-64, 68-70, 78-97, 100-108, 136.

[28] *Ibid.,* pp. 85-87, 93, 95-97.

Mystae." [29]   This he said though he had earlier attributed
their longevity to a combination of better soil, more propi-
tious heavens, superior diet, better water, more wholesome
air, calmer and more temperate living and greater stamina.[30]
" That the *Antediluvian Patriarchs,* as well as the *Postdilu-
vian,* were in their respective times, the most absolute Mas-
ters of the aforesaid Science [astronomy], of any Men on
the Earth, and that from them it has been convey'd down in
its Pureness to us, is what I know not how to disbelieve." [31]
Besides, a primitive year with four seasons seemed natural
to Beaumont by " Analogy with the four Elements, the four
Humors in Man's Body, the four Quarters of the World,
the Ages, the parts of the Days and Nights, &c." Each
tempered the others, and orderly variety was pleasing to contemplate.[32]

Burnet had contended that mountains could not have been
scooped out of the sea-channel, nor squeezed up while it was
squeezed down, for then the two would be equal in quantity,
and the whole land surface would be covered with mountains.
Beaumont agreed that the areas of sea and land were equal,
and that the average depth of the sea was one quarter of a
mile, while the greatest deeps and the highest mountains were
each two miles, but solved the difficulty and disposed of the
excessive earth by postulating the gradual rise of a mile from
the seacoast to the base of the mountains. The rest of the
land mass was accounted for by a sharp acclivity of another
mile to their summits.[33]   But his most far-reaching suggestion was that the earth particles in settling out of the

29 Beaumont, *op. cit.*, p. 97.

30 *Ibid.*, pp. 93, 94.

31 *Ibid.*, p. 86.

32 *Ibid.*, p. 87, also pp. 90-93.

33 *Ibid.*, pp. 64-66.

original chaotic mixture would not have been affected merely by the laws of gravity.[34]   The whole mass was full of ferments " from the infinite variety of seminal Principles . . . contained." [35]   These jarring forces caused discord but formed a world mixed in due proportions to suit God's design rather than one of pure elements.   A world of unmixed elements would not have been habitable.   Probably at first, as Moses seemed to say, water covered the earth.   Then these ferments forced up mountains and left valleys and sea-channels, as seeds even now are capable of raising bodies of " many Tuns Weight."   Mountains were not so prominent in comparison to the earth's diameter as the protuberances on an orange.   Then Beaumont casually inserted a statement remarkable for the epoch, to the effect that no present mountains were original, and that the only way of solving the phenomena of marine fossils on mountains was a belief that sea and land had changed places and were continuing the process.[36]

[34] Beaumont, *op. cit.*, pp. 26, 27.

[35] *Ibid.*, p. 26.

[36] *Ibid.*, pp. 27a-30a.   This is an early mention of that problem of fossils in connection with the earth's history which became such a live issue shortly after this time.   Beaumont declared that he intended to write a tract on the subject, but he seems to have neglected the fulfilment of his promise.

CHAPTER IX

RAY, THE BIOLOGIST

In addition to these minor fireworks there appeared several more elaborately and logically developed books inspired by Burnet and the interest in cosmogony aroused over the discussion of his theory. Very popular and often quoted was the work of John Ray (1628-1705), a Fellow of the Royal Society, an authority on botany and to a less degree on zoology. His *Wisdom of God Manifested in the Works of the Creation,* first published in 1691, reached its twelfth edition in 1759; but his more important work was *Three Physico-Theological Discourses* on the creation, the deluge and the final conflagration respectively, which was first published in 1692. With the account of the final conflagration he combined an exposition of the phenomena connected with the end of the world.[1] Knowledge of the first and the third epochs he attributed to revelation, while tradition from Noah had transmitted the record of the deluge.[2]

Ray believed in an antecedent chaos created by God from which He made other "beings." After having formed earth and water, God created "the Seeds or Seminal Principles of all Animate Bodies, both Vegetative and Sensitive; and disperst them, at least the Vegetative, all over the super-

[1] Both these books consisted of sermons originally delivered at Cambridge before 1660 when he was ordained. He was a fellow of Trinity College there from 1649 to 1662. At least the *Wisdom of God Manifested in the Works of the Creation* was translated into several foreign languages.

[2] Ray, *Three Physico-Theological Discourses* (London, 1693), preface, (unpaged but pp. 2-4).

ficial part of the Earth and Water." [3]   He mentioned without rejecting it the theory, which he attributed to the Stoics, that creation took place when all seven planets were in the first degree of Aries.   Their conjunctions in Capricorn and in Cancer marked the destruction of the world by water and by fire respectively.[4]

Ray mentioned and discussed the four elements, fire, air, earth and water, as " simple " terrestrial bodies, but seemed to do this as a concession to common opinion and to believe that metals, oil, salt, stones etc. were as simple as they.   He believed that God created a definite number of particles of

---

[3] Ray, *op. cit.*, pp. 2-7, 46, 47, especially pp. 6, 7.   Ray advocated strongly the idea that the germs of all creatures were created by God since they were the work of intelligence, and that this must have been done during the hexaemeron since creation stopped at the end thereof. To prove its possibility he referred to Leuwenhoek's work on bacteria and to the practically infinite divisibility of dyes and odors in solution. *Ibid.*, pp. 49-60; Ray, *The Wisdom of God Manifested in the Works of the Creation* (London, 1759), p. 325.

[4] Ray, *Three Physico-Theological Discourses* (London, 1693), pp. 268, 269.   This theory cropped up constantly in the writings of the seventeenth and the eighteenth centuries.   Whiston mentioned a Chinese tradition concerning the conjunction of the sun, the moon and the five planets in the days of their fifth king and dated it B. C. 2012, about 900 years posterior to the flood.   Whiston, *Six Dissertations* (London, 1734), pp. 194, 197.   He said that Seneca, *Quaest. Nat.* 1. 3, c. 29, quoted Berosus, a commentator on Belus, for the conjunctions of stars,—i. e., planets, in Capricorn and Cancer as the cause of the deluge and the final conflagration respectively, and that the interval was known as the great or Platonic year.   Whiston, *A New Theory of the Earth* (Cambridge, 1708), pp. 278-280.   Then he added that the real cause was the approach to one another of the moon, the earth and a comet, and said that, if the comet did not visit the solar system in the interim, the era between such catastrophes was a cometary year rather than a Platonic one.   *Ibid.*, pp. 184, 444-446.   About twenty years later he identified the maleficent visitant with Halley's comet, which has a period of 575-576 years.   Whiston, *A New Theory of the Earth* (London, 1755), pp. 185-199, 451, 461-467, 471; Whiston, *Six Dissertations* (London, 1734), p. 214.   *Cf.* also *infra*, pp. 120-124.

each type. The only difference between the first group of bodies and the second was that the particles of each member in the first list were more numerous. None of the original particles was transmutable in kind by the force of any natural agent even fire. This persistency of type protected the universe from dissolution, and as well secured the perpetuity of all species in the world and prevented the production or creation of any new one. He gave our ignorance as a reason for our belief in the disappearance of fossil species, which was perhaps merely apparent, and hinted that some specimens might not be remains of real animals.[5] He made an interesting calculation concerning the number of species. Of beasts, including serpents, he said there were 150 species known and 50 unknown, of birds 500 known and 166 unknown, of fish, including shell-fish, which were five times as numerous, 3,000 known and 1,500 unknown, of insects 20,000 and of plants 18,000, both known and unknown.[6]

Since the earth and the water as they subsided in the chaos were separated by gravity,[7] " it is reasonable to think

[5] Ray, *The Wisdom of God Manifested in the Works of the Creation* (London, 1759), pp. 59-61; Ray, *Three Physico-Theological Discourses* (London, 1693), pp. 147-160, 328-330, note before p. 132. On page 70 he said, however, that few doubted the transmutability of the elements.

[6] Ray, *The Wisdom of God Manifested in the Works of the Creation* (London, 1759), pp. 21-25. Such computations were a favorite pastime, especially in calculating the necessary capacity of the ark. Ray showed his greater biological knowledge in the larger numbers he suggested and also in his appreciation of the limits to his information. Catoir declared, for example, that there were hardly more than 150 genera of animals. Catoir, *Disputatio Theologica de Arca Noachi et Diluvio* (Gröningen, 1704), sec. ix. Even Buffon nearly a century later pleased himself by such calculations. He declared that there were 300 species of quadrupeds and 1,500 of birds. Buffon, *Oeuvres complètes* (Paris, 1831-1832), vol. v, p. 338 (*Époques de la nature*, first published in 1779). *Cf.* also *infra*, pp. 437, 438.

[7] Ray, *Three Physico-Theological Discourses* (London, 1693), pp. 6-9.

that the Waters should stand above and cover the Earth." [8]
Then the waters were collected into one place by the elevation
of the land into continents and mountains, while the ocean
bed was left at the original level.[9] Perhaps the elevation
resulted from " subterraneous Fires and *Flatuses*," [10] somewhat like gunpowder in their effects, which at present caused
earthquakes and the volcanic eruptions always associated
with them. The Bible (Ps. 104: 7) connected the noise of
thunder, a well-known characteristic of earthquakes, with
this collection of the water. At first the fire raised the parts
now mountains, then spread its influence to the rest of the
land and to the borders of the sea,[11]

till at length the weight of them was too great to be raised, and
then the fire brake forth at the tops of the Mountains, where it
found least resistance, and disperst it self in the open Air. The
Waters also, where they found the bottom sandy, or yielding,
made their way into all those Cavities the fire had made and
left, filling them up as high as the level of the Ocean.[12]

Therefore even the waters of seas apparently without outlet,
like the Caspian, were connected through a watery abyss so
that all the oceans, seas and streams were united. Nevertheless, many cavities, even below the ocean, were filled with air,
and produced the wide diffusion of earthquakes and eruptions. The areas of sea and land were probably equal, but
certainly their masses must be, and the depth of the one
exactly balanced the height of the other.[13]

To this division of sea and land succeeded the formation
of living creatures, at " first the more imperfect," [14] plants,

---

[8] Ray, *op. cit.*, p. 9.   [9] *Ibid.*, pp. 8, 9, 24.

[10] *Ibid.*, p. 10.   [11] *Ibid.*, pp. 10-26.

[12] *Ibid.*, p. 26.

[13] *Ibid.*, pp. 25, 32-34, 76, 84-86, 202-206, 215, 216.

[14] *Ibid.*, p. 7.

and then animals. For the production of animals two methods were possible and consonant with Scripture: first, the creation of seeds or miniature animals and their dispersal over the surface of land and water, to which God gave temporary power to hatch and bring them forth; second, to avoid His creation of anything imperfect, the formation from waters and earth of the earliest animals in full perfection. The creation of perfect animals would have been analogous to the method employed in the case of Adam. Perhaps only two of a kind were produced since two unclean animals in the ark proved sufficient to repopulate the earth and only two of the human race were brought into existence. However, fishes and birds were created in abundance; and, because of their wide dispersion although they lacked powers of locomotion, plants must have been generated in quantity.[15] Ray expended considerable time in a disproof of the present spontaneous generation of animals and plants, an atheistical doctrine according to him.[16]

Ray discussed the deluge in detail, and had no difficulty in finding sufficient water. The waters above the heavens or lower part of the air must have been approximately equal to those on or below the earth's surface since the Bible correlated them. By elaborate calculations as to annual rainfall, the floods caused by occasional thunderstorms and the amount of water poured into the sea by rivers, Ray concluded that rain unaided could furnish the equivalent of twenty times eighty oceans. Nevertheless, he felt that the chief reason for the catastrophe was either a gradual displacement of the center of gravity, which brought it nearer the eastern hemisphere and then restored it to its original location, or a

[15] Ray, *op. cit.*, pp. 7, 8, 46-49.

[16] Ray, *The Wisdom of God Manifested in the Works of the Creation* (London, 1759), pp. 298-326.

pressure upon the surface of the Atlantic and the Pacific Oceans, which forced the waters down into the abyss and out upon the land through cracks in the earth's crust. This, by the way, was a reason he propounded for the marine fossils which had been discovered on the land. The shell-fish were carried along with the ocean water through the abyss and out at the fissures.[17] The suggestion was similar to another he offered about fossils.

As for fossil Fishes, some make their Way into the Earth up the Veins of Water, opening into the Banks of Rivers, where they lie till they grow so great that they cannot return: In which Veins they find Air enough to serve their Turn, needing not much by reason that they lie still, and move but little. Others in Times of Floods are left in the Meadows, and with the Water sink into the Earth at some Holes and Pores that the Water finds, or makes, by which also they are supplied with Air.[18]

In spite of his affirmation that fossils were genuine organic remains, Ray tried to explain away their presence on mountain summits by flat denial of the facts and by the attribution of sporadic cases to the acts of animals including men and monkeys. He felt that the great layers of shells in other places, which suggested a period of habitation by fish more extended than the twelve months of the deluge, hinted that at the creation only enough land for Adam's use was uncovered and the retreat of the sea from the rest of our continents was gradual. Another hypothesis was that the deluge changed parts of the sea-bottom to dry land. Since that epoch there had been many variations in the surface of the globe. The relative positions of sea and land had altered;

[17] Ray, *Three Physico-Theological Discourses* (London, 1693), pp. 62-230, especially pp. 70-81, 84-124, 161.
[18] Ray, *The Wisdom of God Manifested in the Works of the Creation* (London, 1759), pp. 76, 77.

and the hills had been washed down, while the valleys and the sea-bed had been filled.[19]

The major difficulty with a change in the center of gravity as the cause of the flood was that it left America dry; but that continent was "in all probability unpeopled at that time," and flooding it was unnecessary.[20] However, Ray was perfectly willing to accept either hypothesis on further proof.[21]

On Scriptural authority Ray rejected a new flood or the extinction of the sun by sun-spots as the cause for the end of our planet and believed in a final conflagration. He thought that this was revealed to Adam and transmitted by Seth to tradition. One possible reason for such a finale was an outbreak of the central fire described by Descartes in his account of the formation of the earth.[22] On the other hand, the existence of such a fire had not been demonstrated; and a

[19] Ray felt that this fact foreboded a future levelling of the earth and its flooding by the sea unless some other means of destruction supervened, but added that the action did not seem to proceed perceptibly fast and there might be natural causes to counteract it. Ray, *Three Physico-Theological Discourses* (London, 1693), note before p. 132, pp. 144-149, 163-230, 283-314. In the same book, pages 296-305, on the ground of its rarity, Ray translated *De Mundi Fabrica*, by Joseph Blancanus, which was quoted also by Hakewill, *An Apologie or Declaration of the Power and Providence of God in the Gouernment of the World* (Oxford, 1635), pt. i, p. 148. Blancanus had declared that a spherical shape was natural to the earth and that our mountainous earth was constantly being reduced by rains and rivers, so that unless fire destroyed the earth it would some day be flooded. At creation by God's command the greatest part of the land was translated to another place, so that it formed mountains and left a hollow for the sea. Similar statements were made in Blancanus, *Sphaera Mvndi* (Bologna, 1620), pp. 81-85, 94, 98, 99.

[20] Ray, *op. cit.*, p. 122.

[21] *Ibid.*, p. 124.

[22] Ray said that Descartes himself denied the verity of the method of creation propounded in the *Principles*. Ray rejected it wholly, but was not averse to the idea of a central fire since that was implied in the Bible. Ray, *op. cit.*, pp. 316-322.

safer belief was that the cause of the catastrophe would not be a natural one.[23]   The destruction would be followed by a renovation of the earth, perhaps that it might be inhabited by a new race of beings.   Another agency than fire would be superior if total annihilation were desired.   The advantage of man was not the sole purpose of the universe.[24]

Apparently Ray desired to be conservative in his statements.   Constantly he contradicted his own conclusions or so weakened them by modification that the final result was indeterminate.   Perhaps one reason was that the treatises were first delivered as sermons and printed only after thirty years, during which time he probably revised them and incorporated new ideas and discoveries.   As theses in separate sermons, inconsistent statements would not be noticed; and they were not eliminated with sufficient care before publication.   Probably his work was read only by those who agreed with him.   An instance of his desire to agree with both the old and the new ideas occurred in his discussion of the " signatures " of plants.   Since he was a botanist of some importance, he rejected the theory as " rather fansied by Men than design'd by Nature"; but immediately declared that " noxious and malignant Plants do many of them discover something of their Nature by the sad and melancholick Visage of their Leaves, Flowers, and Fruit." [25]

[23] Ray, *op. cit.*, pp. 322, 332.   The whole account of the final catastrophe appeared, pp. 237-363.

[24] *Ibid.*, pp. 353-363.   In the *Wisdom of God* he enlarged on that last statement.   He refused to affirm that minerals and salts were created wholly or primarily for man's use.   Animals were " *made to enjoy themselves as well as to serve us* " (p. 175), though they were useful also to impel to study by their variety, to inspire to admiration of the Creator and to punish as scourges.   The stars, especially the more distant ones, invisible to the naked eye, must have had some other purpose than twinkling for us.   Ray, *The Wisdom of God Manifested in the Works of the Creation* (London, 1759), pp. 98, 99, 175-185, 366-375.

[25] Ray, *op. cit.*, pp. 113, 114.

CHAPTER X

Leibnitz, the Philosopher

Towards the end of the seventeenth century a noted philosopher composed, as did Descartes, an account of cosmogenesis, which like his predecessor's, has been forgotten, although his dicta on metaphysics and psychology are studied to the present day. Leibnitz (1646-1716), in January 1693, inserted a brief summary of his *Protogaea*, written three years earlier, into the *Acta eruditorum* of Leipzig pp. 40 *et seq.*[1] The treatise as finally published was shorter than Descartes's and much more hazy in its ideas. It explained neither the whole universe nor its details, such as magnetism. Leibnitz agreed with Descartes in believing that the earth was originally a molten, fiery fluid. Over this a coat of scoriae formed and darkened it. The arguments which led him to this conclusion differed, however, from those of his predecessor. Instead of *a priori* reasoning that particles in a vortex would behave in a given manner, Leibnitz observed the earth around him. He thought he saw that scoriae were a form of glass and that under the influence of fire all earth and stones became glass except those parts which flew away into the air. Therefore glass was the basis

[1] Reference by Scheidt in his Preface to the *Protogaea*. He also said that his friend had planned to publish the theory but had died before he could. Leibnitz, *Opera Omnia* (Geneva, 1768), vol. ii, pp. 184 and note and 196, 197. The treatise itself fills pp. 201-240. De Luc, *Lettres physiques et morales sur l'histoire de la terre et de l'homme* (The Hague and Paris, 1779-1780), vol i, pp. 313-333, reviewed Leibnitz's system, calling it logical, but denying that it fitted the facts. De Luc dated the first publication of the *Protogaea* 1683, *ibid.*, vol. i, p. 314. A brief account of Leibnitz and his theory was given by Geikie, *The Founders of Geology* (London and New York, 1897), pp. 7, 8.

of the earth; and, when it was corroded or distilled by the
dissolving or the agitating of waters or of vapors, it hid
itself under all forms.[2] The original fluidity of the earth,
which gave it a regular form without excrescences, was due
to internal motion or heat,—that is, fire or light, which permeated the whole. This fire was the moving cause given in
the Bible as the beginning of the creation. The first step
in the process was the separation of light and darkness or
actives and passives; the second, the distinction of various
passives from one another,—that is, the division of dry land
and water. They were distinguished by a difference in resistance. Leibnitz apparently believed that what happened
was a consolidation of the earth's crust. The process destroyed its heat and light. The water, which had previously
been vaporized by the heat, fell upon the surface, and washed
out the fixed salts. The crust, as it contracted with the cold,
left cavities filled with water and air, and, because of the
inequalities in its matter and its heat, solidified with an uneven surface of hills and valleys. The waters by their weight
prepared for themselves a ditch in the hitherto soft foundations and thus aided in the production of hills. Finally the
expansion of the gases or the weight of the water within
the cavities of the crust fractured it; and the water flooded
forth and laid down sedimental strata, which hardened.
Diverse strata were deposited by the successive floodings.
At last a state of equilibrium in the structure of the crust
was reached. Solid matters, therefore, had a double origin.
They were either cooled from fire or deposited from water.
Some of the fused matter formed in layers on top of that
already hardened. Not all the roughnesses of the earth were
due, however, to its first concretion. There had been many
later earthquakes, floods, conflagrations, eruptions and
gradual deposits of sediments from stagnant water, the

[2] Leibnitz, *op. cit.*, vol. ii, pp. 201-203.

effects of which had been superimposed upon the original skeleton of the ocean bed and the vast mountain ranges.[3]

Leibnitz believed in the existence of two great cavities within the earth. When the waters first retreated from the surface, they filled the upper cavity and air the lower. At the time of the flood the walls of the upper reservoir were fractured, and the water poured forth. After that devastation it found its way by secret passages into the lower cavity.[4] As the crust over the upper cavity subsided in ruins,[5] the formerly level sedimentary strata were broken and inclined, as can be seen in mountainous districts, such as Norway. The cracks or veins gave a place for the formation of metals, perhaps by means of fire, sulphur, salt, water and earth or stones.[6]

More than half of the essay discussed fossils, giving pictures and descriptions of them. The author declared that they were once real fish. One suggestion he offered was that a great lake filled with fish might have been overwhelmed with earth by an earthquake or some other force. As this soil was changed to stone, it preserved the form of the fish; and the animal remains were replaced, largely under the influence of the great fire of nature, by the metallic matter scattered through the mud.[7] Another method of forming fossils was employed when the sea covered the mountains. After the earth's crust was broken, the mud containing shells flowed down into the cracks until the water sank away and the sediment was stranded and became rock. In addition, many shells and animal remains in the early days were cast

[3] Leibnitz, *op. cit.*, vol. ii, pp. 201-205, 233-237, 240.

[4] *Ibid.*, vol. ii, pp. 205, 206.

[5] Here he leaned to Burnet's theory, as he acknowledged. *Ibid.*, vol. ii, p. 206.

[6] *Ibid.*, vol. ii, pp. 207-212.

[7] *Ibid.*, vol. ii, pp. 214-217 and elsewhere.

up by great storms. They were dropped by waters seeking to pass through narrow gaps. This was true especially with the remains of terrestrial animals, such as elephants, which the waters of the vast flood left at the narrow openings through which the liquid was received into subterranean reservoirs.[8]

In 1749 after Leibnitz's death his friend, Christian Ludovic Scheidt (1709-1761), historian and archivist, composed a preface for the *Protogaea*.[9] Scheidt discussed at considerable length the question of the flood and the attribution of fossils to it. He called this Leibnitz's doctrine, though Leibnitz himself mentioned other sources of fossils. Scheidt thought that fossils had more than one origin. He gave lists of scholars who had dealt with the problem and with the end of the world, and said that Germany was full of men studying the rocks and communicating with one another.[10] He neither denied nor accepted Leibnitz's explanation of the flood. He, however, claimed to adhere to the literal sense of the Bible. Moses wrote of cosmogenesis merely succinctly, leaving to philosophers a field in which to exercise their talents. However, God created the universe from nothing by His own word, "*FIAT*." He could have made all in a moment but evinced His care and planning by a division of the work into days. The result was the best of all possible worlds. The flood was due to the superior waters in the air and to those from the subterranean abyss. Enough subterranean liquid to cover the earth was forced out because the surface of the ocean was depressed by some unknown force actuated by God. This last statement shows that Scheidt, like most of

---

[8] Leibnitz, *op. cit.*, vol. ii, pp. 217, 218, 220, 221, 229.

[9] *Ibid.*, vol. ii, pp. 181-198, especially pp. 181, 196-198.

[10] *Ibid.*, vol. ii, pp. 182-194, 196.

his contemporaries, believed in a free communication between the waters of the ocean and those of the abyss.[11]

Leibnitz in his philosophical writings said little that bore directly upon the creation of the universe. In his correspondence with Dr. Samuel Clarke, an English prelate, he declared twice that it was impossible and futile to suppose that God might have created the world earlier than He did. Before creation all time and space were perfectly uniform; hence no time or place was more suitable than any other. Now the universe was unlimited in space though not in time.[12] He seemed strongly to disbelieve in the existence of a vacuum, and rejected the idea of the earth's attraction by the sun through an empty space. If God caused such action of bodies on one another at a distance, it was surely a miracle, since it exceeded the powers of creatures. If not miraculous, it was false, a scholastic, occult quality.[13] This objection to the Newtonian theory of gravitation was common and prevented its general acceptance on the continent for many years.

Leibnitz's views of creation aroused few comments, perhaps because their complete publication was delayed until the late eighteenth century when the emphasis had shifted and the Newtonian doctrine, which he had rejected, had been generally adopted. Another reason for the slight number of contemporary references may be the lack of detail. His *Protogaea* was rather the sketch for a theory of cosmogony than a complete picture.

[11] Leibnitz, *op. cit.*, vol. ii, pp. 191, 192, 194-196.

[12] Leibnitz, *The Philosophical Works of Leibnitz* (New Haven, 1890), pp. 249, 270-274. Fourth and Fifth Papers in reply to Dr. Clarke's Third and Fourth, secs. 15 and 55-75 respectively.

[13] *Ibid.*, pp. 253, 254, 284, 285. Sections 46 and 118-123 of the same papers.

CHAPTER XI

Le Clerc, an Early Modernist

JEAN LE CLERC OR CLERICUS (1657-1736) was an influential French Protestant theologian. In 1684, after some. twenty years of preaching in Geneva and a period in Grenoble, he settled in Amsterdam. At first his duties were merely clerical, but later he added professorial responsibilities in a seminary. His influence was spread by his voluminous publications, at least seventy-three of which are known. The most important was a Biblical Commentary published at intervals from 1693 to 1731. The first volume contained the book of *Genesis*. Each page began with a very few lines of text, followed by a paraphrase of approximately equal length and a very long commentary.

Le Clerc showed the new critical spirit. In spite of lip service to Moses's authorship of the Pentateuch, he proved from Moses's own statements that some parts consisted of documents which the great law-giver merely incorporated or perhaps edited, and that other portions were obviously explanations and addenda by later authors. On the ground that Moses omitted any such claim, he denied a direct revelation by God of the events which had occurred in the earlier ages. On the other hand, he declared that practically all of the five books was the work of Moses, that the repetitions and other stylistic shortcomings showed them to be an unrevised collection of the writings by the Hebrew prophet. Since Moses's purpose was to teach religion to the Jews, he omitted many matters. This was the reason why, for example, he spoke of the sun and the moon as created for times and seasons,—that is, to designate solemn festivals appointed to the Jews, rather than for the more important solar purpose of giving warmth and raising plants. Moses at the same time mentioned casually the creation of the stars to show how far they were from being gods, and that they were merely the instruments of the Almighty to benefit man.[1]

Most of Le Clerc's ideas were not new. He believed that the world was not eternal but had been founded by God. Matter had been created antecedently from nothing, but the Mosaic account referred only to its shaping. The heavens mentioned in the first verse of Genesis were not merely the abode of the blessed and the angels, but were the three heavens, the airy heaven, the stellar and the third that contained the seat of God. The earth at first bore no living thing but was covered with water, the abyss. Over it was nothing but a vast emptiness of air. The motion of the spirit, which was not a wind but the divine power presiding over unformed extension, was not the motion of a setting bird, but that of wings,—i. e. flying.[2] On the ground of insufficient data, Le Clerc refused to philosophize about the cause and the nature of the light formed on the first day; but he said that it, like the sun, encircled the globe so that the day was the period when it was above the horizon. The first day consisted of twelve hours of light preceded by an infinite myriad of years, during which there were no changes in the darkness to divide it into parts.[3]

Though the word firmament sometimes meant the whole space of the airy and the stellar heavens, in the account of the second day it meant merely the airy interval up to the clouds,

---

[1] Le Clerc, *Mosis Prophetae Libri Quinque* (Amsterdam, 1735), Preliminary dissertation *De Scriptore Pentateuchi Mose*, and *Genesis*, paraphrase, p. 6, and commentary pp. 10, 11.

[2] *Ibid.*, pp. 1-5.

[3] *Ibid.*, pp. 5-7.

which were the waters above the firmament, while those on the surface of the earth were the ones below. Le Clerc doubted the popular theory of a watery abyss below the earth's crust. That a serener air might rest upon the globe, God wished by means of heat, perhaps from the light just created, to remove the clouds that rested upon the earth and veiled it with an eternal fog. The choice of firmament as a name for this space referred to the belief of the Chaldeans and apparently of the Jews that the earth was in the center of the universe and held in place (compressed, made firm) by the force of the surrounding heavens.[4]

God's command to the water and the earth to bring forth animals meant that He formed them of those materials. After the seventh [5] day He created nothing. The creation of man may have taken place either inside or outside of Paradise. This was a definite tract of territory on the Euphrates. The four rivers mentioned in Genesis were not a combination of two which afterwards split, as Bochart asserted, but four flowing from a single source in the garden. Their courses had been so changed by earthquakes that the present complete failure in the identification of two was not remarkable, while the Tigris and the Euphrates no longer fitted Moses's description.[6]

Adam and Eve knew the use of language, since they were created as adults. God did not desire them to experience the great difficulty of developing a language but gave them the ability of mature persons. Their knowledge of words was particularly necessary that they might understand God when He spoke to them. The language was not Hebrew, which was a Canaanitish dialect, but a primitive speech, equally

[4] Le Clerc, *op. cit.*, pp. 7-9, 65.

[5] Le Clerc here followed the example of some authors in speaking of creation as taking seven days instead of six.

[6] *Ibid.*, pp. 11-13, 16, 18-24.

close to all Oriental tongues.[7]   It was used by Adam in naming the animals as there was occasion.   This act took more
time than one day, especially since he was unable to judge
their characters with abnormal facility and speed.   Their
being led to him was not credible.   American animals and
birds, which were different from those in Asia, " do not seem
to have gone to Adam to receive names."   In spite of por-
trayals in earlier centuries of fish presenting themselves before the first man, Le Clerc thought such action obviously
impossible.[8]   This learned French divine agreed with those
who attributed the ill effects of the forbidden tree to the fact
that the fruit was poisonous or unwholesome.   It was forbidden because man could have discovered its lethal properties for himself only by long use.[9]

Though his suggestions seem to us so mildly heterodox, Le
Clerc was bitterly inveighed against; and perhaps these doctrines, as well as the suspicion of Socinianism, were a cause
of his exclusion from the chair of dogmatic theology at the
Remonstrant seminary in Amsterdam, although he was permitted to hold those of philosophy, belles-lettres, Hebrew and
church history.   The views that his contemporaries deemed
so radical were expressed with such an imposing background
of scholarship that his Biblical Commentary, which was subjected to fierce attacks, was nevertheless influential in de-
stroying traditional prejudices and in demonstrating the necessity for a more scientific inquiry into the origin and the
meaning of the sacred books.

[7] Le Clerc, *op. cit.*, pp. 4, 26 and also preliminary dissertation *De
Lingua Hebraica.*

[8] *Ibid.*, p. 25, " non videntur ad Adamum ut nomina acciperent ivisse."

[9] *Ibid.*, p. 24.

CHAPTER XII

WHISTON, THE MATHEMATICIAN

DURING the decade before 1690 genuine scientific progress was being made, which was destined to revolutionize the concepts of cosmology. Sir Isaac Newton (1642-1727) published in 1687 his *Principia,* in which he rejected Descartes's theory of vortices because it did not fit several of the phenomena. He substituted for it the theory of attraction or gravitation, to which his name has been popularly attached. Except in England his doctrines did not oust the Cartesian hypotheses for nearly two generations. Swedenborg was the last eminent exponent of Cartesianism, but as late as 1740 official recognition of the dying theory was granted in France in the division of a prize offered for an essay on tides among three Newtonians and one Cartesian.[1] Newton's doctrines, which are now more generally known than those of Descartes, presented a new conception of the universe for harmonization with the Mosaic account. Except for a few general statements in the *Scolium Generale* at the conclusion of his *Principia,* in which he attributed the creation and preservation of the world to the direct action of God, Newton himself did not attempt more than a portrayal

[1] Newton, *Philosophiae Naturalis Principia Mathematica* (London, 1687); Grant, *History of Physical Astronomy from the Earliest Ages to the Middle of the Nineteenth Century* (London, 1852?), pp. 20-44, 69, 73, 74, 88, 133, 152, 160, 309, 323-327, 345, 346, 481, 482, 527, 528, 530-532; Berry, *A Short History of Astronomy* (London, 1898), pp. 210-247, 291, 293; Delambre, *Histoire de l'astronomie au dix-huitième siècle* (Paris, 1827), pp. 1-51; Faye, *Sur l'origine du monde* (Paris, 1884), pp. 97-103, 110.

of the universe in its present state and of its laws. Their correlation with the Scriptural narrative was left for his friends and disciples. The task was undertaken by William Whiston (1667-1752), a man of great learning and acute but ill-balanced intellect. During his later years he adopted many fads, but always he was interested in science. In spite of poverty he spent time and money on a coast survey and on an attempt to find a method for figuring longitude. He was especially proficient in mathematics and succeeded Newton as professor of that subject. The Cartesian philosophy that he had studied at Cambridge he rejected as fictitious after he had heard some of Newton's lectures and had read the *Principia.* For some time he was a friend of the greater philosopher, who permitted the publication of his *Arithmetica Universalis* by the younger man. To Newton, as well as to Wren and Bentley, Whiston submitted *A New Theory of the Earth* in manuscript.

In England interest still centered around the work of Burnet. Although Woodward in his first book antedated Whiston by a year as a critic of Burnet, his theory was based on a remoter principle and will be considered later. Whiston revised Burnet's system, and made it more complete and more probable.[2] The *New Theory of the Earth,* printed in 1696 while Whiston was chaplain to the Bishop of Norwich, was the first of his very numerous books, and, except perhaps for his translation of Josephus, the most popular

[2] De Luc, *Lettres physiques et morales sur l'histoire de la terre et de l'homme* (The Hague and Paris, 1779, 1780), vol. i, p. 254. De Luc (1727-1817) summarized very fairly and discussed all of the systems preceding his own, especially those that purported to harmonize the Mosaic account with the facts of natural history. His account of Burnet, Whiston and Woodward was in vol. i, pp. 243-312. Another account of Whiston, which emphasized his scientific achievements, was given by Delambre, *Histoire de l'astronomie au dix-huitième siècle* (Paris, 1827), pp. 51-60. Delambre gave the date of his death as 1755.

though not the most valuable. At least six editions of it had appeared by 1755 with an unusual number of changes, some of which incorporated his answers to Keill and other critics. The most conspicuous alterations dealt with the flood and his attempted identification of Noah with the Chinese emperor Fohi. In the first edition [3] he had placed Noah at the foot of the Caucasus, where Tartary, Persia and India touch one another, both before and after the deluge. He quoted Sir Walter Raleigh and Heylyn for Tartary as a landing place; but after 1700 he seemed to accept the more general opinion, which located Ararat in Armenia.[4] The flood began while the people slept. By 1708 he had evolved the idea that Noah or Fohi lived in Peking. A partial fracture of the earth's crust on November 28, 1662 Anno Mundi, and violent rains accompanied the catastrophe for approximately the first nine hours; but they occurred in Armenia, so remote from Peking that the earliest effect in China was its inundation by the waters as they had flowed thither from the localities where they first fell. The greater part of them did not reach China until the ark was safely afloat. Then the ark gradually drifted westward, because of the general current in that direction, and landed on the mountains between Armenia and Assyria. When Noah's three sons and their descendants came south to Shinaar, the father, probably because he was unwilling to

[3] Whiston, *A New Theory of the Earth* (London, 1696), pp. 119-123, 310-314, 325.

[4] The authors he mentioned may be found as follows: Raleigh, *The History of the World* (Edinburgh, 1820), vol. i, pp. 236-268 (1st ed., 1614) ; Heylyn, *Cosmography in Four Books* (London, 1674), introduction, pp. 6, 7, bk. iii, pp. 126, 149, 152 (1st ed. about 1648). Heylyn himself contradicted Bochart and Josephus on this subject. Bochart, *Opera Omnia* (Leyden, 1712), vol. i, cols. 13-22, 30-32, 38, map opposite cols. 77, 78. Whiston's statements concerning the flood in his notes to Josephus do not always agree with those in his other books.

join in the construction of the Tower of Babel, presumably travelled east to China and left there other descendants.   The Chinese language and writing were so different from those introduced by the confusion of tongues that their origin must have been unique.   No mention of Noah and his activities after the flood occurred in Scripture except his age at death; hence he must have travelled to China or to some other district outside the limits of that known world concerning which the Bible treated.   The knowledge, the history and the government of the Chinese were superior to ours because Noah's wisdom surpassed that of his sons. The Chinese account of Fohi coincided with our traditions about Noah.[5]   The sixth edition, however, regretfully decided that Fohi was some six hundred years the younger of the two.[6]   This version agreed with Burnet as to the probable preservation of some men in America as well as in Asia at the time of the deluge.[7]

Besides these English editions, Whiston's work was translated into German and influenced the universities in that country.

The theories of Whiston and Burnet found wide acceptance also in Germany, mainly through the all powerful mediation of

[5] Whiston, *A New Theory of the Earth* (Cambridge, 1708) (2nd ed.), pp. 133-141, 202, 203, 368-382, 384, 393; Whiston, *A Vindication of the New Theory of the Earth from the Exceptions of Mr. Keill and Others* (London, 1698), pp. 37, 49-52; Whiston, *A Second Defence of the New Theory of the Earth from the Exceptions of Mr. John Keill* (London, 1700), p. 17.   Keill (1671-1721), a Scotch astronomer of some note, was one of Newton's first disciples and especially ardent in upholding his doctrines.   His scientific work was discussed by Delambre, *op. cit.*, pp. 158-179.

[6] Whiston, *A New Theory of the Earth* (London, 1755), edition vi, p. 141.

[7] *Ibid.*, p. 405.   In the second edition, Whiston, *A New Theory of the Earth* (Cambridge, 1708), p. 403, he had declared that they all perished.

Gottsched, so long, from his professor's chair at Leipsic, the dictator of orthodox thought, who not only wrote a brief tractate of his own upon the subject, but furnished a voluminous historical introduction to the more elaborate treatise of Heyn. In this book, which appeared at Leipsic in 1742, the agency of comets in the creation, the flood, and the final destruction of the world is fully proved. Both these theories were, however, soon discredited.[8]

Like Burnet, Whiston endeavored to explain not only the creation but also the flood, the final conflagration and the ultimate fate of the world. He, too, decided that the earth's last state would be the same as its first, though he believed that this would be as a comet rather than as a star. But the form of the *New Theory* betrayed the mathematician. Book I consisted of Lemmata, Book II of Hypotheses, Book III of " Phaenomena " and Book IV of Solutions or applications to the phenomena of the philosophical principles expressed.

Like Burnet again, Whiston declared that the account in Genesis referred to the formation of the earth alone out of chaotic matter previously created by God from nothing. Such statements as seemed inconsistent with this view resulted from the adaptation of difficult philosophical truths to vulgar capacities.[9] On the fourth day the sun, moon and stars, which had been created earlier, were placed in the firmament. This interpretation necessitated merely a change in the narrative from the past tense to the pluperfect, a natural emendation since the Hebrew had no pluperfect tense.[10] On the other hand, Whiston also declared that the first appearance of light was

---

[8] White, *A History of the Warfare of Science with Theology in Christendom* (New York and London, 1910), vol. i, p. 206. For Heyn's book, cf. *infra*, pp. 190-192.

[9] Whiston, *op. cit.*, introductory discourse, pp. 4-16, 21-43, 58-73, 87-94.

[10] *Ibid.*, introductory discourse, pp. 15-17.

when the superior Regions of the Chaos were become so far clear and defecate, that the Rays of the Sun in some degree could penetrate the same, enough to render a sensible Distinction between Night and Day, or that space the Sun was above, and that it was beneath the Horizon. And agreeably, The Sun, Moon, and Stars, are then said first to *Be*, or to *be made*, when afterwards the Air was rendred so very clear and transparent, that those Luminaries become conspicuous, and their Bodies distinctly visible.[11]

Our globe was originally a comet and the chaos mentioned in the Bible was its atmosphere, which did not reach so far as the moon.[12]   The sun and the stars were probably created by another method; but each of the planets arose from a chaos, similar to that which gave birth to our globe.   The mass of the comet was about equal to that of a planet, but its volume was incomparably greater.   The central part was a solid so heated by its approach to the sun that it could not cool in many thousands of years.   Around this was a mixture of solid particles, fluids and vapors, elevated by the solar heat and kept in motion by the comet's eccentric orbit so that they were prevented from the subsidence that they would experience if its orbit became circular and regular.   The main bulk

11 Whiston, *op. cit.*, introductory discourse, p. 24.

12 *Ibid.*, introductory discourse, pp. 33, 34; Whiston, *A Vindication of the New Theory of the Earth from the Exceptions of Mr. Keill and Others* (London, 1698), pp. 2, 3; Whiston, *A Second Defence of the New Theory of the Earth from the Exceptions of Mr. John Keill* (London, 1700), pp. 3, 4. Keill, *An Examination of Dr. Burnet's Theory of the Earth. Together with some remarks on Mr. Whiston's New Theory of the Earth* (Oxford, 1698), pp. 179-184, 189, 190, asserted that the atmosphere of a comet could not be the primitive chaos since such an atmosphere was transparent and the central solid would reflect the sun's light so that the atmosphere would be bright and not dark. Whiston replied that this solid was cooling; hence it was no longer luminous in itself; and that the inner sections of a comet's atmosphere were opaque, not transparent.

of the chaos consisted of dense fluids heavier than the floating particles of earth so that later they settled upon the
cometary nucleus beneath the other portions of the chaos. A
regular circular orbit with the concomitant consolidation of
solids and liquids upon the comet's surface would produce a
planet suitable to sustain life. Any change of this nature
must, however, be a definite act of God. It was not a necessary mechanical effect. Such a change took place in our
earth six or seven thousand years ago.[13] Then the orbit
became perfectly circular; and there was no diurnal rotation,
so that the length of the year and of the day were equal.
Thus Whiston attempted to meet the difficulty raised by the
brevity of six days for the work of creation, though even yet
the need for divine action was obvious.[14] This was furnished by Christ, especially in the formation of man,[15] " it

[13] Whiston, *A New Theory of the Earth* (Cambridge, 1708), introductory discourse, pp. 40-42, text, pp. 50-55, 73-82, 214, 215, 283-294,
298-300; Whiston, *A Vindication of the New Theory of the Earth from
the Exceptions of Mr. Keill and Others* (London, 1698), pp. 4, 5;
Whiston, *A Second Defence of the New Theory of the Earth from the
Exceptions of Mr. John Keill* (London, 1700), pp. 4-7.

[14] Whiston, *A New Theory of the Earth* (Cambridge, 1708), introductory discourse, pp. 52-54, text, pp. 57, 58, 85-118, 125-133, 293, 294,
297, 298, 305, 308, 312-315, 317, 328. Keill, *op. cit.*, pp. 193-199, said
that days and nights six months in length would kill animals and plants
because of excesses in temperature. Hence diurnal rotation commenced
at creation. Whiston reaffirmed his stand, saying that with twilight and
moonlight there would be hardly one week of darkness. Neither heat
nor cold would be excessive. Whiston, *A Vindication of the New Theory
of the Earth from the Exceptions of Mr. Keill and Others* (London,
1698), pp. 9-13.

[15] Whiston, *A Second Defence of the New Theory of the Earth from
the Exceptions of Mr. John Keill* (London, 1700), p. 9; Whiston, *A New
Theory of the Earth* (Cambridge, 1708), pp. 321, 322. He spoke also of
the Spirit of God moving on the face of the waters and thus impressing
on matter those characteristics which differentiate the various types of
objects. *Ibid.*, pp. 291, 292; Whiston, *A Vindication of the New Theory
of the Earth from the Exceptions of Mr. Keill and Others* (London,
1698), p. 5.

being both unfit and impossible for the Divine Nature it self, or at least that of the Father, to be so much, and in such a manner concern'd with the Corporeal World, and the sinful Race of Mankind " as we believe Christ to have been.   Man was " a Being compounded of a Spiritual and Immortal Soul, and of a Material and Corruptible Body: . . . in both these he was to be made in the likeness of that Divine Person who created him." [16]

During the first day or year the particles of the atmosphere settled.   They were deposited somewhat in accordance with their gravity, but the water and the earth were still mixed. Water filled the " pores " of the earth, while some particles of both still floated in the air.   As the air cleared, the light could penetrate it.   For this reason creation was said to have begun in the evening and the day to have followed.   On the next day the earth became more solid; more water sank; and, since there was more than enough to saturate the ground, it covered the surface.   Some of it by the heat of the sun and of the central hot body became vaporized and joined that which floated above the air or firmament and had not yet been precipitated.   The air supported the " Superior Waters " as it now does the clouds.   The " Inferior " ones were those in the seas and the pores of the earth.   In the course of these two days the strata became solidified.   As the solids settled upon the abyss, which was a region of dense and heavy fluids, the different columns or sections sank farther or less far into it according to their specific gravity, and thus formed valleys and mountains.   Whiston declared that in fact the mountainous areas were not so dense as the others, and that he had proved them porous by their springs, their volcanic character and their susceptibility to earth-quakes.   During the succeeding three months of night the

[16] Whiston, *A New Theory of the Earth* (Cambridge, 1708), p. 322.

air became cold and a large part of the superior waters fell
and ran down into the hollows. This left the land especially
"moist and juicy" and fit for the germination of plants.
Because of a deficient water supply, there existed no ocean,
but only seas and lakes. The vapors left in the sky or raised
by the sun as it rose above the horizon still obscured that
luminary's face.[17] By the fourth day the atmosphere was so
cleared of mist that first the moon and then the sun became
visible.[18] The original formation of the seeds for plants and
animals was by God alone.[19]

As far as our Microscopes can help us to discern the Make and
Constitution of Seeds; those of Plants evidently, and by what
hitherto appears of Animals too, are no other than the intire
Bodies themselves *in parvo*; and contain every one of the same
Parts and Members with the compleat Bodies themselves when
grown to maturity. Since therefore, consequently, all *Gener-*

[17] Whiston, *op. cit.*, pp. 61-66, 82-85, 297-316; Whiston, *A Vindication
of the New Theory of the Earth from the Exceptions of Mr. Keill and
Others* (London, 1698), pp. 15, 16.

[18] Whiston, *A New Theory of the Earth* (Cambridge, 1708), pp. 316-
318. Keill, *op. cit.*, pp. 188-190, denied this. Keill also said that had the
earth been a comet it could not have had a satellite, the moon. Or the
lunar sphere must have been made, not revealed, on the fourth day.
Ibid., pp. 190, 191. Whiston responded that comets varied and perhaps
some had satellites. Whiston, *A Vindication of the New Theory of the
Earth from the Exceptions of Mr. Keill and Others* (London, 1698),
p. 8.

[19] Whiston, *A New Theory of the Earth* (Cambridge, 1708), pp. 290,
291. Whiston referred here to Dr. Bentley, *Sermon 4*. Unlike Burnet
he gave definite references to books. Burnet, like most of his predecessors, merely listed authors. In one place Burnet mentioned several
names and said, "These Authors I have examin'd my self: But there are
many others . . . which I leave to be examin'd by those that have
Curiosity and Leisure to do it." Burnet, *The Sacred Theory of the Earth*
(London, 1722), vol. i, bk. iii, p. 50. Of course in his *Archaeologiae
Philosophicae* he gave long quotations. He listed many more authors
than Whiston but a much smaller percentage of them were moderns.
When the two quoted Scripture, both generally gave exact references.

ation is with us nothing, as far as we can find, but *Nutrition* or *Augmentation of Parts*; and that agreeably thereto no Seed has been by any creature produc'd since the beginning of things,[20]

what happened on the fifth day was that

those Seeds, or little Bodies of Fish and Fowl which were contain'd in the Water, (or moist fruitful Ἰλὺς of kin to it,) were now expos'd to the kindly warmth of the *Sun,* and the constant supply of a most gentle and equal Heat from beneath; they were neither disturb'd by the sudden Alteration of the Temperature of the Air from the Violence of Winds, nor by the Agitations of the Tide; (which was both very small, in these small Seas; and by reason of the absence of the *Diurnal-Rotation,* imperceptibly easy, gentle, and gradual;) these Seeds, I say, when invigorated with the Divine Benediction, became now prolifick.[21]

Whiston limited the spontaneous generation of animals to the period before the Fall and attributed it to the length of the day, which gave continuous heat, and to the greater warmth from the central body, which had since then become somewhat cooled, and which was nine or ten miles nearer to Paradise than it had been to the tropics since the earth's change in shape to an oblate spheroid.   In addition, the soil, being " loose," freely admitted the ascending steams, which were caused by the central hot core, and, being moist and juicy, could nourish the embryo.   The only spot where this production of animals occurred was Paradise.   Eden was a particularly fertile section of Assyria and was free from winds and storms.[22]   Upon this happy world man's sin brought

[20] Whiston, *op. cit.,* p. 290. Bentley described seeds under the microscope as obviously containing minute but perfect plants. Bentley, *The Folly and Unreasonableness of Atheism Demonstrated* (London, 1699), pp. 113, 114, 128, 129.

[21] *Ibid.,* pp. 319, 320 also p. 295.

[22] *Ibid.,* pp. 230-234, 326, 332-336, 341-347.

unpleasant results. Whiston tried to explain these by the suggestion that consumption of the fruit from the tree of knowledge for a day,—i. e., a year, or even longer, like any other intemperate diet, might make man sickly, miserable and mortal. The change in the earth's shape and in its orbit, together with the beginning of its diurnal revolution, he attributed to a comet of small size,[23] which at that time hit "obliquely upon the Earth along some parts of its present Equator." [24] Since the center of the earth was largely fluid, the change in motion would cause the liquid to assume the form of an oblate spheroid. Such an alteration would crack the crust. The central body would, therefore, be nearer to the flattened poles and would moderate their temperature. All the planetary orbits were originally circular because such a course was more suitable and more just to the inhabitants whom Whiston postulated for each planet. God's wisdom would necessarily begin with a perfect, uniform, regular motion for the celestial spheres, and then by the attraction of comets passing through the planetary system change it to fit the state and the behavior of the creatures inhabiting each planet.[25] One proof that the impulse to this change came from the outside was that the central body did not revolve quite so fast as the exterior crust.[26] The belief in a loose central core, generally conceived as hot, floating in liquids,

[23] Whiston, *op. cit.*, pp. 41-49, 111, 112, 131, 337-339.

[24] *Ibid.*, p. 111.

[25] *Ibid.*, pp. 55-57, 60-64, 125-133, 327, 328, 344-346, 349.

[26] For this Whiston quoted the Royal Society of London, *Philosophical Transactions* (London, 1665-1933), no. 195, art. 3, 1692, pp. 563 *et seq.*, Halley, "On the cause of the Change in the Variation of the Magnetic Needle; with an Hypothesis of the Structure of the Internal Parts of the Earth." Halley (1656-1742) was an authority on many phases of astronomical discovery. His contributions to the science were summarized by Delambre, *op. cit.*, pp. 116-140. Whiston, *op. cit.*, pp. 109-112, 234, 349.

was prevalent during this period.   Whiston as well as Burnet enlarged on it in his comparison of the earth to an egg.[27] Keill denied the usefulness of any such hot central solid on the ground that heat did not penetrate stones even so far as five feet; hence volcanic eruptions must come from heat nearer the surface; and springs were due to water raised from the sea, not to vapors from a subterranean abyss, raised by internal heat through fissures in the crust.[28]   Whiston reaffirmed his statement that vapors from the abyss, forced to the surface by the central heat, caused springs, and declared that this central hot body was not enclosed by a solid wall but by a fluid and then by porous earth that contained innumerable perpendicular cracks.[29]

The flood Whiston attributed to the approach of a much larger comet, which he finally identified with Halley's.   The earth passed through its tail, a process which consumed about two hours, and carried off a large portion of its atmosphere. This settled, at first as rain, and deposited a new coat of solid and gaseous matter upon our planet.[30]   The additional weight changed the solar year, which originally corresponded to the lunar, by an increase of five days, while the length of the month was even reduced; and thus all the ideas of the survivors as to the calendar were disturbed.[31]   The fertility of the soil and the healthfulness, temperateness and serenity of the atmosphere were changed by the diminution of ex-

[27] Whiston, *op. cit.*, pp. 220-222, 326.

[28] Keill, *op. cit.*, pp. 185-188.

[29] Whiston, *A Vindication of the New Theory of the Earth from the Exceptions of Mr. Keill and Others* (London, 1698), pp. 6, 7; Whiston, *A New Theory of the Earth* (Cambridge, 1708), pp. 84, 220, 221, 327.

[30] *Ibid.*, pp. 181-212, 252-255, 368-370.

[31] Whiston tried to prove that the antediluvian year consisted of twelve months and exactly three hundred and sixty days by the assertion that after the flood all or most nations continued to use those numbers. *Ibid.*, pp. 144-168, 173-181, 188, 192-201, 204-209, 261, 262, 402.

ternal and internal heat because of the alteration in the earth's orbit, the increased depth of the crust and the filling of the cracks by cometary waters and debris and by the acquisition [32] of "heterogeneous mixtures," [33] or, as Whiston called them elsewhere, " Sulphureous and Sultry " and " Nitrous and Freezing *Effluvia* or Exhalations," sustained by the present "gross atmosphere." [34]   To these he attributed the storms, the thunder and the " Pestilential Infections, in our present Air," [35] so different from the antediluvian. The comet which caused this catastrophe was six times the size of the moon and passed twenty-four times as near. Therefore it raised a great tide in the interior of the earth. Had the earth been wholly fluid, the tide would have been one hundred miles in altitude; but probably it was only half that height.   However, the tide within the crust and the pressure of the water on the surface, which forced the earth crust down into the abyss, reopened and even increased the fissures formed at the beginning of the earth's diurnal rotation, especially those in the less compact mountainous regions. The waters within the globe were ejected and added to the flood.   Through the same fissures at the end of the deluge most of the water was reabsorbed, but enough remained to form oceans on the surface.   Though part of the earth dried quickly, possibly some of the lowlands were submerged for hundreds of years.   In many localities the strata showed evidence of their slow deposition by the sea.   Another effect of the comet was to attract the earth into an elliptical orbit. Perhaps the later rains mentioned in the Bible came from a second passage of our globe through the tail on the comet's return from its perihelion.   Their comparative mildness re-

[32] Whiston, *op. cit.*, pp. 246, 247, 349-361, 385, 386.
[33] *Ibid.*, p. 246.
[34] *Ibid.*, p. 357; also pp. 350, 358-361.
[35] Ibid., p. 359; also introduction, p. 56.

sulted from the lesser density in that portion of the tail.   It
was much more distant from the nucleus.[36]

Whiston agreed with those who tried to explain fossils by
attributing them to the flood.   Since he had decided that the
finny species as a whole survived the catastrophe, he concluded that many individuals must have been killed by poisonous particles from the comet or stifled by mud so that
their bones sank to the bottom and were embedded in the
strata.   Because he had proved by astronomy and by history
that the date of the deluge was just after the autumnal
equinox,[37] he was forced to explain why the fossil plants

[36] Whiston, *A New Theory of the Earth* (Cambridge, 1708), pp.
203-205, 212, 254, 256, 261, 371-378, 382, 383, 385, 386, 392, 393,
395-402.   Whiston wrote a separate book, *The Cause of the Deluge
Demonstrated* (London, 1714), to prove the flood due to Halley's comet
specifically.   He gave elaborate mathematical calculations of the previous
appearances of the comet to show that once its presence coincided with
the date of the flood.   Again Keill rejected Whiston's method both of
producing and of removing the waters.   He attributed all to a miracle.
Keill, *op. cit.*, pp. 19-21, 32, 33, 177-179, 199-223.   Whiston repeated his
arguments and conclusions in his later books.   Whiston, *A Vindication
of the New Theory of the Earth from the Exceptions of Mr. Keill and
Others* (London, 1698), pp. 13-23, 46-49; Whiston, *A Second Defence
of the New Theory of the Earth from the Exceptions of Mr. John Keill*
(London, 1700), pp. 15-20.   Whiston, *Six Dissertations* (London, 1734),
p. 214.   *Cf.* also *supra*, p. 93 note.   During the eighteenth century the
cometary origin of the flood was a common belief, especially in Germany.
Besides the book by Heyn already referred to, which quoted Whiston
(*cf. supra*, p. 113) and dissertations by two of his pupils (*cf. infra*, pp.
190-192), a similar doctrine was propounded by John Nicholas Catoir.
With mathematical proofs he enlarged on the theory that the flood was
due to the tail of a comet, but referred to Cluver, *Geologia*, caps. xii and
xiii, a German book, as his authority.   Catoir, *Disputatio Theologica de
Arca Noachi et Diluvio* (Gröningen, 1704), secs. xviii-xx.   He felt all
phenomena connected with the deluge were "types".   *Ibid.*, secs. xxxiii,
xxxix-xlvi, xlix.   Unlike Whiston, he believed that the flood began and
ended in the spring.   *Ibid.*, secs. xxxix, xlvii.

[37] Whiston, *A Vindication of the New Theory of the Earth from the
Exceptions of Mr. Keill and Others* (London, 1698), pp. 21, 22; Whiston,

seemed to be those of spring, and asserted that only on the retreat of the waters late in March and especially in May were they torn up by storms and currents with the soil attached and often carried to far-distant countries.   Plants were not, however, wholly destroyed by the deluge.   Later the muddy waters, in subsiding, buried in level strata, which had been deposited according to specific gravity, shells, bones and vegetables over the whole earth including the mountains. These strata were later broken and elevated or depressed by the globe's resettling into shape after the distortion caused by the deluge.[38]

Whiston explained the final conflagration also as due to the near approach of a comet, presumably the same celestial visitor.   This might draw the earth so far out of its orbit that it would be burned up by the sun.   More probably the comet would remove the surface waters.   By the enormous tides it would produce in the abyss it would cause great fissures in the crust and the waters would be drained into the abyss.   The comet would heat or replace the air by its own atmosphere of vapors that had been newly raised to a high temperature at its perihelion.   This external ardor, together with the heat from the central body, which would no longer be moderated by the cold waters and the air, would suffice to burn the outer crust.   The fluids of the abyss itself could not be rarefied by the most violent heat.   After the crust had been reduced to a chaos similar to the original condition, it would

The Accomplishment of Scripture Prophecies (Cambridge, 1708), pp. 98, 99; Whiston, *A New Theory of the Earth* (Cambridge, 1708), pp. 142, 143, 202-204, 206, 209-211, 417, 418, 423, 424. He believed that the season for the first act of creation was the fall, which corresponded to the evening of the first day. *Ibid.*, pp. 215, 297, 298.

[38] Whiston, *op. cit.*, pp. 266-272, 412, 414-417, 422-425. With this explanation of fossils, which he called "more Philosophical than any other," Keill agreed on the ground that it fitted the phenomena mentioned by Woodward. Keill, *op. cit.*, p. 217.

reconsolidate on the same abyss into a state similar to that of the primitive earth.   There would be neither ocean nor seas. Since the comet by rubbing against the earth would retard its diurnal motion till the time of its revolution exactly corresponded with that of its annual course in its orbit, there would be perpetual day in one hemisphere.   The other would be supplied with a supernatural light, permanently fixed above the horizon.   By the same cometary interference the earth's orbit might be made a circle or an ellipse of a different shape. Since there would not be again the special providence by which at the time of the earlier catastrophe the moon was equally accelerated with our earth, the two planets would part company.[39]   After the Last Judgment, as Burnet had already claimed, the earth would desert its present position and no longer be one of the planets.   Whiston as usual attributed this dislocation to a comet.   Any comet by a gentle blow to the terrestrial globe might make it change its orbit to a very elliptical one,—that is, become a comet itself.   Thus again we meet the full cycle of change dear to Burnet and to his contemporaries.[40]

[39] Whiston, *op. cit.*, pp. 276-282, 440-449.
[40] *Ibid.*, pp. 282, 449.

CHAPTER XIII

WOODWARD, THE COLLECTOR

DE LUC criticized Burnet and Leibnitz as having invented logical systems with little resemblance to the real universe. They were men of thought, not of observation. Woodward, the opposite type, put down many things which resembled reality in color and in shape,—that is, in appearance, not in fact. He showed the great difference in the study of nature between the eyes of the body and of the understanding.[1]

What primarily impressed Woodward was the abundance of marine fossils in all parts of the world, even on the summits of mountains. Much work throughout Europe was being done in collecting such materials. Dr. Robert Plot (1641-1696), who, however, believed fossils to be mere stones, had published two constantly quoted books, *A Natural History of Oxfordshire* and *A Natural History of Staffordshire*.[2] These works purported to discuss the natural and artificial things of England both for science and for trade, and contained what is now considered natural history together with a farrago of old wives' tales and queer rural customs. Both books were reviewed in the *Philosophical Transactions*.[3] Woodward commended as well a recent

[1] De Luc, *Lettres physiques et morales sur l'histoire de la terre et de l'homme* (The Hague and Paris, 1779, 1780), vol. i, pp. 254-312, especially pp. 265, 266, 276.

[2] Plot, *The Natural History of Oxfordshire, being an Essay toward the Natural History of England* (Oxford, 1677); Plot, *The Natural History of Staffordshire* (Oxford, 1686).

[3] Royal Society of London, *Philosophical Transactions* (London, 1665-1933), no. 135, 1677, pp. 875 *et seq.*, no. 184, 1686, pp. 207 *et seq.*

Natural History of Northamptonshire by Morton.[4] The
Germans were enthusiastic in the study of fossils and geology, perhaps because their country presented the greatest
variety of specimens in Europe. Just beyond their borders,
Dr. Scheuchzer, professor of mathematics at Zürich, like
many other scientists on the continent, became a convert to
Woodward's views. He published the Latin translation of
the Englishman's work under the title *Geographia Physica*.[5]

John Woodward (1665-1728), a physician, a geologist
and a Fellow of the Royal Society, had an unusual collection
of fossils.[6] He boasted that he had travelled over all England taking notes concerning the contents of mines, grottos,
and other excavations, and had sent a questionnaire throughout Europe, Asia, America and Africa [7] before he wrote his

[4] Woodward, *A Supplement & Continuation of The Essay towards a
Natural History of the Earth* (London, 1726) (1st ed., 1714?), part ii,
p. 45. Addison quoted from Dr. Plot. *The Spectator* (London and New
York, 1898), nos. 447, 607.

[5] Woodward, *op. cit.*, part ii, preface and pp. 4-8. The members of the
Institute of Bologna supported Woodward's diluvial theory but the
Tuscan geologists fought it. Whitehurst, an Englishman, in his *Inquiry
into the Original State and Formation of the Earth* (1778), and Wallerius,
a German, tried to sustain Woodward's thesis that all strata were made
by the flood. Jéhan, *Dictionnaire de cosmogonie et de paléontologie*
(Paris, 1854), art. "Géologie (Histoire de la)," cols. 629, 643.

[6] Harris, *Remarks On some Late Papers, Relating to the Universal
Deluge: And to the Natural History of the Earth* (London, 1697), pp.
164, 165. These collections of natural history, especially of minerals,
were popular during the seventeenth and the eighteenth centuries. Both
kings and private citizens possessed them. Buffon and De Luc had
notable cabinets of such rarities and De Luc mentioned many others.
The miners had even learned to lay aside unusual specimens for sale to
collectors. De Luc, *op. cit.*, vol. iii, p. 380 and elsewhere. Hutchinson
was employed by Woodward to assist in gathering his collection. Jéhan,
op. cit., art. "Géologie (Histoire de la)," col. 628.

[7] Woodward, *An Essay toward a Natural History of the Earth*
(London, 1695), pp. 3-7; Harris, *op. cit.*, p. 164.

Essay in 1695.[8] This was meant to be the preliminary sketch for a future work on the subject and showed a distinct lack of organization. Unfortunately, although there was a continuation of the *Essay,* written in Latin and translated in 1726, to which the title *The Natural History of the Earth* was occasionally affixed, Woodward seems never to have carried out his project. At almost the end of the *Supplement,*[9] Woodward said: "I have offered my Sentiments," about earthquakes and such catastrophes

with the Observations whereon they are grounded, elsewhere; intending, as I shall see Men's Minds settled, and turning to these Studyes, if God shall give me Leisure, to methodise what I have wrote, and to treat of the same Subjects more at large, together with some others of like Sort.[10]

Harris [11] quoted from this incomplete larger work a section which he had obtained from the author. It discussed the confusion of the floating bodies as they subsided. Holloway in his introduction to the translation of 1726 quoted other passages.[12]

Since fossils were Woodward's primary interest, it was natural that his cosmology should begin with the deluge, to which he attributed all these fossiliferous strata,[13] and work

[8] The third edition was published in London in 1723. It had some changes in detail and order, but few in theory.

[9] Hutchinson, *Moses's Principia* (London, 1724), pp. 80, 85, ridiculed him for this failure. Cockburn, *An Enquiry into the Truth and Certainty of the Mosaic Deluge* (London, 1750), p. 182, declared Woodward's larger work never appeared. In 1744 Buffon said the same. Buffon, *Oeuvres complètes* (Paris, 1831-1832), vol. i, p. 229.

[10] Woodward, *A Supplement & Continuation of The Essay towards a Natural History of the Earth* (London, 1726), part ii, pp. 110, 111.

[11] Harris, *op. cit.,* pp. 34-36.

[12] Woodward, *op. cit.,* pt. i, pp. 9-36, 39-104.

[13] Woodward, *An Essay toward a Natural History of the Earth* (London, 1695), pp. 72-80, 112-114.

back to a primitive world and a creation that might have produced such a catastrophe. He resembled Whiston in the belief that the processes of creation and of recovery from the deluge were analogous.

Woodward agreed with most other commentators in accepting a primordial chaos out of which the particles settled in accordance with their specific gravity. Gravity was the chief means whereby the universe was supported and managed. It was not intrinsic in matter but due wholly to the direct and persistent power of God.[14] Strangely enough, however, in the light of this idea that the heaviest part of matter must be nearest the center, he believed that the middle of the earth was, in the primeval world and again after the flood, a sphere of water. Into this reservoir, which Moses named the abyss, was drained the water which covered the globe both after its first consolidation and after its second solidification subsequent to the flood; and out of it came the waters of the deluge. Still nearer the center was a central heat that continuously raised vapors from the abyss. Perhaps this internal fire implied a solid terrestrial core, such as Burnet and Whiston mentioned; but Woodward's statements were not explicit. He did say that the outer crust was thin but strong since it was in the form of an arch. He apparently pictured the crust as having been laid down in horizontal strata over a sphere of air. Then by a force within the earth, probably the central heat, the strata were elevated, fractured and crumpled. Mountains were produced where the strata were solid and supported themselves in their new positions, while clay, gravel and other unstable layers sank back into their former locations and became plains. All mountains of the primal earth were formed simultaneously

[14] Woodward, op. cit., pp. 53, 97, 265; Harris, op. cit., pp. 30-39; Woodward, A Supplement & Continuation of The Essay towards a Natural History of the Earth (London, 1726), especially part i, pp. 9-18, 32, 144, 145.

at creation, and the essential outlines of the earth's surface
were established. After their destruction by the deluge, they
were reestablished in a similar manner at one time. Woodward called the islands and the eminences thrown up by volcanoes mere heaps of rubble. Through the fissures in the
crust the waters that had covered the surface then ran down
and filled the abyss.[15] Vapors raised from the abyss were
the cause of most springs and rains, of temperature and
barometric changes, as well as of sulphurous and nitrous
exhalations which accompanied earthquakes, infected the air
and caused thunder and lightning when they were raised to
the clouds by the sun's heat. The vapors also caused vegetable growth. Of course the abyss, which communicated
with the ocean by chasms in the sea bed, occasioned earthquakes. The central heat caused volcanoes, hot springs and
similar phenomena, which proved its existence.[16]

Woodward, though he denied Burnet's assertions that the
primitive earth had no mountains, seas, seasons or metals,
and that the rainbow was unknown, agreed with his predecessor as to its immense superiority in fertility. He suggested
that the fruitfulness might once have been so great as to
produce valuable grains as profusely as thorns and thistles,
which he declared were not unknown before the Fall. On the
other hand, instead of a general productivity, the fertility
perhaps consisted in the presence of a greater proportion of
the " Terrestrial Matter " needed by valuable plants as com-

[15] Woodward, *op. cit.*, part i, pp. 7, 8, 122, 126-128, 136, 139-145, 152,
153, 164-168; part ii, pp. 58, 59, 96-123; Woodward, *An Essay toward a
Natural History of the Earth* (London, 1695), pp. 46-55, 60-70, 79-81,
97, 110-112, 117, 133-146, 153-165, 188, 189, 231, 238, 246-257, 264, 265;
Harris, *op. cit.*, pp. 20, 39, 44, 169-171, 197, 198, 210, 211, 252.

[16] Woodward, *op. cit.*, pp. 117-131, 133-146, 189, 197-215; Woodward,
*A Supplement & Continuation of The Essay towards a Natural History
of the Earth* (London, 1726), part i, pp. 31, 32, 116-143, 146-151; part ii,
pp. 57-59, 104-107, 112, 115; Harris, *op. cit.*, pp. 169, 252.

pared with that requisite for weeds.[17] " The Animal and Vegetable Remains of that Earth shew it to have been much more fruitfull and productive than ours." [18]   Possibly the earth was not uniformly fertile.   Obviously the purpose of this productivity was to afford man leisure for the praise of God and the contemplation of His works.   When, after the Fall, the fertility and the leisure became a snare and led to luxury and sin, God in kindness and mercy removed it.   This was the primary reason for a deluge.   The mere destruction of mankind could have been more expeditiously and economically effected in other ways.   But a re-dissolution and a precipitation of the earth's crust in such a manner as to mix the fertile surface soil with sterile mineral matter would produce a planet where the toil of agriculture would prevent leisure and luxury.   In addition such a re-formation of the crust would obviate the danger of the soil's exhaustion. The upper surfaces of mountains were continually worn down.   While these changes were slight, they restored the fertility of the valleys.[19]   Therefore the deluge must have been universal, as could indeed be judged by the wide dispersion of fossils.   Their condition, especially that of the plants, proved that the date was the end of May.   The suggestion of Ray and of Dr. Camerarius in Germany that the fossils might have been deposited at creation when the waters were withdrawn was inadmissible since the Bible distinctly stated that the dry land appeared on the third day and the

[17] Woodward, *op. cit.*, pt. i, pp. 37, 38, 51-66; Woodward, *An Essay toward a Natural History of the Earth* (London, 1695), pp. 56, 84, 85, 100-102, 245-277.

[18] Woodward, *A Supplement & Continuation of The Essay towards a Natural History of the Earth* (London, 1726), pt. i, p. 61.

[19] Woodward, *op. cit.*, part i, pp. 35, 37, 38, 50, 61; part ii, p. 96; Woodward, *An Essay toward a Natural History of the Earth* (London, 1695), pp. 56, 57, 60, 61, 83-95, 99-106, 231, 237-241; Harris, *op. cit.*, pp. 28, 61, 110.

first animals were created only on the fifth. Moreover, the shells were attached in such a way as to show their growth in the bed where their fossils remained; and not all the animals, of which the deposits consisted, were of the same age. The production of so many living creatures for immediate destruction did not seem sensible.[20]

Woodward had much to say concerning the manner of the flood. Only after the mountains, which Moses mentioned, were covered, had the waters poured out of the abyss in sufficient quantity to dissolve and to hold in suspension the earth's crust. Though Woodward in his supplemental volume asserted that he had not mentioned the cause of the earth's dissolution, he made a number of statements that at least bore on the subject. He attributed it to the direct act of God and to the ministry of the waters and the principle of the abyss. As the gravity which still held all things together and at creation and after the flood had induced the subsidence of matter was the immediate and constant act of God, so a partial removal of this force would permit the dissolution of all mineral and metallic matter, though not its dispersion through space. Mineral particles were attached merely by apposition, while organic remains consisted of fibres so intertwined that they were held together and subsided as wholes after having floated about during the months of the flood.[21] The destruction of so many aquatic creatures Harris, an admirer of Woodward, explained to his master's critics as

[20] Woodward, *op. cit.*, preface, pp. 157-165, 274, 275; Woodward, *Fossils Of all Kinds* (London, 1728), part ii, pp. 52-54, 121, 125, 126; Woodward, *A Supplement & Continuation of The Essay towards a Natural History of the Earth* (London, 1726), pt. i, pp. 38, 46, pt. ii, pp. 16-26, 61, 134-138.

[21] Harris, *op. cit.*, pp. 16-36, 43, 82, 83; Woodward, *op. cit.*, pt. i, pp. 5, 6, 38, 39, 155-166, 168, pt. ii, pp. 27, 38, 61-75, 91-97, 100-103, 108, 109; Woodward, *Fossils Of all Kinds* (London, 1728), pt. i, p. 45; Woodward, *An Essay toward a Natural History of the Earth* (London, 1695), preface and pp. 29, 74, 75, 165, 166.

due to the commotion of the water and to the great glut of dissolved earthy and stony matter, which choked the fish, and of noxious salts, which poisoned them. The fish that survived must have been preserved by a particular providence to repeople the seas.[22]

After the tumult and confusion of the deluge, which transported the relics of antediluvial animals and plants to strange districts, God reestablished the principle of gravitation. All the matter in solution settled in strata wherever it chanced to be, generally in accord with its specific gravity so that the heavier strata were lower. Organic remains were in the strata where the gravity of the mineral matter resembled theirs. For this assortment an enormous quantity of water was necessary. Of course, if at the beginning of the process lighter matter was below heavier, it might be so near the center of the earth that its final resting place was lower than would be anticipated. Further changes in the relative gravity of the strata had been effected by the swift currents at the final retreat of the waters, by the rains of the intervening centuries, which had removed light fossils and stones from their original resting places and mixed them in inextricable confusion, and by the vapors from the abyss, which had raised metallic particles up the fissures in the crust. The belief in the earth's dissolution could be substantiated from the Bible. In passages later than Genesis like the books of Amos and Peter the terms " dissolve " and " melt " and " destroy the whole world " were used to describe the flood. The fact of the dissolution was also established by the tradition to that effect among Greeks and Romans, and by the books of the " Sibyll," of the fathers etc.[23]

[22] Harris, *op. cit.*, pp. 81, 82.

[23] Woodward, *op. cit.*, preface and pp. 29-33, 75-79, 153, 167-169, 179-196, 233, 234; Woodward, *A Supplement & Continuation of The Essay towards a Natural History of the Earth* (London, 1726), part i, pp. 48,

As has been implied, Woodward's work, as well as Burnet's and Whiston's, aroused much comment from bitter opponents, largely pamphleteers, who preferred to remain anonymous, and from stalwart champions, both in England and on the continent. Perhaps the most enthusiastic of the defenders, Dr. John Harris, declared that Woodward's book *" vindicates, supports* and *maintains the Mosaick Account of things,* as exactly *agreeable* to the *Phaenomena of Nature."* [24] This coincides with De Luc's comment that Woodward looked upon nature directly instead of upon the mirror held up to nature by classic authority. Except for the Biblical authors, he seldom quoted any but his contemporaries; and among them he referred more commonly to men still acknowledged as outstanding scientists than to philosophers or theologians. By 1690 a new spirit of independence and rejection of authorities was evident among even second-rate men. Though it seldom went to the extent of rejecting the Biblical narratives of the creation and the flood, it did attempt new explanations for these, and no longer based its appeal to belief on lists of authorities. Even the theologians, notably Le Clerc, in their Scriptural commentaries and sermons shared in the new spirit, as has been pointed out. After Newton's time, the fundamental principles of the heliocentric theory were accepted, although there were sporadic denials. The emphasis changed from a discussion of the universe as a whole to a consideration of the earth in particular. Thanks to the telescope, the universe kept expanding into system beyond system until it reached its present state of incomprehensibility. The mind of the ordinary man ceased to attempt to grapple with its immensity, and per-

---

144, 145, 165-168; part ii, pp. 32-49, 61-75, 97-103, 107, 108; Woodward, *Fossils Of all Kinds* (London, 1728), pp. 8, 54, notes on pp. 10 and 12; part ii, pp. 63, 68, 121-125; Harris, *op. cit.,* pp. 36-42, 207-210.

[24] *Ibid.,* p. 44.

mitted the scientist unchecked to exploit theories concerning it that had no relation to the Bible.   The harmonization of the Mosaic statements on creation with the facts of the earth's surface occupied the general attention.   The phenomena of fossils became ever more important, together with other signs of immense age in the terrestrial strata.   Some commentators solved the difficulties of fossiliferous deposits in Woodward's manner by a hypothetical dissolution of the earth's crust at the deluge, but an increasing number demanded long eras for the slow changes that shaped the earth. Buffon asserted that the period since creation had been as much as 75,000 years.   These tendencies were evident in the period just discussed, but they were ever more noticeable with the progress of the eighteenth century.

CHAPTER XIV

Cosmological References in Belles-Lettres

At all times literature has been alive to the current scientific hypotheses. In figures of speech and allusions the poet, the essayist, the orator and especially the dramatist have shown themselves attentive to the popular scientific doctrines. On the other hand, poetic conventions have often inspired language and images expressive of an outmoded science. Occasionally essayists or didactic poets have gone further and expounded favored theories or eulogized conspicuous scientists. It would be impossible to mention all the instances of this truth during the seventeenth and the eighteenth centuries but a few examples from English literature of the tendency may be interesting.

The first place in any such discussion naturally belongs to John Milton (1608-1674), because of his superiority as a poet, because of his dominating influence on English readers and because of the volume of his contribution. His *Paradise Lost* (1668) and *Paradise Regained* (1671) were definite attempts to enlarge the Mosaic account and at the same time to correlate it with the scientific ideas that he favored.

Generally he spoke as if he accepted the Ptolemaic hypothesis, probably because he deemed it more stimulating to poetic imagery; but in Books V-VIII of *Paradise Lost,* when Raphael, at God's command, related to Adam and Eve the history of the fall of the angels and of the creation, and, inasmuch as Eve preferred to hear the story from her husband, expounded to Adam alone the system of the stars, he seemed to favor the heliocentric theory. Adam declared that the idea of the stars circling around the earth was unreasonable because it required the use of too great means for the end proposed.[1]   Thereupon Raphael made answer:

> " This to attain, whether Heaven move, or Earth,
>   Imports not, or if thou reckon right; the rest,
>   From man or angel, the great Architect
>   Did wisely to conceal, and not divulge
>   Hid secrets, to be scann'd by them, who ought
>   Rather admire: or, if they list to try
>   Conjecture, he his fabric of the Heavens
>   Hath left to their disputes, perhaps to move
>   His laughter, at their quaint opinions wide,
>   Hereafter, when they come to model Heaven,
>   And calculate the stars, how they will wield
>   The mighty frame, how build, unbuild, contrive
>   To save appearances, how gird the sphere,
>   With centric and eccentric scribbled o'er,
>   Cycle and epicycle, orb in orb." [2]

Raphael refused to affirm either the geocentric or the heliocentric theory,[3] advising Adam against the investigation of Nature's secrets with the following reflections:

> " Whether the sun, . . .
>   Rise on the earth, or earth rise on the sun; . . .
>   Solicit not thy thoughts; with matters hid,
>   Leave them to God above; him serve and fear;
>   Of other creatures, as him pleases best,
>   Wherever placed, let him dispose." [4]

[1] Milton, *The Poetical Works* (London, 1862), *Paradise Lost* (1st ed., 1667 or 1668) bk. viii, ll. 15-57.

[2] *Ibid.*, bk. viii, ll. 70-84.

[3] *Ibid.*, bk. viii, l. 117.

[4] *Ibid.*, bk. viii, ll. 160-170.

Milton's account of creation was slightly less neutral and more definite. He visualized an infinite universe as at first divided into heaven, hell and chaos. Perhaps originally heaven and hell were made from chaos. They were bounded only on the side toward chaos, which lay between them, and into which wide gates led from each side. Through these openings the defeated angels fell. After the revolt of the angels, Christ at God's command divided off a portion of chaos with golden compasses. Upon the part thus circumscribed brooded the Spirit of God. It infused vital warmth and virtue into the fluid mass and expelled downward the cold dregs. The Spirit combined like things and formed the earth, while the various elements departed to their places, and the " etherial quintessence of heaven " rose and formed the stars, probably including the planets, and an outer spherical wall to separate the visible universe from chaos. In this wall there was but one opening, directly above Eden and the Holy Land. It led to heaven and served as a highway for the angels. After the Fall its size was diminished. Milton probably believed in four concentric spheres of earth, water, air and fire, and placed the waters above the firmament in a crystalline sphere somewhere beyond the stars. Despite his acquaintance and dalliance with the heliocentric system and his meeting with Galileo in Italy, his account of creation and the picture of the world in his poetry implied a stationary central earth, surrounded by solid orbs or spheres, to which the planets and the stars were affixed, and by which they were moved. He mentioned several times the music of the spheres. Each sphere was governed by an angel, who was perhaps assisted by inferior angels; and the globes might even have other inhabitants.[5]

[5] Milton, *op. cit., Paradise Lost*, bk. ii, ll. 1000-1010, bk. iii, ll. 417-428, 480-485, 500-542, 565-570, 689, 707-720, bk. v, ll. 176-183, 577-579, 620-627, bk. vii, ll. 163-175, 219-242, 264-273, 620, 621, bk. viii, ll. 144-

After, or perhaps before, the separation of the elements,
God by His word created light.   It sprang from the deep [6]
and

> " from her native east,
> To journey through the airy gloom began,
> Sphered in a radiant cloud, for yet the sun
> Was not; she in a cloudy tabernacle
> Sojourn'd the while." [7]

The firmament was the transparent elemental air which filled
the whole space of the visible universe, though Milton had
previously asserted that the ether was there located.   On the
third day the waters were driven from part of the earth's
surface by the production of mountains and valleys.[8]   When
God formed the celestial bodies,

> " first the sun,
> A mighty sphere, he framed, unlightsome first,
> Though of ethereal mould : then form'd the moon
> Globose, and every magnitude of stars,
> And sow'd with stars the Heaven, thick as a field :
> Of light, by far the greater part he took,
> Transplanted from her cloudy shrine, and placed
> In the sun's orb, made porous to receive
> And drink the liquid light, firm to retain
> Her gather'd beams, great palace now of light.
> Hither, as to their fountain, other stars
> Repairing, in their golden urns draw light,
> And hence the morning planet gilds her horns ;
> By tincture, or reflection, they augment
> Their small peculiar." [9]

149; *Ode on the Morning of Christ's Nativity*; Warren, *The Universe
as Pictured in Milton's Paradise Lost* (New York and Cincinnati, 1915).

[6] Milton, *op. cit., Paradise Lost*, bk. iii, ll. 8, 9, bk. vii, ll. 243-245.

[7] *Ibid.*, bk. vii, ll. 245-249.

[8] *Ibid.*, bk. iii, l. 720, bk. vii, ll. 264-308.

[9] *Ibid.*, bk. vii, ll. 353-367.

On the sixth day of creation full-grown animals literally broke from the earth. Adam himself was created outside of Paradise and was led thither through the air by God. Paradise was on top of a wooded mountain, but it had hills of its own as well, inasmuch as later Adam surveyed the hemisphere of the earth from the highest one. All animals except fish were brought by God in pairs before Adam, who was endowed with sudden knowledge of their natures so that he gave them appropriate names. Later he discovered Eve, but did not completely fathom the method of her creation.

During the first six days the poles of the earth were erect so that it enjoyed a perpetual equinox; but after the Fall God bade his angels tip the poles and carry out such other changes as might destroy the perfection of the earth and introduce excessive heat and cold, storms, thunder, disease and all the malevolent effects of the stars. Sin and Death were admitted by the path by which Satan had travelled.[10]

Milton assigned more than one purpose for creation. In *Paradise Lost* he spoke of the innumerable angels who fell and the need for repeopling heaven by the faithful lest Satan exult in his work. This has always been a popular doctrine.[11] When Satan himself assigned a reason, he stated that God created and governed the world for His glory and demanded

[10] Milton, *op. cit., Paradise Lost*, bk. vii, ll. 452-472, 492, bk. viii, ll. 300-305, 312-317, 342-354, 460-490, bk. x, ll. 230-326, 650-715, 846-850, bk. xi, ll. 118-120, 377-380, bk. xii, ll. 639, 640, 649.

[11] *Ibid.*, bk. i, l. 344, bk. vii, ll. 150-161; bk. ix, l. 144. Some other authors who believed this the reason for the creation of the visible world and of man are as follows: St. Augustine, quoted by Swinden, who also accepted the theory. Swinden, *An Enquiry into the Nature and Place of Hell* (London, 1727), pp. 88-90, 176-178, 275; Kircher, *Itinerarivm Exstaticvm* (Rome, 1656), pp. 357, 358; Swedenborg, *Miscellaneous Theological Works* (New York, 1863) *The Earths in the Universe*, secs. 3, 30, 126, and elsewhere in his works; Jordan, *The Creation of the World* (London, 1827) (1st ed., 1611), pp. 18, 19, 36, 37.

glory from men and angels, both good and bad. Christ responded that God's word produced all

> " Though chiefly not for glory as prime end,
>   But to show forth his goodness, and impart
>   His good communicable to every soul
>   Freely." [12]

Milton's account is of greater importance than his scientific knowledge warranted, since the grandeur of his conceptions and the beauty of his language made it a part of the literary heritage of the English race, so that later writers frequently superseded the Biblical version by the Miltonic and defended it as ardently as though it were Scriptural.

During the eighteenth century poets and writers of belles-lettres dallied with the topic of cosmology both seriously and casually. One of the two most important and characteristic authors of the early eighteenth century, Alexander Pope (1688-1744), referred to " ' our Copernican system ' ". The other, Addison (1672-1719), in the *Spectator* for July 2, 1712 alluded to the immensity and the complexity of the universe and described it briefly in terms of the heliocentric system. A month later, to be sure, he wrote his famous hymn, *The Spacious Firmament on High,* as if he had never heard of any cosmogony except the Ptolemaic.[13] Perhaps he thought it more poetical. Steele (1672-1729) in a rhapsody on the magnitude and wonder of the visible universe apparently accepted not only the heliocentric theory in general, but also the Cartesian vortices.[14] Other allusions to scientific hypotheses concerning the heavens occurred as

---

[12] Milton, *op. cit., Paradise Regained,* bk. iii, ll. 111-120, 123-126.

[13] Stimson, *The Gradual Acceptance of the Copernican Theory of the Universe* (Hanover, 1917), pp. 91, 92; *The Spectator* (London and New York, 1898), nos. 420, 465, July 2, 1712 and August 23, 1712.

[14] *Ibid.,* no. 472, September 1, 1712.

similes in the *Spectator*. Addison talked of Newton's mathematical calculations of the heat of comets and praised his reasoning powers. He alluded to the circuit of the planets around the sun again in the paper of July 9, 1714 as if it were an unquestioned doctrine, and a couple of times surmised that the other planets were inhabited. He spoke of maps of sun-spots and frequently mentioned telescopes and microscopes with their results. However, he was scornful of experiments and dissections and of the Royal Society as a whole.[15]

Richard Blackmore (1650?-1729), a doctor, composed an entire poem on the creation in 1712. It was a somewhat commonplace description of the universe. Though few now would consider him a great author, he was sufficiently distinguished to be included by Samuel Johnson in the list of British Poets whose lives he wrote, and Addison waxed enthusiastic over the poem.[16] Blackmore's opinion on the relation of earth and sun was given in Book I:

> Copernicus, who rightly did condemn
> This eldest system, form'd a wiser scheme;
> In which he leaves the sun at rest.[17]

William Cowper (1731-1800) in 1785 in the third book of *The Task* showed that the facts of creation were still subjects for poetry. He was much exercised over the attempt to repudiate the chronology settled during the preceding

[15] *The Spectator* (London and New York, 1898), nos. 21, 101, 262, 275, 281, 303, 420, 519, 543, 565, March 24, June 26, Dec. 31, 1711 and Jan. 15, Jan. 22, Feb. 16, July 2, Oct. 25, Nov. 22, 1712 and July 9, 1714. A similar praise of Newton was enunciated by Grove who wrote a few of the papers, Grove, in no. 635, Dec. 20, 1714.

[16] *Ibid.*, no. 339, March 29, 1712.

[17] Blackmore, *Creation; A Philosophical Poem*. It is published in an edition entitled *The British Poets* (Chiswick, 1822), vol. xxviii, pp. 75-251, and the quotation is on page 114.

century by Archbishop Usher (or Ussher). Though there were many calculations as to the date of creation, it was generally agreed to have taken place about 4,000 B. C. Usher said B. C. 4004.[18] Cowper wrote:

Some drill and bore
The solid earth, and from the strata there
Extract a register, by which we learn
That He who made it, and revealed its date
To Moses, was mistaken in its age.

A reprobation followed of the folly shown by those who invented fragile theories to account for the universe and disputed with their opponents over hypotheses so soon discarded. He was vehemently opposed to both deists and atheists.[19]

As might have been anticipated, the litterateurs, with the exception of Milton, display the attitude of intelligent gentlemen toward the subject of cosmology rather than offer any new or scientific contribution to theories; but this very fact shows how widely the doctrines had penetrated society.

[18] Joly, *Man Before Metals* (New York, 1883), p. 4, quoted from Ed. Lartet, " Nouvelles recherches sur la coexistence de l'homme et des grands mammifères fossiles, réputés caractéristiques de la dernière période géologique " (*Annales des Sciences Naturelles*, 4e Série, t. xv, p. 256), a statement to the effect that there were no fewer than 140 different opinions about the date of creation, between whose extreme variations there was a discrepancy of 3194 years. Draper, *History of the Conflict between Religion and Science* (London and New York, 1928), pp. 184, 185, 187, 188, affirmed that the number of opinions was not less than 132. He added that the date was generally supposed to be recent, 5000-4000 B. C., and that creation took just six ordinary days. Adam was created perfect in intelligence and morality. The flood occurred A. M. 1656 on November 2, though Whiston postponed the date to the twenty-eighth. A contemporary account of chronological diversity is to be found in the anonymous book, *An Universal History, from the Earliest Account of Time to the Present* (Dublin, 1744). *Cf. infra*, p. 195.

[19] Cowper, *Poems* (New York, ?), bk. iii, *The Garden*, of *The Task*, ll. 150-154 *et seq.*

CHAPTER XV

Grew, the Rationalizer, and Moncharville, the Fantast

The year 1700 did not mark any immediate diminution in the flood of attempts to show that the Biblical account of creation was in accord with the new science. Each year witnessed a fresh theory. Those of 1701 and 1702 by Grew and Moncharville were less elaborate than most and they were seldom quoted by later authors. Both believed in intelligent inhabitants of the other planets.[1] Otherwise they were quite unlike. Grew was a doctor, scientific in his interests although he retained a belief in many pseudo-scientific doctrines, such as the importance of numbers, the effects of the moon and other astrological tenets.[2] Moncharville on the other hand resembled no one and nothing save the caricatures of the scholastics, since he spun from his own inner consciousness a system of the universe whose connection with the real world was so slight as to be almost non-existent. Its chief merit seemed to him its disagreement with all earlier schemes.

Nehemiah Grew (1641-1712), who was an authority on botany, was a Fellow of the Royal Society. He had been recommended to the members by Bishop Wilkins and edited the *Philosophical Transactions* during 1678 and 1679. His

---

[1] Moncharville, *Preuves des existences, et nouveau système de l'univers* (Paris, 1702), pp. 10, 29, 30; Grew, *Cosmologia Sacra* (London, 1701), pp. 10, 88, 89, 91.

[2] *Ibid.*, pp. 248-254.

Cosmologia Sacra was conspicuous for its endeavor to supply
natural explanations for the prophecies and the miracles of
the Bible, particularly the Egyptian plagues.   Though a firm
advocate of the heliocentric theory as developed by Newton,[3]
he said that Joshua commanded the sun to stand still

> very properly: forasmuch as what he said, was in the hearing
> of all the People . . . to whose best Understanding, it behoved
> him to speak.   Whereas, had he said, *Earth, stand thou still;*
> to them, it had been perfect Gibberish.   Neither can any Man
> prove the contrary, but that the Sun did thereupon really stand
> still: that is, cease for a time, from the Rotation it hath upon
> its own *Axis;* whereby the Earth also stood still.[4]

Another thesis of his, common in that day, was the derivation of all Gentile knowledge from the Scriptures.[5]   Moses
was much the earliest of all writers, at least of those whose
works have been preserved.   Because of the overlapping
lives of the patriarchs he was not far removed from Adam,
and therefore the knowledge of his earliest progenitor and
the history of the first ages were easily transmitted to him
without serious erroneous interpolations.   At the most there
were only twenty-five generations between them, but Grew
gave the list of those between Adam and Moses who were
in part contemporaneous as Enos, Noah, Abraham, Jacob,
Joseph and Moses's father.   Moses had records as well,
particularly covering the period from the era of Joseph.
There was no proof that writing had not existed from the
beginning.[6]   The laws attributed by later generations to
Moses had been largely revealed to and by Adam and Noah.[7]

[3] Grew, *op. cit.*, pp. 6-10, 172, 195-204, 316-318, 360-362, 371, 372.

[4] *Ibid.*, p. 172, also p. 203.

[5] *Ibid.*, pp. 144-161, 228, 229, 252, 253, 327.

[6] *Ibid.*, pp. 162-164.   *Cf.* also *infra*, pp. 462-464.

[7] *Ibid.*, pp. 227-235.

Creation was the greatest of all miracles. It could have been completed in an instant or in six days, years or ages. God, however, chose six days of twenty-four hours each because six and four were the perfect numbers. Twenty-four was their product.[8] Matter could not move itself. God by His thought brought into being both matter and motion, and His power was needed for their continuance. His government, as was implied by His act of creation, was universal. It pertained to the most casual as well as to the most important matters and even the most remote effects must have been foreseen and planned.[9] All the world and its creatures were made and existed " for the Use and Benefit of Sensible Creatures. And all inferiour Creatures, for the Service of those above them." [10] After the six days God rested from creating, " that is, from doing any thing, without the Co-operation of Second Causes," [11] such as angels good and bad, men, animals or inanimate nature. Creation took place nearly six thousand years ago, in the autumn in order that the fruits might be ripe [12] and in order that Adam soon after his fall " might see Winter coming on, and all Nature in a sort of dying Condition, like himself, or putting on Mourning for his Fall." [13] Adam himself was created with a mind whose perfection corresponded with that of his body, so that

---

[8] Grew then gave other combinations of the sums or products of these numbers in the number of tribes, the seventy-two Elders, the preparation for the Passover and for the Day of Atonement on the tenth of the month, Moses's forty days at the Mount, the size and furnishings of the tabernacle and the ornaments of the High Priest. The shape of the tabernacle resembled that most perfect rectangular figure, a cube; and the proportions were those of a man. Grew, *op. cit.*, pp. 194, 248-254.

[9] *Ibid.*, pp. 4, 5, 17, 23, 30, 85, 86.

[10] *Ibid.*, p. 23, also pp. 24-30.

[11] *Ibid.*, p. 195.

[12] *Ibid.*, pp. 8, 91, 92, 184, 195.

[13] *Ibid.*, p. 184.

" he then knew many things, by some sort of Intellectual Instinct." [14]   His intuition into the natures of various animals inspired appropriate names.   Both he and his righteous descendants till the flood were vegetarians.   Such moderation in diet was one reason for their longevity.[15] After that time

the Earth and Air being now in a worse condition; and so the Vegetable Diet; Animals were allowed.   And the rather, with respect to the Colder Climates; probably uninhabited before the Flood.   Wherein, as there is less variety of delicious Plants; so Flesh is more requisite and desirable.   Likewise, to answer God's Intent, of reducing the Life of Man . . . But withal, to give more Vigor unto Mens Minds, though it abated that of their Bodies,

as carnivorous animals are the more sagacious.[16]

As to the rest of the universe, the moon and the other planets were probably terraqueous globes with atmospheres and inhabitants.   The fixed stars were suns, around which circled planets.   All the celestial bodies had power and influence over the earth, man's body and the other material objects.   The sun, although it was probably not hot in itself, by its heat had the chief control of vapors and exhalations and therefore of meteors.   Solar heat was probably caused by the mixture of the light rays with air because any ordinary heat would be dissipated by the distance between the solar body and the earth and an extraordinary temperature would alter the sun's substance.   The moon aided in the growth of seeds, shell-fish, hair and teeth, and governed the humors in man's body and various diseases, especially lunacy and epilepsy, as well as the tides.[17]

[14] Grew, *op. cit.*, p. 184.

[15] *Ibid.*, pp. 184, 185, 227, 229, 231-233.

[16] *Ibid.*, pp. 232, 233.   [17] *Ibid.*, pp. 7, 8, 10, 88, 89, 91.

Moncharville in the following year produced a remarkable system of the universe opposed to the ideas of Plato, Aristotle, Descartes, Democritus, Epicurus, Gassendi and all " physiciens." [18]   After having worked it out he consulted the Bible, the " *source de la divine & vraye Philosophie* " [19] with infinite knowledge in physics as in metaphysics and in morality; and much to his satisfaction found various passages to confirm him, especially Ezekiel ch. I.[20]   Almost all that to a modern reader seems to come from the Bible is the affirmation that from nothing God formed the universe completely in six days.[21]   Moncharville denied corporeal and continuous fullness and also an inanimate vacuum.[22]   God he conceived to be " a point of pure fire " [23] at the center of the universe, or perhaps the fire merely surrounded God.   Thence His activity departed and thither returned.   It both animated matter by its swiftness and penetrated it, so that it moved matter within and without.   It was mind and life.   Matter tended always to repose and chaos, and consisted of large bodies rolled in the air by the spirit that guided them.   The heavier the bodies, the farther from their mover they were carried. The tendency of everything to rejoin the central point caused the spherical form of the universe, through which were scattered an infinity of stars.   The motion of the spirit was spiral, returning again to the center.   Of bodies the natural motion was circular, not direct.   In order that they might move, bodies were made globular [24] because the spirit " which forms all bodies, circulating within, makes them round with-

[18] Moncharville, *op. cit.*, pp. 3, 4.

[19] *Ibid.*, p. 16.

[20] *Ibid.*, pp. 21-29, 60.

[21] *Ibid.*, pp. 38, 45.

[22] *Ibid.*, pp. 3, 4, 6.

[23] " Un point de pur feu," *ibid.*, p. 8.

[24] *Ibid.*, pp. 4, 6-13, 36, 37, 61, 62.

out " when not impeded by their contact with other material objects.[25] Since matter was neither infinite nor infinitely divisible, the universe was limited. The stars, like our sun, were surrounded by planets, which they illumined. Such a vile spot as this earth could not be the sole care and object of an infinite being, but there were millions of inhabited earths. Moncharville attempted to reduce matter to one element and declared that all dense bodies consisted of air solidified under different forms by the circulations of nature. The earth absorbed into herself and shaped the surrounding air. Fire, perhaps Moncharville meant the fire at the center of the earth as well as other fires, made bodies take form by " cooking " them. Air was not only the first matter, but also the final product. To it all returned on dissolution, since earth became water and that changed to air. The process caused our globe to abound in animals, plants, rocks, trees and metals.[26] The spirit of man came from God, that of animals from the stars; hence reason and instinct were respectively spiral and circular in motion. The spirit of animals and their instincts followed the solar movement.[27]

From this brief summary the reasons for the lack of influence in the case of both Grew and Moncharville are obvious. Grew's theories were too commonplace and Moncharville's too fantastic for imitation or even for comment.

[25] Moncharville, *op. cit.*, p. 12:
"qui forme tous les corps,
Circulant en dedans, les rend rounds en dehors; "

[26] *Ibid.*, pp. 4, 10, 13-15, 29, 30.
[27] *Ibid.*, p. 11.

CHAPTER XVI

DICKINSON, THE ATOMIST

MONCHARVILLE's system can hardly be considered seriously. Not so unimportant was Edmund Dickinson's *Physica Vetus et Vera* published in 1703. It upheld the atomic philosophy, which the author attributed to Moses. With its dedication to the Archbishop of Canterbury it continued the tradition of the period. In spite of Dickinson's aversion to Aristotle and the Peripatetics, his theory was based on the four elements, though he combined with them the Paracelsian thesis that the world was made by a combination of salt, sulphur and mercury. But he declared that Moses's account should be taken literally. Like most of his predecessors, he attributed to Moses great knowledge, especially of chemistry and astrology, great faithfulness so that he would not seek to deceive and a special revelation from God who spoke to him face to face.[1] Originally even the common people among the Israelites understood Moses's account. It later became obscure to those who looked through Peripatetic spectacles.[2] Unquestionably Adam, "whom God made and taught,"[3] so that he might understand the natures of things and the art of imposing appropriate names, knew the story of creation and taught it to his sons, who transmitted it to their progeny. There were few generations before Moses. In some fam-

[1] Dickinson, *Physica Vetus et Vera* (Rotterdam, 1703), especially pp. 1-4, 32, 33, 35, 36, 69, 70, 126, 127, 130-132, 306-325.

[2] *Ibid.*, pp. 1-4.

[3] *Ibid.*, p. 17, "quem fecit & erudiit Deus," also p. 7.

ilies, because of the desire for luxury, the tradition became garbled; but it was retained longer in the family of Heber and Abraham, as was proved by Job, who was descended from Hagar and Abraham. If Hagar's child knew the truth, assuredly it was taught to Isaac by his father. Dickinson gave an elaborate and lengthy proof of the great natural talent among the Israelites, inherited from the patriarchs, and of their excellent training, which even included tuition in schools established by Abraham, Sem and other heads of families and later carried on by the priests and the elders. These qualifications argued that they were capable of comprehending the history of the creation and that they had some knowledge of it. Probably Moses at God's command wrote the books of Genesis and Job during his stay in Midian and sent them to the Israelites to strengthen their faith. This he would not have done had he not known that his statements corresponded to the common notions, although they had been corrected by revelation where errors had crept in, and that the Hebrews were sufficiently intelligent and docile to be fit recipients of the doctrine. He did not present his view in the form of an argument needing proofs, but as a statement of received truths. His was far the oldest and truest account of creation.[4] Aristotle, like the other Greeks and the Egyptians learned from the Jews. In return he taught them his philosophy until they could no longer understand the Mosaic account and denied its truth.[5]

The first act in the genesis of the world was the creation of matter out of nothing, since there was nothing from which to create it. This matter, from which were later formed the earth and the visible heavens, was a mass of tiny particles,

---

[4] Dickinson, *op. cit.*, pp. 2, 3, 7, 17-28, 48, 49, 130, 193, 263-309.

[5] *Ibid.*, pp. 4, 30-45, 60, 234, 235, 263, 270, 277, 278, 302, 324.

with small empty spaces everywhere.[6]   The heavens consisted
of the lower heaven or expanse, which included the so-called
airy and stellar heavens, and the upper heaven or empyreum.
The still higher third heaven was the home of the angels and
the seat of the blessed.   Since it was immaterial, Moses did
not mention it.   Moses called the total mass of matter at first
heavens and earth, for it included the whole creation, then
earth, since it was motionless and thick.   Later he named
it abyss, because it was a confused mass of immense depth or
even with no bottom, and finally waters, since it consisted of
multitudes of particles easily moved or fluid.   The last name
was not used until the lazy and impotent matter was moved
by the spirit from God.[7]   All motion was aroused and preserved by God.   The particles into which all matter was
divided were of different shapes and figures.   When they
were agitated by the divine mind and hit one another, similar
particles united to form the four elements.   As Moses said,
the Spirit of God moved on the face of the waters,—that is,
moved the particles slowly and gently to assist their union,
but not as a bird incubates an egg.[8]   At first they associated
by the apposition of plane faces, which were held together
without any glue or cement because they fitted so closely.

[6] Dickinson, *op. cit.*, preliminary remarks, pp. 38-45, 59, 64, 65, 191-196.
Dickinson declared that his theory, which both in its fundamentals and
in many of its later phases resembled the ideas of Democritus, far antedated that philosopher. *Ibid.*, pp. 198, 199.

[7] *Ibid.*, preliminary remarks, pp. 4, 6, 29, 45, 50-55, 64, 65, 73, 193-199,
221, 222, 231-237, 246-249, 255.

[8] *Ibid.*, pp. 4, 33, 34, 64, 65, 67, 73, 199-203, 247.   Dickinson sometimes leant to the idea that the Spirit of God was perhaps a wind but
elsewhere he denied this and asserted that it was God Himself.   On p. 67
he said "*Spiritus* . . . non ita intelligendus est ac si per *Spiritum Dei*
vellet *magnum ventum* notari; . . . sed ipsum Deum."   On p. 200 he
declared that the Hebrew word "tam *ventum*, quàm *spiritum* notat; nec
imprudentèr quoniam motum istum . . . meliùs appellatione Venti, quâm
spiritûs exprimi judicabant."   *Cf.* also p. 328.

There were two kinds of motion, that of preparation and that of separation. The motion of preparation, which lasted the whole time of darkness, was transverse. It mixed the atoms so as to bring together those alike. Then these cohered and formed not the elements but the molecules thereof. The motion of separation was circular, and rotated the whole mass of the abyss so as to produce fire and light. Light was merely the efflux of fire, or the pressure of the subtle particles of that element upon the optic nerve. By the second type of motion similar molecules were brought together, though always with an admixture of unlike ones, so that there were nowhere in nature pure elements. The four elements thus consisted of molecules which differed in shape, not in material nature. The smallest were round, and therefore swiftest and subtlest, and formed fire when they were separated from the others. Dickinson called these *pilulae*.[9] The same round form but greater size characterized the *globuli* of water. Other molecules were like sticks. They moved freely and left spaces around themselves. These, which formed the air, he named *longulae* or *bracteae*. The fourth type of molecules, the earthy, was thicker and heavier. They were of many different shapes but most frequently branched. In addition, there were quantities of very minute and highly irregular particles that had been broken off from all these concretions. Because of their angles they were so prone to attach themselves to other bodies that they did not have much apparent effect although they probably aided in moving, preserving and restoring things. They were the angles which caused fire to burn and produced the sharpness of acids. Apparently Dickinson thought that the elements

[9] The shape which he and Descartes attributed to molecules of fire was perhaps borrowed from Democritus and other Greek philosophers; but in the shapes Dickinson assigned to the particles of air and of water, he differed from both the Greek and Descartes. *Cf. supra*, pp. 35-37, 39-41.

were mutually transmutable by erosion and by accretion.[10]

At the same time that God caused the whole of chaos to revolve, He established the laws to govern it. By this, Dickinson meant chiefly the centrifugal impulse of rotating bodies, and perhaps the law which produced the tendency of light bodies to fly from the center and of heavy bodies to seek it. As the abyss rotated, the pills sought to recede from the center.[11] They formed an outer layer, and with their "admirable" speed made a fiery sphere, the empyreum or highest material heaven. This primogenial light, which became the matter of the future sun, was less violent than after the creation of that body. Meantime the thicker, less mobile particles were pressed to the center. They were still too heterogeneous to form one mass, though the whole was denser than before the removal of the pills. Some of the smallest globules were raised to the empyreum and formed the waters later denominated those above the firmament. They served to temper the ardor of the fiery particles, to augment their light after the manner of crystals, to transmit to lower orbs the influence of the empyreum, especially in the form of dew, and probably also to punish men at the deluge and even at other smaller floods when God suspended natural laws. In the days of Noah these waters did not merely augment the clouds; they also drove them headlong. Not only did reason prove the existence of these superior waters, but the Bible said (Ps. 148; 104:3, 13) that God made the heavens from fire and water. Before the pills were raised to the empyreum, there was darkness,—that is, a complete absence of light, not anything corporeal or created by God. It had lasted from

[10] Dickinson, *op. cit.*, pp. 33, 34, 66-70, 193, 196, 203-205, 214, 216, 220, 221, 237, 238, 242-244, 255-259.

[11] Here he clearly reversed Descartes's doctrine that the minute spherical particles would be concentrated in the center of the vortex.

creation till the rising of light.[12]   In one passage Dickinson
said that this was twelve hours; in another he called that
belief false.[13]   The blandly warm primogenial light was of
great use during the days before the sun.   It separated matter
on the first day and the second and aided the growth of plants
on the third.[14]

On the second day a further rotation of the abyss by the
finger of God, which might mean angels, separated out some
of the pills that still remained, pressed still nearer to the
center the thicker matter and released the *bracteae*.   They
were small in diameter, stiff and disposed to rotate around
their centers, so that they required a great deal of empty
space.   Moses named this space, which with the exception of
the celestial spheres reached from the earth to the empyreum,
the *Expansum* because it naturally expanded.   In the
empyreum God had placed the superior waters and those
secret virtues with which He wished to supply the earth by
means of these waters.   The formation of the expanse He
ordered that it might separate the waters in the empyreum
and in the expanse itself from those on the surface of the
earth.   The other uses for this heaven became more obvious
after the third and the fourth days.   The work of the second
did not attain sufficient perfection to deserve the term good.

[12] Dickinson, *op. cit.*, pp. 68-78, 205-221, 237-241, 247, 248, 326, 327.

[13] *Ibid.*, p. 76: Nox or caligo "quae ab ipso momento Creationis, ut
credibile est, ad spatium duodecim horarum fuit in superficie Abyssi, vel
materiae primae." P. 209: "Neque mihi vendibilior esse videatur ulla
doctrina, quàm quae docet Mosem hîc per diem unum satis evidentèr
innuisse, quod illae tenebrae, quae praecedebant luci primigeniae, non
longiùs duràssent quàm duodecim horarum spatio, priusquam duodecim
horarum quoque Lux secuta esset; atque ità diem unum; viginti quatuor
scilicèt horarum spatium confecerant: Fuerunt hae tenebrae (non in-
fiteór) antequàm motus ullus esset; verùm autem non tantùm motus, sed
etiam quies, per accidens, mensura temporis existat."

[14] *Ibid.*, pp. 74-76, 207.

Innumerable thick and irregular bodies floating among the *bracteae* prevented them from moving freely and therefore kept this heaven from becoming rare and transparent. The part near the earth was so congested that the pills from the first heaven could hardly reach it, much less light it. Gradually the darkness throughout the abyss was enlightened as the earth and the water were consolidated. Nevertheless some of the more solid particles remained in the air until almost the fourth day, because they were hindered in falling by the rotation of the *bracteae* on their centers. These pressed as much outward to the circumference of the universe as inward to the center. The force derived from the general rotary motion of the abyss, however, drove the heavier particles towards the center. As the *bracteae* separated from one another and their resistance diminished, the process became more speedy. The only difference between the aerial and the sidereal heavens was the greater density of the aerial because the *bracteae* were closer together and were intermingled with accidental denser matter raised from the earth as vapors. The lowest part of the expanse formed the atmosphere. Its action was stronger, slower and more suited to the nature and use of terrestrial things.[15]

Throughout the expanse were watery and fiery particles that travelled up or down. The gyrations of the *bracteae* carried to the earth exhalations and vapors, rains, dews and those precious effluvia that were shed on all sides by the stars, and in return raised the subtle exhalations of the earth to the sun, the moon and the stars. The waters of the empyreum were thus constantly renewed. The *bracteae,* which were straight and unbending and not easily broken, rotated in circles and occupied a much greater space than their size seemed to demand. In the beginning they were so

[15] Dickinson, *op. cit.,* pp. 69, 79-83, 85, 86, 221-225, 254.

crowded that they had no room to turn separately and became attached side by side so that each orbit contained several. The fewer there were in each orbit, the faster they moved and the rarer the air became. As the pills and their still more minute associates of irregular shape travelled up and down, they penetrated both the orbits and the *bracteae* themselves, and separated them whenever there was room. The sticks had, moreover, a natural tendency on their own part toward separation. For this reason their circulation exerted a marvellous compression on all around, on earth, empyreum, sun, stars and moon, on the sap of plants, causing it to travel slowly enough to nourish the plants, and especially on the sea, the mass of waters inside the earth and the central fire. The greater the number of *bracteae* in each orbit, the stronger was the compression. The wisdom of Moses was shown by his choice of a word, translated firmament, which meant expand but also bind and make firm ("*constringere* atque *firmare*"). This was the means whereby God suspended the earth over nothing. It forced light things to arise and heavy ones to descend. Through cracks the *bracteae* penetrated deep into the earth to supply the central fire, all other subterranean fires and the animals that dwelt below the surface, and aided in the generation of metals and minerals. On the other hand, the destruction of all concretions except what was effected by worms resulted from entrance of the *bracteae* into the pores and their laceration of the substance. All things were therefore constantly losing parts of themselves and depended upon others. However, the *bracteae* by compression restrained from excess the rarefaction and fermentation that they themselves caused and thus conserved the universe. Their motion was not natural like that of the fiery particles of the highest heaven and of the heaven as a whole, but God Himself gave them originally their circular whirling and still directed and preserved it, apparently by

means of the pills. By the activity of the *bracteae* God
separated the remaining constituents of the abyss and gave a
spherical shape to the earth. Winds were due to their revolutions.[16]

The third day saw the separation of earth and water and
the formation of plants. It was improbable that on the first
day God wished the earth to be covered with water only to
remove it two days later. Therefore the water of chaos,
mentioned in verse 2 of the first chapter in Genesis, was
really the primeval loose moving particles, not the element.
The lower *bracteae* pressed the thick matter at the center of
the universe closer together till the particles were in contact
at all points and became a solid mass. Though the force
of the air was everywhere the same, the resistance of the
earth particles varied so that the surface of the globe was
uneven and hills appeared. Most of the round globules were
forced out as the earth solidified, but many remained in caverns and ducts or mixed with the earth and made the soil
humid and sticky. The earth formed eminences where the
greatest number of globules remained, as well as where the
largest proportion of earthy particles was originally located;
hence mountains existed from the epoch of creation.
These globules, which were round, barely touched one another
and constantly rotated, were extremely mobile. They found
hollows on the earth's surface, either because they emerged
there on the first and the second days or because they ran
down thither from the mountains. Some moisture was,
however, retained in earth, minerals, plants and animals to
produce the cohesion of their particles. All the water was
said to be in one place because it was connected by manifest
or secret channels.[17]

[16] Dickinson, *op. cit.*, pp. 83-87, 89, 216, 217, 222-224, 227-230, 237, 238,
258-261, 326.

[17] *Ibid.*, pp. 55, 69, 88-92, 231-237, 242-244, 249.

An additional activity of the third day was the location of the earth at the center of the universe so that the sun, the moon and the stars might pour out their light upon it and always serve it. This situation was assigned to the earth by Moses and all the sacred writers who celebrated its immobility to eternity, its columns, its foundations etc. The earth's immobility was proved not only by reason, but also by the authority of Aristotle, of Ptolemy, of Pythagoras himself, of Abraham and the Assyrians, and, since these last were taught by Arphaxad, of Sem, Noah and the other patriarchs, who learned the truth either by long observation or by Adam's instruction. Our earth was not viler than the heavens. Its particles cohered more closely and its greater density was due to abundance of matter. God called the work of the third day, the adornment of the earth, good twice, while that of the first and fourth was styled good only once and the adjective was not applied at all to that of the second day.[18]

The formation of a central fire at the heart of the earth was simultaneous with the work of the first three days. In the beginning God placed at the center of the abyss a great number of pills and so walled them in that they were unable to escape when the abyss was rotated. By the pressure of the earthy particles and of the expanse they were compressed and assumed the force of fire. They were and are the cause for the generation of plants, of vapors, especially those that watered the earth before rain (Gen. 2: 5, 6), of minerals and of metals. That the formation of metals was not completed during the first week but was gradual was proved by the omission of their production in the Mosaic narrative. The variety of metals depended upon the influences of the planets, except that gold consisted of solar particles concreted and compacted in suitable earthy matter. The earth sur-

---

[18] Dickinson, *op. cit.*, pp. 115, 250-255.

rounding the central fire was particularly hard, although not so dense but that fiery particles could leave through its cracks in sufficient numbers to accomplish their work. This work included assistance in the interchange that existed between earth and heaven. The central fire, since it was constantly dissipated, must be as constantly replenished and nourished. Air found its way thither through the cracks in the earth's crust. The sea continually received sulphurous matter from the sky and the land. Either directly or by way of streams it was brought down in rain, snow, hail and thunder into the sea. The sea water, which was heavy with sulphur and salt, sank to the depths of the ocean and thence through channels of varying sizes to the central fire. The elastic pressure of the air aided in forcing it thither. Part was rarefied by the heat and raised towards the surface. It made minerals and metals; it produced and increased vegetables. Dickinson attributed to this central fire the warm vapors found by miners. Unlike most of his predecessors, he did not consider it to be the cause of volcanoes and hot springs. These he declared had been discovered to be due to the union and the conflict of sulphur and certain salts.[19]

Besides the central fire there was in the earth a great receptacle of waters. It, as well as springs and rivers, was made at the same moment as the sea; and the circulation of the waters commenced at once, as this was necessary to prevent stagnation. From under the seas the water sank into the earth by small and large channels and was again driven out, but in the process brought nourishment to the central fire, supplied fat humidity for the formation of minerals and metals, and assisted the growth of plants. Vegetables and animals did not grow from water itself but from the viscous matter hidden therein. Plants did not retain the hundredth

[19] Dickinson, *op. cit.*, pp. 88, 92, 93, 96, 101-105, 189, 244, 252, 253, 260, 262.

part of the water, whose only purpose was to dilute the viscous substance so that it might enter the plants. It was forced in at the roots by the pressure of the subterranean air, and later the surplus moisture was exhaled. The subterranean water supplied in addition the vapors that were raised by the fire to preserve the commerce with the skies. The ducts and receptacles of water underground were of various sizes and were made in the same manner as the rivers, by the collection of water into one spot and the excessive solidification of the surrounding earth, which prevented its dispersal. The greatest subterranean passage of all was the one that engulfed the water near the north pole and poured it out again at the south. This well-authenticated whirlpool and duct carried even ships and such debris through the center of the earth. Within the earth in many places were branching channels leading to lakes, seas and springs, and some which ended in earthen walls. The last-mentioned tubes, where the force of the water was slight, sometimes became filled with earth while fresh channels opened up. This was the reason for the great quantity of shells, the bones of terrestrial and marine animals, the wood and the parts of ships that were buried deep in the earth. Dickinson even added some plates to illustrate the inner constitution of the globe, and showed a ship with all sails set, stranded upright at the end of a blind alley. Not only were the waters, separated on the third day, important to the earth in subterranean depths; but they were of use also in the form of dew, rain and the like to bring to the earth all the celestial effluvia gathered into the expanse. The effluvia gave life, vigor, secret strength and special properties to all things on our planet. In addition, by floods and violent storms, both at the deluge and at other times, the waters served as a means of punishing man.[20]

[20] Dickinson, *op. cit.*, pp. 88, 92, 94-101, 109, 110, 239, 244, 245, 326.

While these changes were taking place at creation, God Himself formed the seeds of all plants,—that is, the plants themselves in miniature, and then scattered them on the dry land and left them to the earth, as a secondary cause, to produce. That it might perform this service, He ordered humid vapors to arise from the depths of the earth and to irrigate the whole surface of the land. A nutritive terrestrial sap was forced into the pores of the seeds by the heat from above and below and by the expansion of the air. The particles that supplied the place of the sun continually descended, and with the *bracteae* penetrated the earth as deep as the roots and even much deeper. The entrance of the *bracteae* made larger openings for the nutritive saps. The saps, as was still the case, attached themselves to and coalesced with the suitable parts inside the seed, and so increased it that it broke its outer coat, germinated, produced roots and grew. The saps were so shaped and disposed by the fabric of the pores that each vegetable exhibited the characteristics peculiar to its species. Because of the greater vigor of nature at the epoch of creation, plants reached perfection in one day, so that there was no need to change the days of the account in Genesis to years. The whole earth was made beautiful, and the face of the earth on the third day was lighted not only by the primogenial light but also by the colors of flowers and fruits and by the reflection of the pills from the vast expanse of water.[21]

The work of the fourth day was the construction by God Himself of the sun and the other heavenly bodies in the expanse. Although the *bracteae* were not calorific, there was mixed with them a quantity of fiery particles, which were effluvia of the first heaven or had been separated from the abyss by the rotation of the second day. This diffused heat, together with the warm vapors raised by the central fire,

---

[21] Dickinson, *op. cit.*, pp. 5, 88, 92, 105-115, 253.

was able to produce plants though not animals or minerals. On the fourth day, in order that they might act more strongly, God collected into celestial spheres, all these subtle particles, although this action was contrary to their natural motion; and He imposed upon them a new motion.   The fixed stars were fiery in nature and had innate light; but they were con-creted, not lax and mobile like the sun.   That lucent body consisted of the purest fire and the subtlest sulphur and had so many vortical motions that the surface was constantly changing and seemed to have mountains and valleys.   By its rays, which were really particles of its substance, the sun's body would soon have been dissipated had it not been surrounded by a thicker matter whence it could obtain nour-ishment.   This encompassing layer was replenished by the *bracteae* in their whirling, as they carried from one globe to another exhalations from each.   The sun by its internal motion threw to the surface numerous thicker molecules like scum.   Both these and the thick surrounding matter hindered but did not prevent the passage of the sun's rays.   Since the spots were constantly renewed as well as destroyed by the effluvia from the sun and other bodies, the subtle solar matter could never be scattered too profusely.   The sun poured out on inferior things not only light and heat but also qualities which affected man's character and body.[22]   It, the planets and the fixed stars, especially since the power of the stars was strengthened by their concentration into constellations, had as a gift from God all the powers attributed to them by " sober and learned Astrologers." [23]   The belief in and the knowledge of astrology were ancient.   In the Bible Abraham, Jacob, as he showed by the skilful increase of his flocks,

[22] Dickinson, *op. cit.*, pp. 79, 104, 116-123, 126, 128, 129, 133-135, 223, 228-230.

[23] "Astrologi sobrii doctique," *ibid.*, p. 137; also pp. 122-133, 135, 136, 189, 250, 254.

Joseph, Noah, Moses and Amos were clearly proficient in astrology. Dickinson himself was convinced of its truth. He apparently thought one reason for the existence of so many planets was the necessity for their moderating one another's effects. Each was made of salt, sulphur and mercury and of all four elements in varying proportions.[24] He found an easy way to avoid such complexities as epicycles in the older astronomy without having recourse to the mistaken Copernican, Tychonian or Cartesian theories. In the beginning God's spirit set the heavenly bodies rolling, and still by means of angels ruled their motions including those of comets.[25]

In the same manner in which God created the seeds of plants and then left the earth to bring them forth, He produced animals on the fifth and the sixth days. He wished that from the waters should be brought forth the fishes and the reptiles which lived therein, and from the earth the herds, the terrestrial reptiles and all beasts. However, the fish had earth to strengthen their flesh and bones and the land animals had water to make their flesh soft. Birds, which contained a more nearly equal mixture of water and earth, were formed on the same day as the aquatic animals, although not from water. Though all four elements were necessary for each animal, Moses did not ascribe the development of any animals to air or to fire. Both air and fire were too subtle and agile for such a purpose as well as for the complete nourishment of any animal. Not from ether, although it was more closely allied to spirit than the other elements, but from earth, which was sublimated into a fire, God Himself made the souls of animals and placed them into eggs, which He had created in quantity and had scattered over the earth.

[24] Dickinson, *op. cit.*, pp. 122-133, 135-137, 189, 250, 254, 270-272, 274, 275, 301-303, 309, 310, 322, 323, 329-331, 333.

[25] *Ibid.*, pp. 125, 126, 224-227.

They developed into the proper species by the addition of nutritive matter from the earth and the water into which they were placed. As the pores of vegetable seeds shaped their nutriment, so the pores throughout these eggs shaped the saps which entered. The souls of animals, which were corporeal that they might be completely unlike man's spiritual soul from the heaven of heavens, returned at last to the earth whence they were drawn. The production of all animals in one day rather than in a period of years was not marvellous but due to the will of the omnipotent Creator. The freshness and richness of the earth perhaps aided the process.[26]

All this visible world of animals, stars and sun, was ordered to serve man, the microcosm, who was created on the sixth day. His dignity was shown by the difference in method. He was created only after consultation and deliberation. His spirit or *anima* came from heaven, and in that respect he surpassed all animals and equalled the angels. Moreover, instead of permitting the *anima* of man, as of beasts, to form his body, God from carefully selected red clay shaped his frame as one would a statue. Perhaps for this occasion God even assumed human form. Adam's original comeliness of body as of soul was presumably lost after the Fall. Since the sixth day, however, it had been the soul of the infant that from nourishment had developed its body. It made "pores" of definite type throughout the body and by the expansive force of the air or of its own ethereal heat sent through them nutritive saps. The pores by a kind of mechanical action like that of vegetable growth shaped the nourishment into suitable form. The heart was the seat of the soul, which must act through tools but had a life of its own in addition.[27]

[26] Dickinson, *op. cit.*, pp. 140-154.

[27] *Ibid.*, pp. 155-167, 173, 174, 176, 177, 179-182, 184, 185, 188-190, 253.

Dickinson's account, while fairly clear and interesting, was verbose and repetitious. After an introductory part that contained general statements, he took up the work of the six days in turn. Then he repeated his introductory comments with some additions and discussed the four elements. These pages gave another version of the same facts from a different angle, and reiterated most of his statements concerning the first three days. He even added an appendix on the waters that he might discuss them once more. His other appendix about the light in the ark was practically a restatement of what he had previously developed in detail, as were his accounts of the Israelites in Egypt and of Moses. To be sure, occasional contradictions added a spice of variety. On the other hand, he obviously accomplished his aim. He interpreted the Mosaic narrative and such scientific concepts as he chose to accept in a way to harmonize them; and one feels that the archbishop must have been pleased with the offering.

Dickinson (or Dickenson) (1624-1707) was a doctor. As was evident in his book, he was especially interested in chemistry and even in alchemy. He believed that the philosopher's elixir was obtainable, and that, in fact, it had been obtained by Noah. Charles II, to whose attention he had been called by the remarkable cure of a tumor for the Earl of Arlington, established him in a laboratory under the royal bedchamber. The two rooms were connected by a private staircase.[28]

[28] *Dictionary of National Biography*, art. " Dickinson."

CHAPTER XVII

WITTY, THE ANTICARTESIAN, AND DERHAM, THE ASTRONOMER

Two years after Dickinson's attempt, John Witty published a similar volume, entitled *An Essay towards a Vindication of the Vulgar Exposition of the Mosaic History of the Creation of the World*. Witty was less dogmatic than Dickinson in most of his statements and presented several alternative theories from which the reader might choose. His chief opposition was to the Cartesians but occasionally he demonstrated that even their theories were in accord with the Biblical account.[1] He believed the earth a planet with diurnal and annual motion and gave proofs thereof. Some of these depended on the Newtonian doctrine of gravitation, which he did not question. He was inclined to think that each star was the center of a planetary system similar to the solar. All the systems were formed at the same time as ours and from the same original matter, created by God out of nothing in the form of a chaos. He wavered as to the exact day the stellar systems were formed, but seemed favorably impressed by the doctrine that they, like the solar system, were started on the first day and proceeded by like steps so that all the systems reached perfection at the same time. Full perfection in the case of the stellar groups was attained on the fourth day unless the planets had inhabitants. He did

---

[1] For example, Witty, *An Essay towards a Vindication of the Vulgar Exposition of the Mosaic History of the Creation of the World* (London, 1705), pp. 59-61.

166

not deny the possibility, even the plausibility of this hypothesis, but seemed unwilling himself to believe it.[2]

Witty, like so many others, felt that the doctrine of the fall and the redemption of man, on which he declared revealed religion to be based, must be discarded if the account of creation given in Genesis was not literally true. But the ordinary explanation in reality agreed with the " *best Philosophy* ",—that is, science. Besides, science never had advanced and could never advance beyond probability. Deductive systems were based on some general statement, such as the essence of matter; but the fact that this was unknowable invalidated the results. On the other hand, induction from a few particulars was unsound, especially since there were many causes that might concur in the production of the phenomena. Indeed " philosophical " theories had generally been ephemeral. In addition, revelation was intrinsically reasonable and to be expected of a good God, desirous of man's redemption; and specifically the narrative of creation in the Bible was not contrary to what we knew in other ways. Then, however, Witty went on to say that God at creation acted immediately and not by means of secondary causes and that the laws of nature were not in force.[3]

The work of the hexaemeron, 6000 years ago, was the whole material universe and took merely six days of normal length, except for the lapse of a considerable period between the impression of motion on matter and the appearance of light, so that the planets had [4] " *time to come to a tolerable consistency, and to revolve upon their Axes, (the first appearance of Light being the tendency of the Sun and fix'd Stars towards something of a perfection).*" This " *solves very intelligibly the most material Philosophical Difficulties*

---

[2] Witty, *op. cit.*, pp. 41-46, 48, 102, 104-113, 159-176.

[3] *Ibid.*, pp. 3-40 and preface.

[4] *Ibid.*, preface, pp. 5, 41-45, 48, 78, 113, 114.

in the History." [5]   Probably the reason for a creation which
took time was to instruct the angels in the nature of the
universe by showing them its gradual formation.   Besides,
since the world was created out of nothing as a chaos and then
formed into an orderly whole by motion, this motion implied
succession and therefore time; and there was no reason why
that time should not have been six days.   The matter of
chaos was divided into a vast number of parts, which then
were perfected in the same manner as our solar system.
Many systems were no harder to form in six days than a
single one, if they all began at the same moment and proceeded by equal steps.   At the end of the fourth day all the
systems reached perfection; but Moses's design was, for
man's instruction, to tell particularly of the earth.   The
chaos, which was dark, formless, fluid, inactive, was agitated
by the incubation of the Spirit.   This was not the universal
soul of nature or a plastic force, since such a force could not
operate without heat.   It was not a wind, for which there
was no place before the creation of the *expansum,* and which
could not exist until there was a sun to cause it.   Therefore,
it was really the Holy Spirit.   God both created matter and
put it into motion.   Perhaps from the division of the chaos
into parts, which in four days were reduced to globes in various vortices,[6] commenced the operations of secondary causes.

Witty said that many [7] ridiculed the idea that light, the

[5] Witty, *op. cit.*, preface.

[6] *Ibid.*, pp. 7-9, 43-49, 65, 66, 111-114, 138, 181.   In spite of his dislike
of Cartesianism, Witty could not escape its fundamental hypotheses.

[7] Though Witty represented that his opponents were chiefly Cartesians,
whose influence was almost paramount by this time in the universities, particularly on the continent, there were many other groups who ridiculed or
rejected the Scriptural narrative. A large proportion were society gentlemen who called themselves Deists and free-thinkers and who were generally accused of atheism. They included as well the "modernists" of the day.

work of the first day, preceded the sun, but foolishly since we did not know what light was. Then he gave various doctrines on the subject, including Descartes's, and showed how on each hypothesis the narrative might be true. If light was inherent in the lucid body, it might easily be created before its collection into a system,—i. e., the sun. This theory of light was held by few. If it was due to the motion of fine particles, they might well be numerous enough by the first day and in sufficiently rapid motion to be somewhat luminous. Or if light was in the observer's eye, the medium through which the sun's operation was conveyed, a part of which was then in being, might be called light as well as the sun. He quoted Bishop Patrick (*On Genesis,* cap. I, p. 6 or 9),[8] who said that perhaps the first light was " a portion of hot luminous Matter made to move about the Earth till the creation of the Sun, in order to hasten its perfection." [9] On this first day bodies gained consistency and began to revolve on their axes so as to produce day and night. All this showed that there was no ground for rejecting the Mosaic narrative on the first day.[10]

The second day's work was the formation of the firmament and the separation of the waters above and below it. As the lighter solids and most of the fluids still dispersed through the systems or vortices subsided, they left clear the expanse or firmament, which divided the systems and also separated the spheres in each vortex. Since much, perhaps most, of the chaos was fluid as was implied by Moses's appellation

---

The Aristotelians were losing their importance, but many arguments were still published to confute them, and belated disciples still composed tracts and tomes to expound dying theses. The authors of the day on the whole did not mention the names of those they opposed, and the groups implicated can be judged only by the arguments employed to refute them.

[8] Witty, *op. cit.,* pp. 50-67, 138, 139, 182.

[9] *Ibid.,* p. 181.

[10] *Ibid.,* preface and pp. 65, 67, 139, 181.

of waters, and since in all or most of the bodies except the central spheres of each system there was water, the liquids of all spheres except our own were the waters above the firmament. Then Witty weakened and asserted the possible identity of these waters, which were a cause of the deluge, with the clouds. This identity was commonly accepted. Vapors and atmosphere, generally attributed to solar influences, were exhalations from the earth and possibly resulted from the violent " intestine " motion of each planet on the second day, which, by causing agitation and heat of the superficial fluids, would produce vapors. In addition, the sun, though not perfect, might already emit considerable confused light and heat.[11]

The time of the third day was not too brief for the work of draining the earth and the production of plants. Witty gave an elaborate mathematical calculation, based on the amount of water passing Kingston-bridge in the Thames during a day and the number of cubic miles in the ocean, to prove that draining the earth by it alone would take about 159 days. But there were many rivers, often swifter than the Thames. Moreover, a large proportion of the fluids as they subsided from chaos settled immediately into the sea beds, and a considerable amount of those which fell on the land had been drained off during the first two days, so that fully three-fourths of the ocean was in place before the commencement of the third day. Much of what remained was evaporated by the internal heat of the earth and the new influence of the sun, or moistened the earth and filled the lakes, many of which were very large. Thus by the middle of the third day most of the earth's surface would be apparent. Then followed the creation of vegetables. They were not necessarily fully mature until the creation of Adam, since

[11] Witty, op. cit., pp. 68-76, 139, 140.

not until then was their perfection requisite. As was later
the case with animals, the formation of the seeds, which
were miniature adults and perfect in all parts, was the immediate work of God. Witty denied the doctrine that taught
the continued spontaneous generation even of insects and
plants, and referred to the observations and experiments of
Malpighi, Redi and others as disproofs. Perhaps the seeds
were formed, as Bishop Patrick said (*On Genesis*, cap. 1, p.
6 or 9), at the time when the spirit of God began to move
upon the face of the waters. Presumably plants were created
in a considerable degree of perfection since secondary causes
took so little time to bring them to full growth. Witty
contradicted himself, for he declared once (pp. 121-123)
that the relics of the deluge,—i. e., fossils, showed that the
earth had not deteriorated, and elsewhere (pp. 95-98) that
all things necessary for the production of vegetables were
more efficient in the beginning than at any later epoch. The
seeds were superior, the intestine motion in the superficial
parts of the earth was more violent and hence the heat was
greater and the earth was saturated with fluid particles.
Though the sun was not perfect, it had much influence.
Plants differed in the quantity of heat that they required, and
there was enough warmth to produce those that needed the
most. The others were not killed because there were sufficient fluids to prevent their being burned up.[12]

When it came to the fourth day, Witty, in spite of what
seemed to be his real opinion that the stars, the planets and
the sun had been forming from the beginning, said that God
perhaps made them in the brief space of that day to show
His power and, because of the contrast with the excessive
time consumed in the formation of the earth, His care for
man and the great value of human beings. The whole

[12] Witty, *op. cit.*, pp. 9-12, 77-98, 116-132, 140-143, 181, 182.

visible world was made for man's service. The stars, for example, were useful to him in navigation and in travel by land, and further stimulated him to adore God. Even Jupiter's satellites enabled man to discover the speed of light and to find the longitude of various localities.[13]

The creation of Adam and Eve was entirely the act of God. On the sixth day occurred also the preparation of the Garden of Eden and the naming of the animals, but not the Fall. Adam was created perfect. Hence he possessed knowledge of the whole world and an insight into the characters of animals so great that he could easily impose on them thousands of appropriate names in a short space of time. The knowledge of language, communicated by God, was also his immediately, even before the creation of Eve.[14]

An author who was more frequently quoted than either Dickinson or Witty though his ideas were less striking and unusual was William Derham (1657-1735). In 1711 and 1712 he gave in London as the Boyle lectures of the season sixteen sermons that demonstrated the existence and attributes of God from His works at the creation. The book, *Physico-Theology* (1713), which later summarized them, was so popular that by 1742 it had reached its tenth edition. An appendix promised therein, *Astro-Theology* (1714), was published four times by 1721. In 1716 the author was made a canon of Windsor. Derham, who was also a member of the Royal Society, was keenly interested in natural history. He was so able an astronomer that the Society lent him the telescope bequeathed to it by Huygens. It was 126

[13] Witty, *op. cit.*, pp. 99-115, 141, 142, 146, 169-177.

[14] *Ibid.*, pp. 134-137, 143-145, 177-181. Dr. Nichols, whose *Conferences with a Theist* were often quoted, had said that language was not miraculous but framed by Adam and Eve; but Gen. 2 : 20, according to Witty, proved that Adam knew it before her creation, and without it he could not have named animals on the sixth day. *Ibid.*, p. 136.

feet long, and Derham, because of the lack of a sufficiently elongated pole to serve as an attachment, found difficulty in the manipulation of the instrument.[15] He believed in a system of the universe like the Copernician except that the fixed stars were not in a single sphere but scattered.[16] Gravity was " imprinted on all the Matter of the Universe by the Creator's *Fiat* at the Creation." [17] The stars were the centers of other planetary systems that resembled the solar. All these planets had seas, mountains and atmospheres and were inhabited.[18] This was a " a far more probable and suitable use for so many Suns, so many glorious Bodies, than to say they were made only to enlighten and influence our lesser, and I may say inferior, Globe ";[19] and therefore worthier the Creator. Derham declared that we no longer made " the Uses and Offices of all the glorious Bodies of the Universe to center " in the earth or " in Man alone, according to the old vulgar Opinion, that *all things were made for man.*"[20] This change coincided with the fact that the earth had been ousted from the center of the universe. The Scriptural texts that seemed to oppose the heliocentric theory [21] were due to the

[15] Some early telescopes were made in two parts, an eyepiece like a small portable telescope and a separate tube that was similar in outward appearance, which was raised upon a long pole and guided by ropes. The difficulty was apparently to aline the two parts. The length was measured from the eyepiece to the correct location of the other half. As to this telescope, Derham said that it was 126 feet long, though the article on telescopes in the *Encyclopaedia Britannica* reduced the measure to 123 feet. Derham, *Astro-Theology* (London, 1721), preface and pp. ii, iii.

[16] *Ibid.*, pp. xxxviii-xliii.

[17] Derham, *Physico-Theology* (London, 1742), note p. 31.

[18] Derham, *Astro-Theology* (London, 1721), pp. xlvii-lv, 34-41, 55, 128-132, 181, 237.

[19] *Ibid.*, p. 35.

[20] *Ibid.*, p. 39.

[21] *Ibid.*, pp. xviii-xxi.

fact that " the design of the holy Writings is not to instruct
Men in Philosophical, but Divine Matters " [22] and that the
Biblical authors spoke in accordance with the appearance of
things and vulgar notions, not with their philosophical
verity.[23]   The sun's cessation of motion at Joshua's command
and the recession of the shadow on Hezekiah's sun-dial,
which were genuine history and therefore miracles, might
have been an arrest of the earth's movement just as well as
of the sun's.   Or they might have been merely in appearance,
the effect " of some preternatural Refractions, or extraordinary Meteors," as was not improbable.[24]   Comets were
" places of Torment . . . or Bodies appointed for the Re-
freshment and Recruit of the Sun, or any of his Planets, as
Sir *Isaac Newton* conjectureth in his *Princip.* L. 3. Prop.
41 & 42."   The sun, on the other hand, might be the location
of hell.[25]

Derham had made borings in the earth, weighed samples
and concluded that in general the lower strata were the
heavier.[26]

The time when those Strata were laid, was doubtless at the
Creation, when *God said . . . Let the Waters under the*

[22] Derham, *op. cit.*, p. xx.

[23] *Ibid.*, pp. xx, xxi, 39.

[24] *Ibid.*, pp. xxvii, xxviii; also Derham, *Physico-Theology* (London,
1742), pp. 44, 45.

[25] Derham, *Astro-Theology* (London, 1721), p. 164. Also pp. 55, 237.
The last suggestion was the opinion of another clergyman, Tobias
Swinden, who wrote an entire book, *An Enquiry into the Nature and
Place of Hell* (London, 1727) (2d edition), of approximately 470 pages
to sustain his thesis. The belief that comets were the location of future
punishment was common at the time, and was held by Burnet, apparently
in the earlier editions of his works. He was quoted to this effect by
White (Andrew), *A History of the Warfare of Science with Theology
in Christendom* (New York and London, 1910), vol. i, p. 206.

[26] Derham, *Physico-Theology* (London, 1742), pp. 66, 67 and note.

*Heavens be gathered together unto one Place, and let the dry
Land appear;* or else at the Deluge, if . . . we suppose the Globe
of Earth to have been dissolved by the Flood.[27]

As the particles of the chaos subsided, the strata were deposited according to their specific gravity, " according to the
Law of Gravity " [28] or as he called it elsewhere " Nature's
Tendency." [29] This produced an " even, spherical Surface,
every where equidistant from the Centre of the Globe." [30]
Its formation into hills and valleys was " a manifest Sign
of an especial Providence of the wise Creator." [31] Derham
believed in the existence of subterraneous heat, which might,
however, be due merely to " the meeting of mineral Juices," [32]
and in the theory generally associated with it that springs
came from the sea through the earth rather than from rains
and vapors.[33]

[27] Derham, *op. cit.*, p. 66.

[28] *Ibid.*, p. 66.

[29] *Ibid.*, p. 78.

[30] *Ibid.*, p. 78.

[31] *Ibid.*, p. 78.

[32] *Ibid.*, note p. 50.

[33] *Ibid.*, notes pp. 50-52. The belief about springs was held by Richard
Blackmore among others, who in his poem on *Creation* (1712) expressed
the idea, though he mentioned as well the thesis of some that streams
were due to rain and melting snow. *The British Poets* (Chiswick, 1822),
vol. xxviii, poem entitled *Creation*, bk. i, pp. 93-95, bk. iii, p. 143. *Cf.*
also *infra*, pp. 375-380.

CHAPTER XVIII

THREE DECADES OF HARMONIZING EFFORT

THE next thirty years displayed a definite decrease in the number, elaborateness and importance of the books on the relation of science to the Book of Genesis. On the continent the second decade of the eighteenth century gives us little save a theological disputation by Adrian Hubert vander Donck on the first verse of Genesis. Apparently his chief aim was to prove that matter was not eternal. Moses was promulgating a complete history of creation, and must have included the production of angels and of the highest heaven; therefore the first verse was not merely a summary of the whole process. By heaven Moses meant here not only the highest heaven, which was the seat of God, the angels and the blessed, but also the angels, all of whom were created. Since this heaven was perfect, it did not need sun, moon, stars, animals and plants. The later production of all these removed the imperfection of the earth. Inasmuch as the heaven and earth were spoken of as separate from the moment of creation, this highest heaven did not form part of the chaos.[1]

In 1724 appeared another stalwart upholder of the literal interpretation of Genesis, John Hutchinson (1674-1737), who wrote a book, *Moses's Principia,* that exerted some influence. He had aided Woodward in assembling his geological collections. Though he criticized severely his former master, he adopted his major theses that with the

[1] Donck, *Disputatio Theologica, de Divina Creatione Coelorum et Terrae in Principio* (Leyden, 1713), especially theses i-iv and vii-ix.

176

exception of organic remains the earth was dissolved at the deluge and that the method of its re-formation was the same as the method employed at creation. In both cases it started from a chaotic condition. However, Hutchinson denied that the process involved the subsidence of particles in accord with their specific gravity and affirmed that it was a consolidation which resulted from the pressure or expansion of the air. The strata were obviously not in a state that bore any relation to their specific gravity. The reasons given by Hutchinson for the deluge were the causes assigned by Woodward: the destruction of all living, the reduction of the earth's overfertility, which had inspired luxury, and the deposition of fossils in every country as memorials of the catastrophe and as warnings to mankind.[2]

Hutchinson's chief method of reconciling the Mosaic account with the scientific doctrines he affected was the redefinition of Scriptural terms. Like practically all others who mentioned the subject, Hutchinson believed in the creation of matter by God from nothing. His chaos, however, consisted of two parts, a chaos of earth and water, chiefly water, in the form of a hollow sphere, and a chaos of air and airy bodies both within and without this sphere. That part which was within the sphere was named sometimes darkness because it was deprived of light, and sometimes the abyss. The spirit gave motion to the matter on the face of the waters, not to the waters. The spirit was a material and created thing; in fact, it was the airs in motion upon the surface of the deep. The motion was not of a wind but rather of a bird incubating its eggs. The ancients believed in a Mundane Egg. The dual number was employed in mention of both the waters and the airs because the airs

---

[2] Hutchinson, *Moses's Principia* (London, 1724), pp. 9, 14-16, 22-34, 48, 53-55, 68-85, 88-91, 98, 99.

were and the waters were about to be in two places, not only without but also within the sphere of earth. The light upon the surface of the waters was the same air in more violent motion. This motion appeared in different parts alternately, and the air was called light where it was and darkness where it ceased. The firmament was the spirit and light in a rarefied state. Its parts pervaded the pores of the earth, pressed upon it, separated the waters from the earth and solidified the earth. The process produced a hollow globe of earth, with a layer of water on either surface, and with air or firmament at the center and circumference of the whole sphere. Obviously, the waters on the outer surface of the earth were below the upper firmament; and those within were above the lower firmament. The pressure of the air finally cracked the earth, filled some of the fissures with metals and through others forced down the waters.[3]

The collection of the waters into one place and the appearance of the land was therefore caused by the formation of funnels in the earth's sphere so that the water on the surface sank down into the interior and filled it, while the air within rose and changed places with the water. In their subsidence the waters tore off bits of the earth, which they carried with them into the abyss. These settled at the center of the whole as a globe. After the abyss, now an abyss of waters, was full, what liquid remained at the mouths of the funnels was called sea.

To produce the flood, God acted directly. He superseded natural laws and caused a miracle. The waters of the abyss broke out by the original passages with such force as to rend the earth and to enlarge the holes. The " windows of heaven " were these holes or similar ones, through which the air hastened inwards to take the place of the waters.

[3] Hutchinson, *op. cit.*, pp. 2, 3, 6-18, 22-34, 38-40, 71, 72.

Perhaps it entered with such force as to expel the water. Such action produced a dreadful noise. The earth was cracked in so many places as to be in small fragments; but the mountains still subsisted for a time, though in a shattered condition. The wind mentioned in Genesis at the conclusion of the flood was really the spirit described above. The cause for the renewal of the earth was that God had ceased to suspend natural laws and had set the spirit again at work.[4]

In spite of the fact that Hutchinson claimed to follow Moses and declared that " if *Moses* has made one Trip, all the rest is not worth a Farthing," [5] he did not explain the derivation of most of his doctrines from the Mosaic account. Except in the interpretation of the dual number for water and air, he asserted but did nothing to prove the justice of his translations and definitions of the Scriptural terms. The whole book impresses the reader as a rather petulant attack on an unnamed person, who was probably Woodward. Nevertheless, Catcott and his father later adopted Hutchinson's leading ideas and Pike developed them into a logical whole, whose harmony with Genesis was satisfactorily elucidated.

Swinden in his *Enquiry into the Nature and Place of Hell,* already mentioned, made several remarks about the whole universe. He declared that those criticisms of the heliocentric system that were based on the Bible had already been sufficiently answered " by far better Pens." [6] Elsewhere he spoke of the heliocentric system as certainly true. He seems also to have adopted Descartes's vortices, which he attributed to Huygens. Though the stars might be suns at the centers of their vortices, and might be surrounded by

[4] Hutchinson, *op. cit.,* pp. 38-45, 54-65, 68, 69, 71, 72, 74-87.

[5] *Ibid.,* p. 75.

[6] Swinden, *An Enquiry into the Nature and Place of Hell* (London, 1727), p. 233.

inhabited planets, possibly they were not hells, since perhaps the devil was confined to the solar vortex, and the inhabitants of the others, because they were untempted, possibly remained righteous. Our account of creation gave what was needed for our salvation, and beyond this we were not told. The Bible mentioned one heaven and one hell, and our philosophy must adapt itself to revelation. There was no reason why the solar vortex could not be at the center of the universe, while around all the vortices might be the situation of the empyreum. Such a location of the sun and of the empyreum showed clearly the vast distance by which the devil and evil men were separated from God. It agreed with the general doctrine that opposites were situated as far as possible from each other. The sun's uniqueness and opposition to the other spheres in all respects,—size, location, immobility as contrasted with the motion of all other bodies, —formed the chief reasons for Swinden's choice of it as a location for hell.[7]

Swinden went further than most authors in that he declared the cause for the creation of the present universe was the production of saints to take the place of angels who had lately fallen. One-third of all fell. This was a tremendous number. Seeing no place other than the empyreum, they had felt that because of their immortality they could not be deprived of bliss. Thereupon God, with ease and speed, created this universe, and first of all the sun. This event was the creation of light on the first day. There could be no light without the sun, and besides Moses called it day. On the fourth day He gave the solar sphere a new use in distinguishing the seasons. That meant that the earth was then given its annual orbit. So elaborate an adjustment obviously would require a whole day.[8]

[7] Swinden, *op. cit.*, pp. 142, 143, 145-176, 226-233, 249, 250, 349-351.
[8] *Ibid.*, pp. 88-93, 176-183, 275, 350.

With regard to the earth, Swinden doubted the existence of a central fire, and attributed volcanoes and such phenomena to natural fires in cavities nearer the surface. He was more inclined to accept an abyss of waters as the core of the earth and said that this opinion was fortified by the Bible when it spoke of the abyss or the waters under the earth, of the earth as founded upon the seas, of shutting up the sea with doors and of its breaking forth. This internal reservoir was the source of the more important perpetual springs. The expanse he considered to be the air.[9]

He evolved an interesting theory as to the manner of the earth's destruction by a final conflagration. He started with the suggestion that there were really countless planets in our system, perhaps 6,000 in all, some nearer to the sun than Mercury and others farther distant than Saturn. When by God's decree a planet was to be destroyed, the ordinary method was by its falling into the sun or at least coming near enough to be consumed. Those that we saw in the process of consumption we called comets. They were solid bodies about the size of the earth, all on fire. The vaporable elements made the comet's tail of vapor and smoke. Sometimes the spheres emerged again from the influence of the sun and travelled away out of sight.[10] If a globe journeyed far enough from the heat, the contents of the tail might " ' settle again upon that Nucleus, or Coal of the Comets Body, and perhaps become a much more glorious Planet or Earth than it was before.' " [11] Planets differed in their capacity to bear heat as was shown by the fact that some comets were visible as far from the sun as Mars. The outer planets might well take fire at that distance. At the end of the world, after the righteous had been caught up into

[9] Swinden, *op. cit.*, pp. 83-87, 95-99, 201-203.
[10] *Ibid.*, pp. 100-102, 354-357.
[11] *Ibid.*, p. 357.

the air, the earth with the moon would fall into the sun and be burnt.[12]   Perhaps it might then be tossed out " ' to a new and better Place in the Firmament, and become a new Earth in a new Heaven or Sky, and there be the Scene of the millennial State.' " [13]

In the meantime on the continent, Emanuel Swedenborg (1688-1772) was issuing many books and pamphlets, some of which were of a scientific nature.   The most important works dealing with cosmogony were his *Principia,* which formed the first volume of the *Opera Philosophica et Mineralia* (Leipzig, 1734), *The Worship and Love of God* (London, 1745), the *Arcana Coelestia* (London, 1749-1756) and a treatise *On the Planets in our solar system, and on those in the Heavens; with an account of their inhabitants, and of their spirits and angels* (London, 1758).   This last book was a compilation from several portions of the *Arcana Coelestia.*   Its title gives a just picture of its scope.   The *Arcana*[14] gave an exposition of the books of Genesis and Exodus.   The most important idea from our present viewpoint was that the first eleven chapters through the account of the deluge were purely allegorical, and described the internal life of the earliest people.[15]   *The Worship and Love of God* presented in narrative form the origin of the earth and the story of Adam.   Swedenborg's most important scientific work was the *Principia.*   Five years after its publica-

[12] Swinden, *op. cit.,* pp. 358-360.

[13] *Ibid.,* p. 360.   Swinden seems here to be quoting from a William Wall.   He also quoted from Dr. Nichols, *Conferences with a Theist,* part i, the suggestion that the original chaos, which filled the present orbit of Saturn, contained an " unctious inflammable Matter."   At God's word this subsided to the center and became compacted into a globe. On the fourth day it broke out into the solar flame.   Swinden, *op. cit.,* p. 219.

[14] Swedenborg, *The Heavenly Arcana* (London and Boston, 1839-48).
[15] Through vol. ii, p. 115.

tion it was placed on the *Index Expurgatorius,* but it gained the author a great reputation as well as friendship and correspondence from all contemporary philosophers. The position of the solar system in the Milky Way, the clustering of stars into distinct stellar congeries, the first enunciation of the nebular hypothesis,—that is, the belief in the origin of the planets and their satellites from the sun, together with many other later scientific theories, were promulgated in the *Principia.* The first suggestion has been erroneously considered a discovery of Herschel, the second was an important theory of Kant and the third has been attributed to Laplace. On the other hand, Swedenborg showed himself as the " last eminent reactionary," since he restored the Cartesian gyrating medium.[16] Because of his obsession that everything in the world, large as well as small, must have been made according to one plan,[17] he believed that " all things consist of vortices, the atoms as well as the solar systems." [18] The simplest material particle arose from the vortical motion of the immaterial mathematical point. This point he suggested had existed from eternity, though elsewhere he said it was created. His work was far from clear. He could not " imagine any action at a distance between celestial bodies "; [19] and in spite of his admiration for Newton he did not introduce the eminent mathematician's discovery into his own system of the universe.[20] His theory differed from the Cartesian in that the planets, according to Swedenborg, were ejected by the sun instead of migrating

[16] Clerke, *Modern Cosmogonies* (London, 1905), p. 15.

[17] Arrhenius, *The Life of the Universe as conceived by man from the earliest ages to the present time* (London and New York, 1909), vol. i, p. 116.

[18] *Ibid.,* vol. i, p. 111.

[19] *Ibid.,* vol. i, p. 117.

[20] *Ibid.,* vol. i, pp. 116, 117.

into the vortex of the solar system. When sun-spots increased and obscured the whole surface of the sun, which was the largest of the stars, the dark shell became strained by the imprisoned fire that sought to escape and to expand. The crust was fractured and gathered into a belt around the solar equator. As the vortex rotated, this ring broke into small masses, which became spherical and formed planets and satellites. These were carried away by the vortex until they reached a position of equilibrium with the vortex-ether around them and thereafter moved in almost circular paths. The specifically heavier planets were nearer the sun. Like Descartes, Swedenborg attributed the appearance of new stars to the bursting of such a shell of sun-spots, and declared the solar vortex to be limited by other whirls; but he displayed a broader conception of the universe since he linked the solar system to the Milky Way in a stellar system and surmised that this was part of a still greater whole. This idea was later developed by Wright (1750), Kant (1755) and Lambert (1761).[21]

Swedenborg made the belief in inhabitants of the other spheres an integral part of his philosophy. To him they were of the human race,[22] since " man is the end for which every earth was created and nothing was made by the Great Creator without an end." [23] He rejected the mere illumi-

[21] Swedenborg and his work were treated by the following: White, *Life of Emanuel Swedenborg* (Philadelphia, 1874) (Perhaps the first edition was in England, 1856), especially pp. 40-46, 55, 56, 78-85, 94, 132-134; Arrhenius, *op. cit.*, vol. i, pp. 111-118. For the theories of Wright and the others, *cf. infra*, pp. 242-249.

[22] Swedenborg, *Miscellaneous Theological Works* (New York, 1863), pp. 321-416, entitled *The Earths in the Universe, and their inhabitants; also, their spirits and angels*, the translation of a Latin treatise with similar name published in London in 1758. Also Arrhenius, *op. cit.*, vol. i, pp. 118-124, where he mentioned Pythagoras, Giordano Bruno, William Herschel and Kant as advocates of the same theory.

[23] Swedenborg, *op. cit., The Earths in the Universe*, sec. 112.

nation of the earth as too small a task for the celestial bodies.[24]
The universe consisted of many systems like the solar, each
with a sun at the center, around which revolved planets, all
equally inhabited. Such spirits as formerly lived in human
shape on each planet still surrounded it; and, because they
were similar in genius and temper to the inhabitants whom
they served, they found it difficult to associate with those
from another globe.[25] Because of this difference in temper
and disposition, even their hells were near their own earths
and had no connection with the hell of the wicked on our
earth.[26] Since man was the microcosm of heaven, " the
Grand Man," [27] each of the heavenly bodies with its inhabitants must present some characteristic of man in unadulterated form. For example, the spirits of Mercury delighted
only in knowledge and sought it everywhere. Both they and
their human associates on that planet were interested in the
memory only of abstractions from the material, as laws, forms
of government, things of heaven.[28] In general, Swedenborg
attributed to these inhabitants and spirits the characteristics
associated by astrology with the various planets, though he
somewhat idealized them; but for some reason he considered
the Martians the best of all planetary men, like those of the

[24] Swedenborg, *op. cit.*, secs. 3, 4, 112.

[25] *Ibid.*, secs. 3, 4, 30, 61, 112, 126, 146, 148; Swedenborg, *The Heavenly Arcana* (London and Boston, 1839-48), n. 9967-9970.

[26] Swedenborg, *Miscellaneous Theological Works* (New York, 1863), *The Earths in the Universe*, secs. 109, 137.

[27] *Ibid.*, secs. 9, 86, also secs. 5, 132 *etc.*; Swedenborg, *The Heavenly Arcana* (London and Boston, 1839-48), n. 2996, 2998, 3024-3649, 3741-3750, 3883-3896, 4039-4055, 4218-4228, 4318-4331, 4403-4421, 4523-4534, 4622-4634, 4652-4660, 4791-4806, 4931-4953, 5050-5062, 5171-5190, 5377-5396, 5552-5573, 5711-5727, 9969, 9972, 10030.

[28] Swedenborg, *Miscellaneous Theological Works* (New York, 1863), *The Earths in the Universe*, secs. 6, 10-20, 25, 101, 139 and elsewhere.

golden age.[29]   The reason for such a profusion of men was that many inhabited earths were necessary to produce enough angels.   The purpose for the creation of the universe was man, "that an angelic heaven might be formed of men." [30]

Peter Horrebow, professor of astronomy at Copenhagen, in 1725 and 1740 published another theory in *Clavis Astronomiae,* [31] based on the Cartesian vortices but with certain touches of Leibnitz's doctrines.   Out of nothing God produced matter, indefinite in extent, chaotic, deprived of all light.   It had of itself no motion, and was the passive element, resembling glass.   Light was the active element and was endued with motion, which was constant in quantity. From the continual strife of the two came ether, air and water.   All these were composed of perfectly elastic little balls of glass, which differed in density and radius or size. The movement of the active element produced the vortices. The poles of all the planets were unmoved.   Outside our atmosphere the movement of the vortical matter had more liberty; and our light was due to the mutual interpenetration of this active or hermetic matter, which circulated from west to east, of magnetic matter, which flooded from the two poles, and of a humid matter.   Though Horrebow expounded these strange doctrines, most of his book was merely mathematical astronomy.[32]

[29] Swedenborg, *op. cit.,* where the characteristics assigned to the dwellers on the various spheres were given in the following sections: Mercury, secs. 6, 10-20, 25, 44, 101; Jupiter, secs. 48-62, 68-73, 84; Mars, secs. 85, 87, 88, 90, 93; Saturn, secs. 97-100, 103; Venus, secs. 106-110; the moon, sec. 111; other earths in the starry heavens, secs. 128, 131, 134, 136, 140, 143-147, 149-155, 160-164, 166, 172-178.

[30] *Ibid.,* sec. 126, also secs. 112, 168.

[31] The account of his work was given by Delambre, *Histoire de l'astronomie au dix-huitième siècle* (Paris, 1827), pp. 140-155.

[32] Horrebow, *Clavis Astronomiae* reprinted in *Operum mathematico-Physicorum, etc.* (1740) quoted by Delambre, *op. cit.,* pp. 140, 144, 145.

About the same time Christian Wolf in Germany in his *Cosmologia Generalis* gave an account of the universe as it was, in which he dealt with mathematics, ontology, physics and metaphysics. With no statement of his own choice, he mentioned the three astronomical systems, which he called the Ptolemaic, the Tychonian and the Copernican, but declared that the last was the one preferred by astronomers of the day, and later called the earth a planet. Before the creation of the sun, as was shown by Genesis 1 : 2, the earth was empty, void and dark. However, the sun and the earth were mutually interdependent; and the creation of either must have been immediately followed by that of the other.[33]

With the exception of Hutchinson, the writers of this period developed cosmological doctrines of little influence. Though some of Swedenborg's suggestions were expounded by later scientists, it was apparently without knowledge of their previous elucidation. Therefore, these decades were evidently an era of retrogression and loss of interest in the Scriptural cosmogony.

Horrebow's account of light seems inconsistent. Perhaps he distinguished between an invisible active elemental light and a visible luminosity that resulted remotely from the action of the element.

[33] Wolf, *Cosmologia Generalis* (Frankfurt and Leipzig, 1737), especially pp. 34, 58, 61, 75, 76.

CHAPTER XIX

CONTINENTAL ATTEMPTS TO RECONCILE MOSES WITH SCIENCE

THE year 1740 introduced an epoch of renewed endeavors to formulate an account of creation which should be scientifically sound and to prove that it agreed with the Mosaic narrative. The date marked the publication in Italy of a book by Anton-Lazzaro Moro, *De'crostacei a degli altri marini corpi che si trovano sù Monti, Libri due*. Moro, whose style was extremely prolix, was opposed to Burnet, Whiston and Leibnitz, for he attributed to earthquakes and to volcanic eruptions the changes in the earth's surface; but he tried to coordinate each part of his system with the Biblical account of creation.[1]

Moro's chief thesis was that the marine animals and plants found as fossils in many mountains lived in the sea before the secondary mountains, which were formed after the fifth day, were raised. The organic remains were forced into their present locations and usually petrified when the mountains rose from the bottom of the sea. At that time the water covered the earth to the present height of the mountain peaks.[2] He supported his theory by two modern instances, the appearance of a new island near Paros in 1707-1711

---

[1] Jéhan, *Dictionnaire de cosmogonie et de paléontologie* (Paris, 1854), cols. 629-634, art. "Géologie (Histoire de la)"; De Luc, *Lettres physiques et morales sur l'histoire de la terre et de l'homme* (The Hague and Paris, 1779, 1780), vol. ii, pp. 390, 391, 401, 402. Pages 390-412, 452-512 gave the whole of Moro's system with De Luc's criticism.

[2] *Ibid.*, vol. ii, pp. 391, 392.

and the growth of Monte-nuovo near Naples in 1538. The
mountain was a new volcano.[3] Moro thought that on the
third day, when the earth was wholly covered with fresh
water, God formed dry land by the aid of subterranean fires
which lighted themselves and forced up the level surface of
primitive rock into mountain chains. The fissures afforded
upward passage to melted metals and salts that had been
originally contained in the interior of the earth. The water
became deeper as its area was diminished. The mountains
opened and poured out abundant lavas, sand and cinders,
which in stratified formation covered great sections of the
sea-bottom. Thereupon the still active subterranean fires
raised secondary mountains. They were distinguishable by
strata without marine fossils, since the sea was yet uninhabited. From the crevasses of the primary mountains came
the sulphurs, bitumen and fossil salts that began to give the
sea its salinity. Then,—that is, on the fifth day, the sea became fit for life ; and plants and animals were born and multiplied. The dry earth, which was covered with volcanic
matter, became fertile and produced trees and plants. Both
primary and secondary mountains continued to pour out
fire, sulphur, bitumen, lava, cinders and minerals. These
volcanic products formed the submarine strata that in due
course became plains. Between the deposition of the different layers there was time for them to be peopled ; hence later
strata buried the inhabitant of the earlier. Finally the submarine fires raised the sea bed into plains, hills and mountains
with fossiliferous strata. As the eruptions continued, they
buried not only shell-fish and corals, which were unable to
move quickly, but also other fish caught in basins or lakes,
and overwhelmed cultivated dry land with the works of man
in metal and in wood, such as were discovered in Moro's day
near Modena and elsewhere. The ships that were reputed to

[3] De Luc, *op. cit.*, vol. ii, pp. 392-400.

have been found in mines might be some which had sunk, had been overwhelmed by lava or ashes and then had been elevated with the enclosing strata by the subterranean fires. The fires gradually lost most of their force. The decreased vigor of the fires meant greater repose for the earth, for animals and for men, who increased; and in time the memory of the early catastrophes was lost. As portions of the sea-bottom were raised to produce continents, and others were covered with volcanic debris, the sea level rose and even submerged parts that were once dry land. Some forests and cities, for example, were at the bottom of the Mediterranean.[4] De Luc denied nearly all Moro's statements and said especially that the Italian did not understand the nature of lava, which was slow, barely liquid, covered with a hot crust and glassy. It could not travel far and its heat would destroy any organic matter it entombed.[5]

During the same epoch the theories of Burnet and of Whiston still flourished and were treated as worthy of serious consideration, especially in Germany. In 1742 John Heyn, rector of a university in Brandenburg and lecturer in physical science, published with prefaces by himself two dissertations on comets by a couple of his pupils, Balthasar Friderick Kuntsmann and John Gotthilf Werder. This book, which he entitled *Specimen Cometologiae Sacrae,* was printed to disarm by showing its injustice the criticism he apparently feared of his and their orthodoxy.[6] The first

[4] Jéhan, *op. cit.*, cols. 629-634, art. " Géologie (Histoire de la)"; De Luc, *op. cit.*, vol. ii, pp. 390, 391, 401-409, 457-463, 488, 489.

[5] *Ibid.*, especially pp. 457-475.

[6] Heyn, *Specimen Cometologiae Sacrae* (Leipzig, 1742), especially dedication and prefaces. During the same year, he published a longer book of his own on the same subject: Heyn, *Versuch Einer Betrachtung über Die Cometen, die Sündflut und das Vorspiel des jüngsten Gerichts, Nach astronomischen Gründen und der heiligen Schrift angestellet* (Berlin and Leipzig, 1742).

treatise, which quoted both Burnet and Whiston, attributed the flood to the passage of Halley's comet near the earth, as it twice crossed our planet's orbit. The vaporous atmosphere of the comet by its pressure upon the earth's surface opened the caverns of the abyss and expelled the subterranean waters. In this way the celestial visitant produced sufficient liquid to drown the world. The subterranean waters remained on the surface because the caverns were filled with the air from the comet. The catastrophe was a proof of divine wisdom, which at the creation ordained the comet's course so that at the correct moment it should be the minister both of the divine justice and of the divine power which had preserved it. The courses of the comets had been so arranged that there were only two occasions on which a comet could collide with the earth. The first was this oblique touch at the time of the flood, and the second would cause the destruction of the earth. Kunstmann added that the Bible itself (especially Amos 5:8) corroborated his theory, and mentioned various proofs by Whiston that Halley's comet approached the earth at the time assigned to the deluge, but said that they could not be understood or repeated without abstruse knowledge of astronomy and of chronology. The subsidence of the waters at the conclusion of the deluge, which was attributed by Moses to a wind, was due to the magnetic attraction of the comet on its final departure. It drew the air out of the subterranean caverns and left them empty for the waters.[7]

The second dissertation proved that the Last Judgment, clearly close at hand, was to be preceded by several comets. It explained the various signs in the Bible which referred to that period as the result of one or more comets. For in-

[7] Heyn, *Specimen Cometologiae Sacrae* (Leipzig, 1742), pp. 4, 8, 13, 16-26, 28-30.

stance, the intervention of a comet would cause an extra-ordinary eclipse of the sun; the moon immersed in cometary vapors would turn red; and the tail of the comet would touch the earth, fill it with odor and terror and carry off invincible sinners with clamor.[8]

[8] Heyn, *op. cit.*, pp. 40, 41, 45-53, 57-62.

CHAPTER XX

HISTORIES OF THE EIGHTEENTH CENTURY

THE eighteenth century saw a recrudescence of world histories like those of Sir Walter Raleigh and Bossuet. They resembled their precursors in their emphasis on Biblical history. From this type of annals two examples may suffice. In 1744 there was published anonymously in Dublin *An Universal History, from the Earliest Account of Time to the Present: Compiled from Original Authors.* The nearly one thousand pages of the first volume brought the story down only through Babylonian history. A more popular and much quoted account was written by Samuel Shuckford (1694-1754), *The Sacred and Profane History of the World Connected, from the Creation of the World to the Dissolution of the Assyrian Empire . . . and to the Declension of the Kingdoms of Judah and Israel, under the Reigns of Ahaz and Pekah.* It was first published in 1728 and was republished in England in the thirties, forties and fifties and twice in the first decade of the nineteenth century before the first American edition in 1824. The preface to the first volume gave an account of creation. In 1753 Shuckford wrote a supplemental discourse to this preface, entitled *The Creation and Fall of Man.*

Both authorities believed that Moses's account should be taken literally, not allegorically.[1] He was "the only authentick Writer of what happened before, and for several Ages after, the Flood. He is by universal Consent allowed to be

---

[1] Shuckford, *The Creation and Fall of Man* (London, 1753), pp. iv-xi, 2; Shuckford, *The Sacred and Profane History of the World Connected* (Philadelphia, 1824), vol. i, pp. 12-15, 22-25.

the most antient Historian now extant," [2] and wrote 675 or 275 years before the Trojan War. [3]   Shuckford claimed to have reduced the ancient profane history, especially the antediluvian, to an agreement with that of Moses.   They had originally corresponded before the addition of allegory and fable to the secular narratives. [4]

Moses either had these truths imparted to him by immediate revelation; or we must say that he collected the dogmata of those who lived before him. . . . The early ages had a great stock of truths, which they were so far from having learning enough to invent or discover, that they could not so much as give a good account of the true meaning of them.   A due consideration of these things must lead us to believe, that God at first revealed these things unto men; that he acquainted them with what he had done in the creation of the world; and what he had thus communicated to them, they transmitted to their children's children.   Thus God . . . did in the beginning in some extraordinary manner speak unto our fathers; for there was a stock of knowledge in the world, which we cannot see how the possessors could possibly have obtained any other way. [5]

The lives of Adam and of Methuselah overlapped and covered the period to the flood; therefore, Adam could hand down to Noah all his knowledge about creation as well as other wisdom.   In addition, Moses was divinely guided and instructed. [6]

[2] *An Universal History, from the Earliest Account of Time to the Present* (Dublin, 1744), vol. i, p. viii, also pp. v, 35; Shuckford, *op. cit.*, vol. i, p. 22.

[3] Shuckford, *The Creation and Fall of Man* (London, 1753), pp. vii-x.

[4] *Ibid.*, pp. x, xi; Shuckford, *The Sacred and Profane History of the World Connected* (Philadelphia, 1824), vol. i, pp. 12-15, 22-25.

[5] *Ibid.*, vol. i, pp. 32, 33, also pp. 51-53.

[6] *Ibid.*, vol. i, p. 51; Shuckford, *The Creation and Fall of Man* (London, 1753), pp. xxix-xxxvi, note p. 28.

The *Universal History* presented an elaborate account of the variations among the chronologists as to the date of creation. They ranged from B. C. 3616 to B. C. 6984, partly because of the differences in the Hebrew, Samaritan and Septuagint versions. The *Universal History* quoted ninety-eight opinions, including Usher's, concerning the epochs of creation and of the flood, and seemed to prefer the date given by Josephus, as amended by Whiston and Dr. Wills. This was based on the Samaritan version and assigned the creation to the year 4658 B. C. and the flood to a period 1556 years later. A most interesting fact is that the *Universal History* gave more than a single opinion for some commentators. Generally the variations by the same man differed by only three to nine months, but once by as much as eight years.[17] *The Universal History* gave the usual arguments based on the present physical state of the world, the numbers of mankind and the comparatively recent invention of various arts and sciences to prove that the earth's age could not be great. As to the season of the year when creation took place, it mentioned several which had been suggested, especially the equinoxes, and decided that the autumnal equinox was the most probable.[8]

[7] *An Universal History, from the Earliest Account of Time to the Present* (Dublin, 1744), vol. i, pp. xxxv-xlii. Other accounts of the differences of opinion on this subject may be found in the following places: Horn, *Arca Noae* (Leyden, 1666), pp. 4-8, who declared that Usher's dates should be preferred; Beaumont, *Considerations On a Book, Entitled The Theory of the Earth* (London, 1693), pp. 174, 175; (Mirabaud), *Le monde, son origine, et son antiquité. De l'ame, et de son immortalité. Essai sur la chronologie* (London, 1778), pt. ii, pp. 131-133, 151-176, 178, 179; Shuckford, *The Sacred and Profane History of the World Connected* (Philadelphia, 1824), vol. i, pp. 56-68. *Cf.* also *supra,* p. 142.

[8] *An Universal History, from the Earliest Account of Time to the Present* (Dublin, 1744), vol. i, pp. 11, 48.

Both it and Shuckford agreed that creation took six days, but the days counted from sunrise to sunrise contrary to the generally accepted view. Both gave summaries of the Mosaic relation.[9] Shuckford added the following theses. The creation was through the word, not the thought, of God.[10] Moses " makes the Heavens and the Earth distinct at their first creation." [11] The " Spirit of God moved upon the fluid matter, and separated the parts of which it consisted from one another; some of them shined like the light of day, others were opaque like the darkness of the night; God separated them one from the other," as the first step in forming the world.[12] Then " God thought it proper to have an expansion between the Earth and Heaven, capable of supporting clouds of water." [13] Its formation and the establishment upon it of the clouds were the work of the second day. The Hebrew expression meant properly expansion, and did not have the implications of the English word firmament. Shuckford declared the " lights of Heaven capable of being serviceable to the world in several respects." They furnished light, heat and a measure for time, seasons and years.[14] On the fourth day, God shaped them and " gave the stars their proper places." [15] God created all plants before the earth had been watered by rain or by dew, which was mist rising from the ground, and before it had received tillage from man. Paradise was a garden, undoubtedly planted on the third day. Outside its limits probably trees

[9] *An Universal History, from the Earliest Account of Time to the Present* (Dublin, 1744), vol. i, p. 35; Shuckford, *op. cit.*, vol. i, pp. 21, 22; Shuckford, *The Creation and Fall of Man* (London, 1753), p. xxvii, note p. 6.

[10] *Ibid.*, p. xxvii.

[11] Shuckford, *The Sacred and Profane History of the World Connected* (Philadelphia, 1824), vol. i, p. 23.

[12] *Ibid.*, vol. i, p. 21.   [13] *Ibid.*, vol. i, p. 21.

[14] *Ibid.*, vol. i, p. 21.   [15] *Ibid.*, vol. i, p. 21.

were not in full perfection at first, and they did not bear such fruit as they did within. The earth had put forth only shoots, which grew gradually to perfection. Originally birds as well as beasts were apparently nourished on green herbs rather than on fruits of trees.[16] At that time, and in fact until after the flood, serpents and other animals were not poisonous, since they were received into the ark with no hostility by Noah.

There might, ere this Time [of Moses] be poisonous Juices in many of the Herbs and Plants that grew on the Earth; The same Alteration of the World, which began from the Flood, and conduced to the shortning the Lives of Men, might cause such an Alteration in many Herbs, that Men might not perhaps now find every green Herb and Tree as wholesome, as they had found all in the first World: And the Nourishment of some in the Concoction of some Animals, might breed in them, what to Man and other Creatures might be malignant Poison. At the going out from the Ark, the living Creatures of the World appear to have been none of them hurtful or destructive to Man: But Time produced in many a Ferocity, and in others other Qualities which made them terrible.[17]

Adam and Eve were both created on the sixth day. Adam was created in an adult state; but his mind was not ready stored with ideas, from which he might derive thoughts. Moses did not affirm that he spoke until God made him try to name animals. Then he chose arbitrarily, and might have called them by any other names, for there were no innate names. To teach Adam how to apply a sound or a word to an animal God brought one to him, as was shown by the use of the singular pronoun. The imposition of appellations on all beasts and fowls would unquestionably have been too stupendous a task for one occasion, but the selection of a

[17] *Ibid.*, pp. 229, 230.
60, 253, note p. 8.
[17] Shuckford, *op. cit.*, pp. 229, 230.

term for a single animal would show him how to designate others as he met them.   The presentation of one or more animals to Adam for names was no inspection, at the end of which it was discovered that among the animals was no fit helpmeet for him.   Such instruction of Adam by God proved that our earliest ancestor had no innate language. God gave the first pair ideas to fit the words He used to them. Then they gradually accumulated concepts and knowledge and developed words to express them.   The first language consisted of very simple words that were all nouns or names, and largely monosyllables.   Probably it was Hebrew, though not so developed a form as the Mosaic Hebrew, or Chaldean, which is the same thing, though it may have been Chinese. Shuckford mentioned but rejected the opinions of others, who in general had attributed the first language to a direct revelation from God.[18]

The Universal History gave the accounts of ancients and of moderns who had attempted to explain the beginnings of the world, including Gassendi and Descartes, whose ideas it rejected, and Burnet and Whiston, for whom it seemed to have a predilection.[19]   It declared that Burnet " excelled in the richness of his stile and fancy " and Whiston, whom it especially favored, " in the strength of parts and contrivance." [20]   Though it criticized both mildly, it continually recurred to their opinions.   It is often difficult to distinguish the theories held by the author of the *Universal History* from

[18] Shuckford, *op. cit.*, pp. lxxxi-xc, 5, 15-52, 54-88, notes pp. 6, 8; Shuckford, *The Sacred and Profane History of the World Connected* (Philadelphia, 1824), vol. i, pp. 81, 82, 85-91, 95-97. Shuckford was another who wished to identify Noah with Fohi and believed he settled in Bactria north of India, whence his descendants moved to India and China. *Ibid.*, vol. i, pp. 81-83.

[19] *An Universal History, from the Earliest Account of Time to the Present* (Dublin, 1744), vol. i, pp. 9-41 and elsewhere.

[20] *Ibid.*, vol. i, p. 36.

the conflicting hypotheses that he quoted, but apparently his judgment accepted the following ideas. The universe was created by God out of nothing. He created matter and was the first and sole principle of motion.[21] Angels were " in being long before the *Mosaic* creation, . . . since they were actually present, if not employed in that creation, *when the morning stars sang together, and all the sons of God shouted for joy."* Even " the fall of the apostate angels was some time at least before it." [22] The Mosaic narrative pertained to the solar system only, neither to the earth alone nor to the entire universe. This system was so closely associated as to constitute a single whole. The planets were formed of their own particular chaotic masses in the same manner and time as the earth.[23] It was improbable that the planets came from the Mosaic chaos, both because Moses called it the earth, and because the belief was contrary to the " now undoubted property of the universal gravitation of matter; not to mention the false supposition, which must in that case be made, of the earth's being the center of the world." [24] The Spirit of God, which Grotius believed to have been the Holy Spirit, Cudworth plastic nature, and others a violent wind or some other emanation to dry up the waters, moved the chaos, whose surface was covered with fluid, " and impregnated it with several kinds of vital influence, preparing every part to receive the intended disposition, order and life." [25] Then

---

[21] *An Universal History, from the Earliest Account of Time to the Present* (Dublin, 1744), vol. i, pp. 9-11, 37, 38, 41.

[22] *Ibid.*, vol. i, p. 49, also p. 50.

[23] *Ibid.*, vol. i, p. 41.

[24] *Ibid.*, vol. i, p. 42. Shuckford also accepted the doctrine of the earth's motion around the sun. Shuckford, *The Creation and Fall of Man* (London, 1753), p. 71.

[25] *An Universal History, from the Earliest Account of Time to the Present* (Dublin, 1744), vol. i, p. 41. Cudworth's most influential doctrine was the belief in plastic nature, by means of which God acted. He

" the confused stagnating parts of matter began to range themselves in order; and the grosser parts subsiding, the lighter and more tenuious mounted up." Since the atmosphere was somewhat cleared, the " rays of the sun began to pierce it, and caused an imperfect and glimmering light, yet sufficient partly to dispel the before total darkness, and to distinguish day from night." [26] This opinion was more reasonable than to suppose with Dr. Nichols (*Conferences with a Theist,* vol. i, part i) and others that the substance of the sun and even of the stars was extracted from chaos. More than ninety-nine per cent of the matter in the universe was fiery corpuscles; and, if they had been in the primeval chaos, it could not have been dark.[27]

On the second day the expanse or air, which Moses called heaven, " was perfected, being now freed from the gross terrene particles which before crowded it, and made capable of supporting clouds and aqueous vapours, which were the superior waters, as those on the earth were the inferior." [28] Dr. Nichols was mistaken in his belief that the waters above the firmament were the planetary waters. Despite this identification of the inferior waters with those on the surface of the earth, the author of the *History* apparently believed in a subterranean abyss, which contained enough water to cover the earth, into which the fluid subsided on the third day and from which it was miraculously produced to cause the flood. In his judgment the best opinion about

derived the belief from Aristotle.   Cudworth, *The True Intellectual System of the Universe* (London, 1743) (1st ed., 1678), vol. i, pp. 178-181, vol. ii, pp. 680, 681, 684, 686.

[26] *An Universal History, from the Earliest Account of Time to the Present* (Dublin, 1744), vol. i, p. 42.

[27] *Ibid.,* vol. i, p. 42.

[28] *The History* here quoted Hugo Grotius. *Ibid.,* vol. i, p. 42.

mountains was Whiston's theory that they resulted from the unequal subsidence into the abyss of earth columns whose density differed. This occurred at the original formation of the earth's surface. Mountainous columns, according to Whiston and the anonymous historian, were hollower and lighter than those of the plains.[29] On the third day, as every one agreed, God formed the seeds of plants; but His power must have been employed also to effect the full growth of trees to fruition in one day, although much "might be expected from nature in that vigorous state."[30]

On the fourth day, the air was at last freed from the heterogeneous particles and the vapors that had obscured it. As a result the moon and the other planets, which had kept pace with the earth in their development, the sun, which from the beginning had exercised great influence upon the earth and whose heat and light had increased as the atmosphere cleared, and the stars, which were no part of this creation, became visible.[31]

Fish and fowl were both generated from the water on the fifth day and therefore resembled each other in mode of progression and in being oviparous. Either God or some agent empowered by Him "actually formed both plants and animals, making use of the earth and water, as the matter only whereof he constituted their parts."[32] Perhaps they were created as seeds and perhaps full-grown; but certainly they were produced in quantities, not in pairs. The plants, which according to the author had no locomotive powers, must have been formed all over the world. Probably God created at first all the individual animals that should exist

[29] *An Universal History from the Earliest Account of Time to the Present* (Dublin, 1744), vol. i, pp. 42, 102.

[30] *Ibid.*, vol. i, p. 42.

[31] *Ibid.*, vol. i, pp. 42, 43.

[32] *Ibid.*, vol. i, p. 43.

till the end of the world.   Each egg and seed contained not
simply the full-grown adult in miniature but also the embyros
of all its descendants *ad infinitum*.   Otherwise the only
difference between God's production of animals and that by
animals themselves would be a matter of speed.[33]   The cre-
tion of man " for whose sake the whole was framed " was
more elaborate, and was preceded by a consultation of the
Trinity.[34]   God still created the souls of all men from time
to time as they were needed.[35]   Adam and Eve " were
created in an adult and perfect state, . . . in the greatest perfection both of body and mind " [36] but this did not mean that
Adam was " master of every science and art," knew more on
the first day than any other at the end of a long life and even
surpassed the angels.[37]   God gave Adam an impulse that
informed him of his natural power to speak, but did not
infuse primeval language into him.   He had only a limited
vocabulary, and named merely the commoner animals, plants
and reptiles, not all.   No commentator imagined that fish
were brought to Adam for names.[38]

Both Shuckford and the author of the *Universal History*
agreed that Eden was located in Chaldea near the southern
end of the Euphrates River.   Shuckford was explicit in his
specification that the garden was just north of the Tigris-
Euphrates delta near the Persian Gulf.   Since the author
of the *Universal History* believed that Adam was created in
or near Paradise, he rejected the neighborhood of Damascus
for the birthplace of the first man.   Both writers denied

[33] *An Universal History, from the Earliest Account of Time to the Present* (Dublin, 1744), vol. i, pp. 43, 44.

[34] *Ibid.*, vol. i, p. 44.

[35] *Ibid.*, vol. i, pp. 46, 47.

[36] *Ibid.*, vol. i, p. 44.

[37] *Ibid.*, vol. i, p. 45.

[38] *Ibid.*, vol. i, pp. 149-151.

that the fall occurred on the sixth day. The *Universal History* suggested the lapse of a year and a day; Shuckford several days or even some months, so that the first pair had had sufficient time to observe which fruits they preferred and how they should be cultivated. Our first ancestors knew enough of animals to realize that not all of them spoke, hence considered the serpent superior. But the episode must have occurred early in their lives, since this loquacity did not impress them as a miracle. Shuckford, in accordance with his rejection of supernatural knowledge as a characteristic of Adam, said that by the end of their first day he and Eve had not looked beyond their garden. Their information gradually increased. The next day was the Sabbath so that they might have time to digest the information they had already acquired. They were directed to take care of the garden in order that new knowledge should not utterly swamp them. The use of the future tense in the narrative of the events after the fall perhaps meant that they were not immediately expelled from Paradise but were permitted to linger a while and were instructed and prepared for exile. The delay would, moreover, give time for the preparation of skins for clothing.[39]

Though the accounts of these eighteenth century historians are not so jejune and so slavishly subservient to the narratives of Scriptural and classical historians as those published during the preceding century, their theories are neither striking nor original. Perhaps for this very reason they were popular and often quoted.

[39] *An Universal History, from the Earliest Account of Time to the Present* (Dublin, 1744), vol. i, pp. 48, 53-59; Shuckford, *The Sacred and Profane History of the World Connected* (Philadelphia, 1824), vol. i, pp. 68-70; Shuckford, *The Creation and Fall of Man* (London, 1753), pp. 31, 32, 60-90, 93-100, 151-161, 170, 186, 254, 255, 281-283.

CHAPTER XXI

Buffon, the Zoologist

MORE influential than most of his contemporaries, in spite of some clerical disapproval, was George Louis Leclerc, Comte de Buffon (1707-1788). In 1744 he published his *Théorie de la Terre,* which aroused the Sorbonne to unfavorable comment and action. They demanded the recantation of fourteen among his propositions on the ground that they were contrary to the faith of the Church. Though he is said to have recanted in the 1769 edition all ideas about the formation of the earth and everything contrary to the narrative of Moses,[1] he continued to publish his monumental *Histoire Naturelle;* and in 1778 or 1779 he brought out a volume of this series entitled *Époques de la Nature,* which seemed to affirm all his old theories. He apparently endeavored to preserve amicable relations with the Church by adopting two of Descartes's equivocations. After an assertion that his interpretation of Genesis was merely an effort to reconcile science and theology, which only in appearance could be in contradiction, he continued with the declaration that his system was purely hypothetical and concluded with the statement that he had submitted his ideas to revealed truths and would continue thus to submit them.[2]

In his first treatise Buffon suggested a new use for comets, which he developed in later parts of his *Histoire Naturelle.*

---

[1] Jéhan, *Dictionnaire de cosmogonie et de paléontologie* (Paris, 1854), cols. 635, 636, art. "Géologie (Histoire de la)."

[2] Buffon, *Oeuvres complètes* (Paris, 1831, 1832), vol. v, p. 43, the end of the original first section of the *Époques.* Later he presented his views as if he had never made such concessions.

He believed the origin of the planets the result of a glancing blow given to the sun by a comet. The particles, which were liquefied by the enormous heat of the sun, were furrowed out of its substance as torrents of molten matter, and, after such a separation according to specific gravity that the lightest were farthest from their source, circulated around the sun in almost the same plane. Mutual attraction formed the molecules into globes. The globes by their rotation on their own axes were shaped into oblate spheroids while they were still liquid from heat. Ever since that era, they had been cooling. The matter of the comet possibly became a part of the new planets.[3]

Even before the catastrophic collision comets had played an important part in the economy of the universe. The sun was and must remain fluid, luminous and burning, with its matter most completely subdivided. This state was produced by the weight of all the vast bodies which circled around it. Their orbits resembled the rims of wheels whose

[3] Buffon, *op. cit.*, vol. i, note pp. 108-111, pp. 168-209, which contained art. i, *De la formation des planètes* in *Preuves de la théorie de la terre*, pp. 271-273, vol. v, pp. 12-18, 29, 69-74, 78-83. Pages 74, 81 and 83 called this merely a very probable, not a certain cause for the formation of the earth and the other planets. Elsewhere he forgot this concession and continued to treat the theory as true. Buffon's *Théorie de la terre* was printed in this edition vol. i, p. 103 – vol. iii, p. 71 and his *Des époques de la nature*, first edition 1779, in vol. v. Buffon was one whose theories were discussed by other authors. Arrhenius, *The Life of the Universe as conceived by man from the earliest ages to the present time* (London and New York, 1909), vol. ii, pp. 128-137; Jéhan, *op. cit.*, art. " Géologie (Histoire de la)," cols. 635-637; Geikie, *The Founders of Geology* (London and New York, 1897), pp. 8-12; De Luc, *Lettres physiques et morales sur l'histoire de la terre et de l'homme* (The Hague and Paris, 1779, 1780), vol. i, note p. 116, pp. 377-423, vol. ii, pp. 141, 177, 198-200, 244, 245, vol. iv, pp. 107-109, 128, 134, 135 especially note pp. 135-137 and vol. v, pp. 388, 389, 517-611; De Luc, *Letters on the Physical History of the Earth* (London, 1831), letter i, pp. 10-15. De Luc generally grouped Buffon's theories with those of several other writers in his discussion and refutation.

hub was the sun. The spokes were the radii from the sun to the various celestial spheres. The swifter the speed of the surrounding spheres, the greater would be the friction and speed of the sun, especially the friction in its interior. All this friction caused heat. While the formation of the planets and their orbits resulted in an access of brilliance, enough comets before that time circled around the sun to produce liquidity, fire and light in the solar body. From these and similar premises Buffon derived the conclusions that the stars must be surrounded by planets, and that Jupiter and Saturn did not freeze, though so remote from the sun, because they were heated by the motion of their satellites. Naturally the farther from the solar sphere lay the course of a planet, the more numerous, larger and swifter must be its satellites.[4]

Buffon agreed with some other naturalists of the eighteenth century in a demand for many more than the orthodox number of millennia since creation to permit the development of the earth to its present state. Because of experiments with molten minerals of varying constitution and size, he concluded that the cooling of the earth to the point where water could settle upon it would take approximately twenty-five thousand years. This he called the first epoch, Moses's first day, from a state of chaos with an incandescent terrestrial globe to light. Light was created in an instant but not separated from darkness. God took time to consider the light before He divided it from the darkness,—that is, before the opaque matter of the planets was separated from the luminous matter of the sun.[5]

[4] Buffon, *op. cit.*, vol. v, pp. 75-79, 82.

[5] *Ibid.*, vol. i, p. 175 note, pp. 192-196, vol. iv, pp. 237-425, which gave two essays by Buffon, *Recherches sur la refroidissement de la terre et des planètes,* and *Fondements des recherches précédentes sur la température des planètes,* vol. v, pp. 22, 23, 30, 33-40, 101, 280 and vol. v,

The next epoch, during which the atmosphere was cleared by the precipitation of the water vapors upon the earth, corresponded to Moses's second day and must have lasted at least ten thousand years. The equatorial regions cooled more slowly than the polar because at the equator the earth's diameter was longer. Hence the waters fell first in the arctic and the antarctic zones and formed seas there before they spread to the tropics after those localities became cooled to receive them.[6] During the third epoch or day, fifteen to twenty thousand years long, the water stood two thousand fathoms above the surface of the earth. At first it had certainly covered all but the summits of the highest mountains. Perhaps they always surmounted the waves, since marine fossils were not found in them though everywhere else. Inasmuch as the great beds of coal, together with the strata of calcareous stone, which were the debris of shell-fish, were deposited during the third period, apparently the subsidence of the waters had commenced and had left some sections dry and densely vegetated. Buffon asserted that these epochs corresponded with the Biblical days but neglected to notice that he here attributed shell-fish to the third day instead of to the fifth.[7]

p. 69, title assigned to the Première Époque. This is an illustration of Buffon's constant apparent contradictions. He did not make clear when he considered the blow of the comet to have taken place. He seemed to place this occurrence at both the beginning and the end of the first epoch. *Ibid.*, vol. i, pp. 174, 175, vol. v, pp. 36, 87, 280. Elsewhere he declared the great work of the first epoch to have been the formation of the planets into solid oblate spheroids, cooled to such a point that the vapors of water and air which they had carried away with them from the atmosphere of the sun could settle on the surface. *Ibid.*, vol. i, note p. 175, pp. 196-200, 204-208, vol. v, pp. 11-18, 69-71, 83-86, 116, 117, 164.

[6] Buffon, *op. cit.*, vol. i, pp. 204-206, 272, 273, 298, 299, vol. v, pp. 23, 30, 99-129, 280.

[7] *Ibid.*, vol. i, pp. 116-121, 279, vol. ii, pp. 7-57, 63, 64, 90, vol. iii, p. 68, vol. v, pp. 12, 20-23, 33-39, 133-188, 191-193, 280.

His fourth epoch showed similar lack of clear correlation with the corresponding Mosaic day. Its ten thousand years were a period of gradual marine retreat and of terrific terrestrial upheavals by volcanoes and earthquakes, concerning which he said that we should thank God for not making man a witness of so terrible a world.[8] During the fifth epoch, nature employed the first period of repose for the production in the still torrid northern climes of the first terrestrial animals. They were the species that inhabited the tropical zone to the present time. This period was shorter and lasted perhaps five thousand years.[9] As the earth grew yet cooler in the sixth epoch, the elephants and other warmth-loving animals travelled southward. Meantime the ocean broke through and separated America from Asia and possibly from Europe. The Platonic narrative of Atlantis apparently preserved the tradition of the division between Europe and the New World. An obvious result of the separation was the undermining of the less solid land areas so that the islands of England, Ireland, Sardinia, Corsica, Sicily and probably the West Indies were severed from the mainland. Simultaneously water shattered the barriers at each end of the Mediterranean and flooded the district. It transformed that inland lake, which had previously had no outlet, into a bay of the ocean. Perhaps the division of Sicily from Italy and the formation of the Adriatic resulted from this rise in the level of the Mediterranean. Buffon said little about the creation of man, although he apparently placed it at the end of the sixth period.[10] The seventh epoch was that wherein men had lived on the earth and with gradually increasing skill and knowledge had cooperated with nature in

[8] Buffon, *op. cit.*, vol. v, pp. 23, 191-222, 280, 281.

[9] *Ibid.*, vol. v, pp. 23-30, 49-66, 225-248, 281.

[10] *Ibid.*, vol. v, pp. 21, 23, 30, 31, 231-235, 246-248, 251-315.

amelioration of our globe. They not only had produced superior types of edible vegetation and domestic animals by cultivation but had even altered the climate by demolishing forests and draining swamps. To each of the later eras he assigned five thousand years. Thus the total length of time since creation was approximately seventy-five thousand years. Buffon then prophesied the final refrigeration of the earth so that 132,000 years after its first formation it would become a ball wholly covered with ice. The heat of the sun was not sufficient to sustain life. In fact only about two per cent of our heat came from this source. To prove his statement Buffon mentioned the contrast between the variation in quantity of solar rays in summer and winter and the difference in temperature at those seasons, and also the thermal increase associated with descent into the earth in mines. That the refrigeration of the surface was already far advanced was evinced by the continual encroachment of ice on Alpine summits and in the polar regions.[11]

The time since the creation of Adam was truly six to eight thousand years as was proved by the genealogies in the Bible. We owed submission on this point to revealed truth. But the Bible itself, by its use of the imperfect tense, by its choice of words, by its counting from evening to morning while true solar days extended obviously from morning to evening, most of all by its enumeration of three days before the appearance of the sun, showed that the days of creation were to be considered as extended periods. Moreover, they were not equal in length but proportioned to the work accomplished in each. The truths of reason and of the Bible, since both were from God, must agree; but the Bible talked

[11] Buffon, *op. cit.*, vol. i, p. 188 note, vol. iii, pp. 103-106, 157, 158, vol. v, pp. 11-16, 30, 92-96, 227, 275-280, 296-304, 319-352, 362. The last mentioned page is in a section entitled *Explication de la carte geographique,* which was apparently published with the *Époques de la nature.*

to the people of the time in such a manner that they could comprehend, and did not go beyond common notions founded on the senses. For example, it presented the physics that was accepted in the first ages, with heaven an azure vault and the sun and moon, which rose and set, as the largest celestial bodies. Since the sea was the same color as the sky and seemed to touch it, the people of Moses's day imagined that sea and sky were filled with the waters below and above the firmament respectively; and naturally the inferior waters gave birth to fish and the superior to birds, who seemed to approach those higher waters not far above the clouds. To support the waters above the earth a solid transparent vault, the firmament, was needed, whose windows might be opened to let them fall upon and drown the earth. The stars, which were attached like nails, were in early days indistinguishable from the planets; and therefore the planets were ignored in the history of the creation.[12]

Buffon's own explanation of creation asserted that in the beginning matter was created out of nothing and was formless. After this initial act creation ceased, and all future activity merely shaped this matter. The earth hardened as it cooled and lost the luminosity it had possessed during its first ages. The interior exploded from time to time and elevated the crust, which had solidified first, into hummocks. Thus were formed the first and highest mountains and the original valleys. At the same time cavities or caverns were made in the earth's crust. Finally the whole earth solidified and was equally dense throughout. Probably Buffon meant all of the earth except the crust, since he based much of his geogeny on the continued existence of caverns. The original vitrified rock at the center extended to the surface even yet at the heart of the great mountain chains. Outside this solid rock was at first a vitrified matter which resembled sand since

[12] Buffon, *op. cit.*, vol. v, pp. 33-43.

it was only particles of glass, finely divided by the fire. Still farther outside were the lightest particles, which had been the scum of the molten mass. From this layer of scoriae and pumice stone were made clays and slates. The specific gravity of different sections of the crust and interior was altered during the first epoch by the sublimation of metallic matter and its deposition in the perpendicular faults of the high mountains. At a later period some of the metals were washed out and redeposited in more nearly horizontal cracks in the lower sedimentary mountains. Much of the earth's crust was deposited in horizontal layers when the surface was covered by water, but the fact that the strata were not arranged in accordance with their specific gravity proved that their deposition was successive not simultaneous.[13]

From the present surface of the earth some facts concerning its primitive state and its successive changes could be gleaned. The greater area of land in the northern hemisphere proved that originally it had more protuberances and the southern more concavities. The surface irregularities and the caverns were greatest at the equator since the tropics were the last to be hardened and the rotation was there the greatest. More matter came from the south pole than from the north to swell the equatorial regions, both when the earth was molten and later when the water was flooding from the poles to the equator. As a result a greater area was prepared for the southern ocean. When the waters, together with the volatile matters in the air, fell, they broke and eroded the mountains and filled the valleys with the debris. Their weight and volume also fractured the vaults of the sub-

---

[13] Buffon, *op. cit.*, vol. i, notes pp. 108-111, 122, 123, 136-138, 186, 187, 295, 296, pp. 121, 123-125, 128, 136, 192, 193, 197-204, 272, 273, 281-289, 296-305, vol. ii, pp. 90, 91, 326-328, 425-430, vol. iii, pp. 183-186, vol. v, pp. 19, 22, 23, 29, 34-38, 83, 84, 87, 92-94, 99-110, 113-118, 121, 136, 137, 141-143, 145, 151, 152, 160-162, 192, 193, 199, 201, 205, 219.

terranean caverns and flooded them with liquid. This ingress of the waters into the bowels of the earth, which began during the second epoch, had continued to the present and was the sole cause for the diminution of the waters that exposed the dry land. Since caverns still existed in the earth's crust, as was proved by earthquakes and volcanic eruptions, the process had not ended but would lower the sea level yet farther.[14]

Other superficial terrestrial changes were due to the quality of the deposits from the air. The aerial precipitates combined with the vitreous rock to form acids, salts and clay. The waters carried these in various directions and finally laid down the clays in horizontal strata. By their own weight the strata were solidified.[15] Meanwhile the waters, which had settled first at the poles because those sections had cooled first, gradually spread to the equatorial regions. The fact that all continents and large bodies of land were pointed at their southern extremities was due to the greater amount and force of the water coming from the south pole, which had cooled before the opposite pole. Finally the whole earth was nearly or entirely covered with water, and the first animals were born in the sea. These shell-fish were able to turn the liquid into solid stone. All calcareous rock was the remains of such animals. Its abundance proved that they must have existed in great quantities and for long periods of time. In many species the individuals, as well as those of the earliest plants and terrestrial animals including man, were enormous in size. Such gigantism was produced by the greater warmth of the earth

14 Buffon, *op. cit.*, vol. i, pp. 125, 136-138, 197-200, 204-208, 271, 273, 274, 289, vol. ii, pp. 60, 66, 67, note p. 70, pp. 86, 191, 327, 328, 426, 429, vol. iii, p. 68, vol. v, pp. 23, 83, 84, 110-113, 115-117, 135-137, 164-166, 205-207, 225.

15 *Ibid.*, vol. i, p. 131, vol. v, pp. 137, 141-147, 151, 152, 157, 166, 183-186, 192, 193, 201, 207.

and by the primitive vigor of nature. As the waters and land cooled, many species became extinct or sought more southern habitats. Buffon logically should have believed in an equivalent and simultaneous creation of animals near the south pole, but his own predilections as an inhabitant of northern lands or the evidence of fossil remains so biased him that when he should have said that animals sought a warmer climate by journeying toward the torrid zone he stated instead that they travelled south. The action of the waters meanwhile formed new subterranean caverns. On the surface of the earth the ocean currents shaped the contours of the mountains and the valleys while the land was at the bottom of the sea. Therefore the sides of valleys were parallel even to their least curves. Further carving of the mountains and such erosion as reduced their altitude had resulted from the rains, winds and frosts after the ocean had receded and had revealed them. The deposition of these strata and the molding of these contours clearly were tasks that required ages.[16]

Buffon reiterated frequently the doctrine that the extent over wide areas of parallel strata with the same thickness and with the same constituents, as well as the later sculpture of the mountain contours proved that the present surface of the land was once the bed of the ocean. The present sea bed resembled in its contours the land now exposed. The whole ocean had a constant general trend from east to west. Tides and currents caused by winds carried sediments from one place to another. The waters formed mountains by the deposition of shells and clays and even of matter, such as

[16] Buffon, *op. cit.*, vol. i, notes pp. 122, 123, pp. 121, 123-125, 128, 130-132, 206, 207, 274, vol. ii, pp. 7-57, note p. 70, pp. 72-86, 90, 91, 163, 170, 171, 226-228, 234, 235, 316, 326-328, 388, 426-430, vol. iii, pp. 56, 57, 69, 70, 168, 169, 171, 185, 186, vol. v, pp. 19-23, 32, 33, 65, 66, 94-96, 110, 116, 117, 133-135, 137-141, 144, 152-159, 163-167, 170-176, 191-193, 201, 206, 207, 218-220, 226-228, 230, 231, 238, 245, 251, 252, 263, 264, 286-296.

vegetable remains, brought down by rivers. Coal resulted
from vegetation thus transported to the sea. Some of the
strata were perhaps laid down on the already sloping sides
of primitive mountains as whitewash was applied to a wall.
The primitive mountains were produced by swellings of the
crust as the earth cooled. Both they and volcanoes contained caverns in abundance. When the vaults over the
caverns fell in, as continually happened, the strata were not
simply cracked, but were also tipped to form new or enlarged
mountains. Some few unstratified mountains and islands,
which were merely the summits of submarine mountains,
resulted from earthquakes, volcanic action or, as he called
it in another place, subterranean fires. Since the winds were
more constant and the tides more violent at the equator than
in higher latitudes, the greater chains of mountains and
the most numerous islands were found there.[17]

As the sea was swallowed by the subterranean caverns and
receded, a period of great volcanic activity eventuated.
There had been and still were submarine eruptions, but these
were quickly extinguished by the quantity of water that
gained access to the fire. However, since the cause of volcanic outbursts was a collision between considerable quantities of water and subterranean fire, followed by the
production of steam, which forced to the surface the molten
matter, the recession of the sea because of marine irruptions
into caverns that contained fire presented ideal conditions
for such occurrences. Especially was this the case on the
borders of the new continents. As the waters receded yet
farther, their access to the stores of subterranean fire was

[17] Buffon, *op. cit.*, vol. i, notes pp. 122, 123, 136-138, 295, 296, pp. 116,
118-121, 123-134, 136-139, 166, 167, 205-208, 236, 271, 273, 274, 281, 283-
290, 296, 297, vol. ii, notes pp. 78-80, 83, pp. 42, 46, 61, 63, 64, 66-71, 75,
87, 90, 91, 219-235, 239, 313-315, 326, 388, 394-401, 405, 425-430, vol. iii,
pp. 29, 42, 43, 55, 58-62, vol. v, pp. 114, 115, 147-151, 193.

impeded; and therefore the effects of such conjunctions had continually decreased and would still further lessen. By 1700 more volcanoes were extinct than active. Buffon did not seem content with his attribution of eruptions to steam, even as generated by the salt water of the sea and subterranean fire. He gave two other causes without any attempt at correlation. They were the spontaneous combustion of inflammable matter in great caverns and its ignition by electric sparks from the central heat. Earthquakes, most of whose causes were connected with volcanic activity, were also diminishing in frequency and intensity.[18]

Even at their greatest these terrible phenomena produced, however, but little effect on the surface of the earth compared with that of the waters. Not only before but also after the emergence of the dry land the waters worked upon it. The sea wore away the coasts or piled up sand banks and dunes, while the rivers and rains, which were the waters from the air, eroded the mountains, filled the valleys and formed deltas and new islands along the coast. Buffon's most novel contribution to the theories concerning the effect of the waters was his belief that the sea, driven by tides and the constant east winds, continually wore away and submerged the eastern coasts of the continents while it built up and receded from the western. Thus the location of the land was constantly altered. It was even possible to observe in the strata sections where dry land had been overwhelmed and later relinquished by the sea. This thesis was perhaps the part of his work most heartily opposed by De Luc, an able contemporary.[19]

[18] Buffon, *op. cit.*, vol. ii, pp. 87, 294-302, 317-321, 324-330, 351-354, 358, 383, 394-401, vol. v, pp. 193-200, 202-206, 220-222, 270, 302, 303.

[19] *Ibid.*, vol. i, pp. 125-129, 139-149, 158-161, 165-167, 279-281, vol. ii, pp. 91, 92, 122, 123, 142-148, 165-170, 203, 204, 208-214, 223, 228, 235-243, 245, 249-252, 259, 260, vol. iii, pp. 7-11, 15-19, 39-62, 66-70, vol. v,

Buffon's theory that the earth was experiencing a continuous reduction of temperature arose from his desire to explain the presence of fossil bones and remains from elephants and other tropical animals in Siberia, northern Europe and North America. He believed all terrestrial animals and plants to have been born in the northern climes as the earth gradually became cool enough to produce them. They were formed successively and not simultaneously, so that the tropical animals had a longer history than those of the temperate zones and the reindeer and other polar animals were comparatively modern. These species of animals were not created in quantities but in pairs because that was sufficient. Their creation and even their growth resulted from the union of innumerable living organic molecules which still were employed in animating successively all beings. If the species were destroyed, the molecules would remain and would form new species. So large a number of the molecules were normally in use in various individual animals as to leave no surplus for the production of new types. The molecules were much more abundant and more active in northern climes than in southern; for the aqueous, oily and ductile particles fell with the waters sooner and in greater quantity there. The molecules were produced by the action of heat upon these particles and developed into organic beings. Each group in turn migrated south as the temperature declined and the southern sections, once too burning to support life, became habitable. At first, the mountain tops were suitable for abodes and later the plains. The land connection between America and the old world, probably by way of Asia, remained unbroken until a recent epoch, as was

pp. 110, 162-167, 186-188, 193, 210-213, 252, 255, 258, 265-267, 270, 282; De Luc, *Lettres physiques et morales sur l'histoire de la terre et de l'homme* (The Hague and Paris, 1779, 1780), vol. i, pp. 377-423, vol. ii, pp. 141, 177, 244, 245, vol. iv, pp. 107-109, 128, 134, 135 and note pp. 135-137, vol. v, pp. 388, 389.

proved by the resemblances in fossil bones, especially those of elephants, that were disinterred in the two hemispheres. Buffon even suggested that the connection still existed between the seventieth and seventy-fifth degrees of latitude. Siberia was the first district populated. Even man came into being on the high lands of Asia between the fortieth and the fifty-fifth degrees of latitude, and there evolved an unusual civilization. Buffon rhapsodized over this golden age of knowledge in both the arts and the sciences, when such erudite information as that six hundred solar years equaled exactly 7421 lunar months was discovered. Most of this wisdom was blotted out by the earliest invasion of barbarians from the north and had only lately been recovered. Like so many of their successors and like the animals that had preceded them, the barbarians had been driven south by the increasing cold.[20] Some of the species at first created had become extinct because of the diminishing heat, but those which had remained were unchanged in their general characteristics, though their size had lessened. Even of men there were races of giants until the time of King David. These were still extant only in Patagonia.[21]

Buffon's theory resembled Leibnitz's, though he differed

[20] Buffon, op. cit., vol. ii, pp. 146, 147, vol. v, pp. 30-33, 49-66, 155-158, 221, 225-238, 240, 242-245, 247, 248, 251-256, 263-265, 271-273, 305-315, 322-329, 346-348. De Luc, *op. cit.*, vol. v, pp. 517-611, refuted this theory of the earth's refrigeration and the migration of elephants. The suggestion that America was still joined to Asia Cockburn thought highly probable and Warren had considered possible. Catoir had said that it was probably cut off by the flood, as England was from Norway and Ireland from Gaul. Cockburn, *An Enquiry into the Truth and Certainty of the Mosaic Deluge* (London, 1750), p. 134; Warren, *Geologia* (London, 1690), pp. 248-251; Catoir, *Disputatio Theologica de Arca Noachi et Diluvio* (Gröningen, 1704), sec. xvii.

[21] Buffon, *op. cit.*, vol. v, pp. 32, 33, 65, 66, 134, 135, 138, 228, 230, 231, 234, 238, 242, 243, 271, 272, 286-296. In volume xv, pp. 417, 418, he suggested, however, that American animals, migrating from the old world, had been changed by climate etc. to new species.

from him in some particulars. He discussed the doctrines of his recent predecessors and showed their blunders. His summaries were, on the whole, fair, although some of his statements were erroneous, as when he attributed the date of 1708 to Whiston's theory. Incidentally he mentioned the great applause with which Whiston's hypotheses were received. He discussed the systems of Whiston, Burnet and Woodward in greatest detail, though he also dwelt on those by Leibnitz, Scheuchzer, Steno and Ray and expounded the sketch of a theory by M. Bourget, who died before it could be developed. It was the opposite of Buffon's since it declared the earth to be gradually burning up. The fire would increase until the whole sphere was turned to metals and calcined materials by a terrible explosion and general conflagration. Buffon's attitude towards his opponents was somewhat contemptuous. He spoke of Scheuchzer's *Physica Sacra* as a puerile work fit to amuse children.[22]

Buffon's vagueness, constant repetitions and occasional contradictions make him a source of annoyance to a modern reader; but the overpowering magnitude of his twenty-six or more volumes, the ease of his style, perhaps even the incoherence in some of his conceptions stimulated approbation on the part of his contemporaries. They admired his book as a work of enormous erudition, whose constituent parts could, at the same time, be easily comprehended. The result was great popularity and considerable influence, especially among the less scientific of his audience. Probably gratitude is due him, however, for the popularization, on which later scientists could build, of many scientific facts, such as the formation of the strata by the sea.

[22] Buffon, *op. cit.*, vol. i, pp. 104, 105, 209-241, vol. ii, pp. 313-315. Bourget's work appeared in a memoir printed in 1729 at Amsterdam, published together with his *Lettres philosophiques sur la formation des sels etc.*

CHAPTER XXII

French Theories of the Mid-century

THE middle of the eighteenth century saw the publication of four books on cosmology, three of which contained a mixture of fantastic propositions with scientific observation. The last of the four was in fundamental contradiction to every important theory promulgated during the seventeenth and the eighteenth centuries. All four were French in authorship.

Benoist De Maillet (1656-1738) wrote a book in two volumes that was published in 1748.[1] He asserted that his theory agreed with that of Moses on the formation of the globe and of all living things. His bizarre opinions, which he attributed to an Indian philosopher Telliamed, an anagram of his name, were so popular that several editions were published, and the book was translated into English in 1750. De Maillet was French consul general in Egypt for sixteen years and later lived on the shores of the Mediterranean, especially at Marseilles. He mistook the retreat of the sea in Egypt, which is the effect of delta-building by the Nile, for a general lowering of the sea-level. Some of his doctrines were among those already mentioned as increasingly popular with scientific thinkers. For example, he declared that the surface of the land was once the sea-bottom. There the strata were formed, especially those containing marine fossils. The cause he gave for the present position of the land was not equally sound. He asserted that the

[1] *Telliamed, ou entretiens d'un philosophe Indien, sur la diminution de la mer, avec un missionnaire François.* De Luc quoted from the edition published at the Hague in 1755.

mountains, which had been shaped by the sea currents, and the continents had been revealed by evaporation of the water. Even yet the water was being evaporated at the rate of three feet in a thousand years. De Maillet was audacious in his suggestion that some fossil marine species might have perished through the vaporization of the waters in their habitat.[2]   This was contrary to the almost unanimous verdict that no new species had been formed since creation and that none had been destroyed.[3]

[2] De Luc, *Lettres physiques et morales sur l'histoire de la terre et de l'homme* (The Hague and Paris, 1779, 1780), vol. ii, pp. 270-293, 307.

[3] A few who upheld the dogma that there were no new species and none annihilated were the following: Hakewill, *An Apologie or Declaration of the Power and Providence of God in the Gouernment of the World* (Oxford, 1635) (3d ed.), pt. ii, pp. 19, 20; Kircher, *Arca Noë* (Amsterdam, 1675), pp. 49-51, 75, 76, 94-97, who said that species seemed new because of changes due to climate and to cross-breeding; Ray, *Three Physico-Theological Discourses* (London, 1693), note before p. 132, pp. 147-151, 330; Stillingfleet, *Origines Sacrae* (London, 1709), pt. ii, p. 19; Cockburn, *An Enquiry into the Truth and Certainty of the Mosaic Deluge* (London, 1750), p. 42. On the other hand, Buffon, *cf. supra,* pp. 216, 217, denied both that no new species had come into existence since creation and that none had been destroyed. He also believed in changes due to domestication, climate, etc. De Luc was at first careful to use the word " perhaps " in asserting a destruction of species, but later declared that some species of fossils had definitely vanished. He also believed in a change of species by environment, as of salt water to fresh water fish. De Luc, *op. cit.,* vol. ii, pp. 531, 532, vol. v, pp. 513-516, 613, 664, 666, 667; De Luc, *Letters on the Physical History of the Earth* (London, 1831), letter iii, pp. 129, 132, 133, letter iv, pp. 155, 156, 159, 160, 178, letter v, pp. 185, 191, 194, 215, letter vi, pp. 238, 239. In 1678 Lister declared that some marine fossils were representatives of lost species, Jéhan, *Dictionnaire de cosmogonie et de paléontologie* (Paris, 1854), art. " Géologie (Histoire de la)", col. 618. Robert Hooke was inconsistent and spoke on both sides, but chiefly on the side of past extinction of species, Hooke, *Oeuvres posth.* (1705), especially p. 327 and lecture du 29 mai, 1689 before the Royal Society, quoted by Jéhan, *op. cit., art. cit.,* cols. 620-622. The opinion of an extinction of species was accepted much earlier in England, perhaps because of numerous examples, than in Italy, where so many of the fossils in museums resembled animals

Telliamed's theory that sea animals became land animals by degrees inspired amusement in a famous contemporary, Voltaire. De Maillet declared that all the space of air and opaque bodies and even such parts of stars as were not yet on fire were filled with seeds of everything having the possibility of life. They were most abundant in the thick air and the waters surrounding the opaque bodies. With great difficulty animals and plants might be and were produced by the heat of the sun in mud or waters disposed to fecundity. As the sea receded, they became terrestrial. Though a million individuals perished, it was enough for the species if two of opposite sex survived. Telliamed believed in

still extant in neighboring waters. Moro and his commentator, Generelli, did not allude to the subject. Evidently even by 1750 the belief in extinction was not accepted in Italy. Scilla hesitated to adopt it. Jéhan, *op. cit., art. cit.*, col. 634. Maupertuis arrived at the conclusion, which he called too bold a conjecture for some, that species had been destroyed by sundry catastrophes, from a consideration of fossils and from a hypothesis that originally all species formed a chain of beings. The neighboring groups were very similar. Present conditions showed great gaps in this chain, which must be due to the loss of intermediate species. Maupertuis, *Essay de cosmologie* (Paris? or Amsterdam?, 1750), pp. 128-130. The idea of changes due to environment was widely held, though generally without the realization that this evolutionary doctrine implied a change of species. Besides those already mentioned, Sir Walter Raleigh felt that such variations had occurred as in the color of blackbirds, Raleigh, *The History of the World* (Edinburgh, 1820) (1st ed., 1614), vol. i, pp. 233, 234. Burnet and the anonymous author of the *Universal History* explained the hue of negroes as the result of environment and the inheritance of acquired characteristics. They thought that only a few generations were needed for so radical a change. Burnet, *The Sacred Theory of the World* (London, 1722) (5th ed.), vol. i, bk. ii, pp. 261, 262; *An Universal History, from the Earliest Account of Time to the Present* (Dublin, 1744), vol. i, pp. 47, 48. Leibnitz explained in the same way the apparent disappearance of fossils like the Ammonites, now considered extinct. Leibnitz, *Opera Omnia* (Geneva, 1768), vol. ii, *Protogaea* (1st ed., 1691 or 1693 or 1683), p. 220. De Maillet also accepted these environmental changes. De Luc, *Lettres physiques et morales sur l'histoire de la terre et de l'homme* (The Hague and Paris, 1779, 1780), vol. ii, pp. 337-343 (Wrongly numbered pp. 407-413).

changes of form, really of species, as from water animals to birds. All kinds of birds resembled in form, color and inclinations the varieties of fish from which they and flies were derived and which still existed. As to quadrupeds, they were similar in figure and inclinations to water animals yet existent, such as sea monkeys, sea lions, sea cows, horses, dogs, cats, pigs, camels, wolves, goats and sheep. Quadrupeds, birds and fish all looked alike. From time to time new species were produced in the sea and later emerged on land. Contemporary monsters were probably from the sea. They had escaped or been thrown up on the land. Telliamed, to prove his idea that men also came from the sea, mentioned the common tradition of Tritons or sea men and various tales of such creatures. Monkeys, especially orang-outangs, were to him wild men. As another proof he referred to the authority of Homer, who declared that Ocean and Thetis were the parents of the gods.[4] The truth at the base of this fable was that " 'these memorable men . . . of whom the Barbarism of the first ages has made Gods, owed their origin to the Sea.' "[5] Man's skin was still covered with little scales like a carp's, as could be seen under the microscope. Even yet water and immersion therein healed the sick and gave vigor to those in health. The most suitable locality for migrations from sea to land was in cold countries where the air was filled with fog much of the year and not very different in humidity and temperature from the sea. This was the reason for the multitudes of men with which the northern countries of Europe and Asia had inundated the southern. Men still continued to emerge from the deep; but they were wild; and, if they saw anything extraordinary, they fled in fear back to the abyss. The negroes had lately arisen

[4] De Luc, *op. cit.*, vol. ii, pp. 308, 327, 333-354, 370-376.

[5] De Maillet, *op. cit.*, tome ii, p. 245, quoted by De Luc, *op. cit.*, vol. ii, p. 377.

thence and the barbarous tribes in Greenland and Spitz-bergen.[6]

Telliamed asserted the discovery in the rocks of fossil ships, anchors and other human relics. On the basis of the rate he assigned for the diminution of the sea, and the height at which artifacts of pottery were found, he declared that man had existed on earth four hundred thousand years or more. Telliamed had some comments to offer on the irregularities of the earth's surface. He attributed the twisted strata of some mountains to a strong impulsion while the substance was still almost liquid. The nearly perpendicular strata of other high mountains resulted from the overturn of hills that were originally formed with strata slightly inclined. When they were undermined by currents at their feet, their strata slid and sank so that the layers became perpendicular. On the other hand, such mountains might have been formed in that position. The waters beat against their inner cores and deposited layers of matter as a perpendicular wall was whitewashed with successive coats.[7]

As for the universe as a whole, Telliamed believed that every celestial system had a central body. This was an ardent globe, whose rays caused the surrounding opaque bodies to rotate and to revolve about the inner sphere. During the process the rays lifted from the opaque bodies dust and water particles, which they carried through the ethereal fluid and deposited at the extremities of the vortex because there their own activity became weakened. All celestial bodies passed through three stages. At first each burned as the center of a system and made other globes revolve around it. Then it was extinguished and because of its lightness was carried to the extreme verge of the sphere of activity pertaining to another fiery body. There

[6] De Luc, *op. cit.*, vol. ii, pp. 377-381.

[7] *Ibid.*, vol. ii, pp. 312-319.

it received the particles of water and dust from opaque bodies nearer the heart of the vortex and was flooded by them. Then, as it reapproached the center, after the extinction of the central body and the substitution for it of the nearest planet, it commenced to lose its humidity. The sea gradually evaporated; and, when dry land appeared, the rays of the central star acted on the mud and shallow water and brought to birth aquatic plants and animals, which little by little became terrestrial. Finally, after the water had wholly evaporated, the globe burned anew and became the center of the vortex. When our earth entered the vortex of the sun, it acquired the moon, which was already there. That globe recognized a stronger body, and was obliged to turn around our sphere. De Maillet affirmed that the length of man's life was always the same in reality because it depended upon his nature. The traditions of his living nine hundred to a thousand years arose because of the difference in the orbit of the earth by which years were differentiated. The antediluvian sun, which ruled the earth at that era, was smaller than the present one, or the activity of its fire was so weak that the earth could circle around it in sixty days or less. The carrying off of Europa by Jupiter in the form of a bull and the fall of Icarus when a sun melted the wax of his wings showed clearly that Europe had passed through the seas and that our earth had fallen from the vortex of an ancient sun into that where was located our moon.[8]

Du Luc gave a similar account of another contemporary system, that of M. Le Catt, Secretary of the Academy of Rouen, which appeared in 1750. It was much simpler. At creation matter was arranged according to specific gravity

[8] De Luc, *op. cit.*, vol. ii, pp. 326-333, 354. The total discussion and criticism of De Maillet occurred pp. 267-386. De Maillet's own book seems to be very rare.

(apparently in subsidence from a chaos) so that the heaviest parts were nearest the center of the earth. Therefore the water surrounded a smooth sphere of earth. It would have retained this shape forever had not the Creator formed the moon and placed it in our vortex. This luminary caused tides, whose agitation raised the mud at the bottom into heaps as banks of sand were raised by storms. The valleys between were at length sufficiently spacious so that all the water was drained into them and the continents emerged. By similar actions of the tides the continents were gradually enlarged. The remains of terrestrial animals that had perished in floods were deposited in the borders of the land before it was uncovered. The tides continued to form depressions and eminences but less conspicuously since the earth was more solid. The sea, however, constantly dug its bed deeper and threw out matter on the shores. Finally the seas of the two hemispheres would meet in the center of the earth, and the crust would be weakened and fall in. The new chaos thus produced would again develop a solid core covered by water, and a new world would be formed in a similar way.[9]

During the same year, 1750, Pierre Louis Moreau de Maupertuis (1698-1759) published his *Essai de cosmologie*. He was a famous mathematician and astronomer and had been sent by Louis XV in 1736 as chief of the expedition to Lapland to measure a degree of longitude. His selection in 1746 as President for the Royal Academy of Sciences in Berlin added weight to his opinion. His account of what might be expected from a comet which should hit or approach closely to a planet, together with the paper of Joseph-Jérôme Le Français de Lalande (1732-1807) on the same subject, which was erroneously thought to predict such an event,

[9] De Luc, *op. cit.*, vol. ii, pp. 179-182. The whole account and De Luc's answers were on pp. 179-194.

caused a serious panic in Paris in 1774. The police were forced to interfere and demanded a sight of Lalande's memoir. From lack of time it had not been read at the meeting for which it was prepared. Though the publication of the paper was ordered by the police, the public believed that the fatal prediction had been omitted so as not to announce an unavoidable catastrophe. A comet in 1775 was apparently feared.[10]

Most of Maupertuis's theories were scientifically sound, but some showed the influence of the century's pseudo-cosmologies. He declared that the sun was a large and luminous globe around which moved the six planets and the comets. The matter of the sun was light itself. The stars were like our sun and were probably encircled by planets and comets. The planets were, in all likelihood, inhabited by living beings; but it was rash to undertake to divine their natures. Formerly all species formed a chain with very slight differences between neighboring groups, but this had been broken by some such catastrophe as might be the effect of a comet. The proof of this event in our planet was furnished by marine fossils in inland mountains and by broken and disordered strata. The satellites of the planets were of immediate use to man. Those of Jupiter, because they helped us to calculate the difference in meridians, were important for geography and for navigation. One of Maupertuis's most interesting ideas was that apparently empty spaces in the sky were those where the stars were less luminous and much smaller, or perhaps flattened like disks

[10] Maupertuis, *Essay de cosmologie* (Paris? or Amsterdam?, 1750), pp. 124-126; Maupertuis, *Lettre sur la comète de 1742* (Paris, 1742), written to a lady; Lalande, *Réflexions sur les comètes qui peuvent approcher de la terre* (Paris?, 1774?); Delambre, *Histoire de l'astronomie au dix-huitième siècle* (Paris, 1827), pp. 364, 365, 558, 559. The account of Maupertuis and his work occurred *ibid.*, pp. 352-368, especially pp. 352, 363-367, of Lalande, pp. 547-621.

so that we saw them only when they turned to us their sides rather than their edges. This or the intervention and the removal of planets which circled around the stars was his explanation of new and variable stars.[11]

The following year, 1751, saw the publication of another small book, *Le monde, son origine, et son antiquité. De l'ame, et de son immortalité. Essai sur la chronologie.* It was anonymous, but the author was apparently well known to be M. de Mirabaud. Perhaps it is not surprising that he did not acknowledge the work in France during his lifetime, since its chief thesis made the world much older than chronologists stated. Although Mirabaud denied its eternity, that seemed to be his secret belief. Especially he doubted the creation of matter from nothing, and probably believed in the eternity of matter if not of the universe. He declared that in all early languages the word create really meant form or develop. Though he affirmed that the earth was made by an intelligent being, his editor in 1778 declared that he believed in the eternity of the earth and of mankind. He adopted the heliocentric system, which he called the Copernican, and asserted that its acceptance was universal, though the Bible plainly promulgated the geocentric astronomy. He even correlated the earth so completely with the other planets as to accept planetary inhabitants.[12] Later he said that the Scriptural acceptance of the primitive cosmological system and the miracles of the sun's delay for Joshua and of the shadow's recession for Hezekiah, both of which he himself probably rejected,[13] proved " that for Physics, as for

[11] Maupertuis, *Essay de cosmologie* (Paris? or Amsterdam?, 1750), pp. 90-104, 113, 127-136; Delambre, *op. cit.*, pp. 364, 365.

[12] (Mirabaud), *Le monde, son origine, et son antiquité. De l'ame, et de son immortalité. Essai sur la chronologie* (London, 1778) (2d ed.), pp. v, x, xi, pt. i, pp. 15-17, 40-42, 128-134, pt. ii, pp. 129-150, 160-163.

[13] *Ibid.*, pt. ii, pp. 161-163.

Historical detail of events, the Bible is apparently not our sole & only rule." [14]   The ancients never believed that they could give the date of creation; the Jews, bolder, were the only ones who undertook to do so; other nations ridiculed them for the attempt.   Then he proved that the record was wholly unreliable.   Even the Bible was inconsistent about dates; and the three versions of the Hebrew, the Samaritan and the Septuagint had caused an impossible confusion among chronologists.   The Jews borrowed their ideas from Chaldeans, Egyptians and Phoenicians.   The theory that the other nations drew theirs from the books of Moses was absolutely impossible.   The spirit mentioned in the account of creation by Phoenicians and Jews was the same thing as the Eros of the Greeks.   The universality of the flood he rejected, and attributed the similar statement in the story of Deucalion to his ignorance of the rest of the world.[15]

None of these four treatises had much influence upon the trend of thought, probably because such hypotheses as were original were bizarre.   Nevertheless, they show the attitude of educated Frenchman during the reign of Louis XV. Marvellous pseudo-scientific cosmologies enjoyed an unaccustomed vogue, as well as the new social doctrines better known to posterity.

[14] " Que pour la Physique, comme pour le détail Historique des événemens, l'Ecriture n'est pas apparemment notre seule & unique regle." (Mirabaud), *op. cit.*, pt. ii, p. 164, also pt. ii, pp. 152-165.

[15] *Ibid.*, pt. i, pp. 8, 9, 38-44, 95-104, pt. ii, pp. 150, 151, 166-181.

CHAPTER XXIII

The Deluge, and the Earth it Submerged

THE problem concerning the universality of the flood greatly exercised the intellects of men during these two centuries, especially since the difficulty of explaining the existence in America of pernicious animals and those unlike the animals in the old world was obvious. The chief argument in its favor, other than the authority of the Scriptures, was the wide spread of fossils. Almost without exception they were attributed to the deluge. Nevertheless, the obstacle of insufficient water seemed insurmountable to many. Isaac Vossius (1618-1685) [1] was perhaps the most famous exponent of a partial deluge in the seventeenth century; but there were many others including Edward Stillingfleet, Bishop of Worcester; [2] and the next century saw another bishop in agreement with that view, the Lord Bishop of Clogher, [3] and a Mr. Coetlogon, whose *Universal History of Arts and Sciences* contained an article on Antediluvians [4] that aroused Patrick Cockburn's wrath. Generally this doctrine was linked with the idea that men were limited in

[1] In *De Vera Aetate Mundi* (The Hague, 1661) (2nd ed.).

[2] Stillingfleet, *Origines Sacrae* (London, 1709) (1st ed., 1697), pt. i, pp. 337-339.

[3] Robert Clayton (1695-1758), *A Vindication of the Histories of the Old and New Testament in answer to the objections of the late Lord Bolingbroke* (Dublin, 1752, 1754). The second part inspired an answer by Catcott. *Cf. infra*, p. 234.

[4] Cockburn, *An Enquiry into the Truth and Certainty of the Mosaic Deluge* (London, 1750), pp. 10-20, 198, 199, 339-344, 348-355 *etc.*

number and had not spread far.   A flood which covered only part of Asia would suffice for their destruction.   Sometimes, as in the case of Coetlogon, there was apparently a belief that a few men other than the Noachidae had escaped.   Innumerable books and treatises were published, and sermons were preached on both sides.   Those who favored a universal flood realized the necessity for the production of sufficient water without a new creation of matter, since this hypothesis was anathema to all, and felt themselves compelled to postulate a theory of the earth and its creation that should solve the difficulty.   So Burnet, Whiston and Woodward, with their compeers, felt that their account of creation must also explain the flood.   Two more illustrations of this tendency may suffice: *An Enquiry into the Truth and Certainty of the Mosaic Deluge* by Patrick Cockburn (1678-1749), published in 1750, and *A Treatise on the Deluge* by Alexander Catcott (1725-1779) in 1761.[5]

Cockburn began by the declaration that he would omit any reference to Moses as divinely authoritative, since some critics denied the claim, and would treat him only as a historian similar to the Greek or Roman historians.   He accepted the earth's diurnal and annual motion as a truism, with the remark that such motion was more marvellous than the deluge.[6]   Both creation and the deluge happened in the spring.   The Biblical narrative made clear their occurrence at the same season (Gen. 7: 11; 8: 13, 14).   The fact that Adam apparently found ripe fruits implied merely that the season was not winter since there were spring and summer as well as autumnal fruits.   For the conclusion of the flood, which lasted a complete twelvemonth, spring was a more suitable season, because it would provide immediate suste-

[5] The second edition, considerably enlarged, was printed in 1768. The first edition contained 296 pages; the second, 423 pages.

[6] Cockburn, *op. cit.*, pp. 2, 3.

nance for man and beast and permit preparation for the
winter, and because spring was the more natural period for
the birth of animals. All early nations except the Egyptians,
whose influence probably misled the Jews, began their year in
the spring, as astronomers still did. Finally, Woodward
had proved by a study of fossil plants that they must have
been uprooted in May. Because the prediluvial world was
more fertile than ours, the season was perhaps more advanced; but it was clearly spring. This line of argument
invalidated Whiston's astronomical calculations that attempted to prove the deluge due to the approach of Halley's
comet. It was of course granted by all that the world began
at either the vernal or the autumnal equinox.[7]

At creation everything settled somewhat in accordance
with its specific gravity. Though the earth had mountains,
which were made before the third day, it was completely
beneath the waters. This was why Moses called it invisible.
Light was created on the first day, but Cockburn did not
attempt to explain the meaning of this. On the second day,
after the firmament had removed part of the water, there was
still enough to cover the earth. The firmament was the air
and also the place of the sun, moon and stars. Part of the
primeval waters were lifted into the air as thin vapors or
thick clouds. The waters above the firmament, whence
came the rain at the flood, were therefore obviously the
clouds.[8] On the third day, most of the liquid subsided into
a subterranean abyss, which formed the great deep mentioned by Moses. Cockburn gave several proofs of such an
abyss within the earth. This reservoir, which communicated
by certain " Hiatus's " with the open seas and lakes, was part
of the source for springs and rivers, and was the second
cause of the deluge. He said that the phenomena of springs

---

[7] Cockburn, *op. cit.*, pp. 46, 47, 300, 312-329.

[8] *Ibid.*, pp. 236, 260-263, 267-271, 295, 310.

proved also a subterranean heat,[9] and quoted, though with disapproval, Dr. Halley's supposition that the center of the hollow earth contained a " Globe of Loadstone or lesser earth " and the space between it and the crust was " filled with a subtle luminous vapour, by which he accounted for both the variations of the Compass, and the *Aurora-Borealis.*" [10] From the abyss the water emerged, probably after earthquakes in various places had cracked the surface of sea and land; and to it, by the same cracks, most of the water returned at the end of the flood, though some was re-evaporated and enough was left on the surface of the earth greatly to increase the area of lakes and seas.   The Psalms mentioned thunder and lightning at the creation to hasten the disappearance of the water into the abyss, and Cockburn suggested like phenomena at the commencement and the conclusion of the deluge.   The oceans as well as the waters of the clouds and of the abyss were transported over the land, since they left manifest remains in mountains and valleys.[11]

Vossius and Stillingfleet had claimed that at creation all lands had their own animals, which had been created in quantity, but Cockburn denied their conclusion.   Vegetables, unlike animals, differed and would not grow in some climates and soils; hence God furnished every country in the beginning with proper plants; but animals had the power of movement and instincts to discover food and to preserve themselves.   No more than one pair of each kind was created at first.   That was enough in the case of man, and after the

[9] Cockburn, *op. cit.*, pp. 236, 271-277, 310, 311.

[10] *Ibid.*, p. 311, quoting the *Philosophical Transactions*, nos. 148, 195; Royal Society of London, *Philosophical Transactions* (London, 1665-1933), Halley, " On the cause of the Change in the Variation of the Magnetic Needle; with an Hypothesis of the Structure of the Internal Parts of the Earth," no. 195, art. 3, p. 563 of the vol. for 1692.

[11] *Ibid.*, pp. 257, 291-306, 308-312.

flood enough for the unclean animals at least. Had more
been created, their progeny would soon have swamped mankind. That even so they nearly overwhelmed men was shown
by the great number of fossils, which suggested to Woodward that the flood was needed to relieve an overcrowded
earth. Moreover, after the flood, when the descendants of
Noah came to Shinaar, the offspring of the pairs of unclean
animals in the ark had already become so numerous as to be
a pest and a menace, and to necessitate hunting.[12]

As the animals came of their own accord to the ark, so
God brought them to Adam for names. All species were
preserved in the ark because it was God's will that all once
created should continue so long as the earth remained.[13] In
mentioning the difficulties of regulating the calendar if the
antediluvians did not have a leap year, Cockburn said, " It
is highly probable then, that God would have instructed
Adam in this, as well as other necessary things, if he could
not find out this use by his own observation." [14] Cockburn
suggested that perhaps Eve was not created till after the sixth
day; and, more confidently, that probably the fall was not
immediate, but perhaps after the lapse of two or three years,
since Adam and Eve must have had time to reflect and to
know their condition before God would expose them to
temptation.[15] As to the state of the antediluvian earth,
Cockburn rejected the opinion, which he called general, that
the axis was untipped and that there was a perpetual equinox,
but said that no one doubted its exceeding fertility and
beauty. The plough was invented only after the flood; it
was unnecessary before. The first hills and mountains were
covered with verdure, and produced food for men and

---

[12] Cockburn, *op. cit.*, pp. 27, 36-38, 73, 116-119, 127-129, 131, 134.

[13] *Ibid.*, pp. 42, 124, 125, 134, 224, 225.

[14] *Ibid.*, p. 327.   [15] *Ibid.*, pp. 95, 96.

animals. After the expulsion from Paradise, however, fruits were not sufficient for food since those outside the garden were not so nutritious as those within. Therefore man was allowed bread also, raised by toil, but was not permitted flesh food until after the flood. Cockburn enthusiastically affirmed the doctrine of antediluvian longevity. At the deluge the surface soil, especially on the uplands, was washed off and left barren rocks and sandy deserts. The flood mixed sand, gravel, stone and other debris with the rich, fertile soil that had produced spontaneously. Additional results of the deluge were the increased size of the seas, which had existed from the beginning; and the appearance of marshes and of great lakes.[16]

Catcott, although he was primarily interested in the flood, gave some suggestions about creation. He summed up his conclusions by the statement that the Mosaic account dealing with the manner of the creation and of the deluge was " philosophically just and literally true: and therefore that the biblical philosophy is strictly consistent with nature." [17] He claimed to have " found such a surprisingly-exact agreement between " the works of nature and the word of God, " that they tallied like two indentures, so as to leave no doubt that the author of one was the inditer of the other ";[18] and he devoted many pages to a really scientific exposition of the natural phenomena that he thought bore on the subject, notably fossils, the position of strata, the formation of valleys by running water and the location of loose stones on their slopes and at their mouths. The occasion of his book was the publication of that by the Bishop of Clogher.[19] It was an attempted refutation of the episcopal theses.

[16] Cockburn, op. cit., pp. 48-70, 96, 143-149, 151-154, 156-182.

[17] Catcott, A Treatise on the Deluge (London, 1768) (2nd ed.), p. 411.

[18] Ibid., p. vii.

[19] Cf. supra, p. 229.

God made use of natural causes to form and to reform the earth from a chaotic,—that is, a dissolved, state. Catcott seemed to favor Hutchinson's theories in the matter, but added a few of his own. He proved by experiments that such regular subsidence as was evinced by the present condition of the strata must have required an immensely great quantity of water and very fine subdivisions of matter.[20] The " darkness " was the "dark torpid Air." [21] The Spirit of God was the first agent to reduce the formless terrestrial mass into shape. The word for Spirit was usually translated wind, or air in motion. It acted upon the surface of the fluid, turbid mass; and naturally, by compression, it formed the confused lump into a sphere; but it was too gross to penetrate or to alter the interior. Hence light was next produced. This was universally agreed to be a material substance with " *motion immensely swift and strong* " so that no terrestrial bodies could prevent its passage through their pores. The airs or grosser part of the heavens, the Spirit, even to the present day pressed chiefly on the surface, while the finer, purer, more ethereal part, the light, pervaded the inmost recesses. A stream of light was constantly coming from the fire at the sun into the earth, chiefly in the torrid zone, where it agitated and expanded the waters of the abyss so that to make room it expelled some matter. The matter in the form of vapors was forced up through the fissures in the crust. This light which expanded the abysmal waters may be what Catcott entitled the subterranean heat or fire.[22] He called light " the most subtile as well as the most powerful of any [agent] in nature." It " passes freely

---

[20] Catcott, *op. cit.*, pp. 5, 6, 51, 53, 86, 280-408 *etc.*, note pp. 79 and 80.

[21] *Ibid.*, p. 52.

[22] *Ibid.*, pp. 52-54, 86-89, 91, 92, 200-204, 375. Catcott's father, whose paraphrase of Psalm 104 was published in his son's book, *ibid.*, pp. 419, 420, 423.

through the hardest and closest of terrestrial substances, and when its atoms are collected in a focus, will separate and dissolve the parts of the most compact body. Here then are two very powerful Agents [Spirit and light]; one that displays itself principally by *pressure,* the other by *penetration.*" [23] They were absolutely powerful when directed by such a master as God. The command of God for the formation of the firmament in the midst of the waters,—that is, of the fluid, chaotic earth, not the heavens, was an order to both natural agents to act upon the globe.[24] Wherever both were present, " there would of course be a *struggle* between them, and this struggle would produce an *Expansion,* this expansion a division, and so on." The meaning of the command was,

Let the *Light* and *Spirit* expand and diffuse themselves, and let them press into the mixture, called *Waters;* and let them act *in, among,* or *between* the *parts* of it, and drive the solid parts together, and thereby make a *separation,* and with the parts separated a *division* or wall between the waters,

so that half were on each side.[25] The earth had been created void and empty,—that is, filled with air, " as every *hollow* place in the earth at present is *filled.* As soon therefore as the light had reached this *central* or *inward* air, there would instantly commence a conflict between them, or a struggling this way and that as from a center," as in a bladder half-full of air brought near a fire.[26] Meanwhile the light and air on the outside were pressing downwards, so that the solid parts or the earth would be driven into a shell or crust and " *fluids* be permitted to slip . . . on *each* side of this crust." [27]

[23] Catcott, *op. cit.,* p. 55.   [24] *Ibid.,* p. 55.
[25] *Ibid.,* p. 56.
[26] *Ibid.,* p. 56.
[27] *Ibid.,* p. 57.

Catcott drew a plan which represented the earth at the close of the second day of creation and at the corresponding period after the deluge. There was a circular band that portrayed the earth's shell. Both its convex and its concave edges were bounded by other bands representing the waters, those below and those above the firmament respectively. Still farther outside and inside was located the expanse or air. The power of the expanse came from God. At first the air was dark and still, but then its motion produced light.[28]

To let the dry land appear, the waters on the surface were united to those within.[29]

As the matter of the heavens would be more and more melted down by the intense fire at the focus of the primaeval light, so would the strength of the Expansion be increased, in proportion to the quantity of matter melted, and the degree of agitation; and how great its force must have been on this, the *third* day, may be partly gathered from the extent of its sphere on the fourth, which reached by that time the other *orbs,* and even the fixed *stars.*

Evidently Catcott did not feel that the Mosaic account included the creation of those heavenly bodies.

The Light and Spirit having such an immense sphere of action, and acting very powerfully near the earth (as is certain from the quick growth of *vegetables,* &c. on this, the *third* day) would press strongly upon the outward surface of it; and by the continual and new admission of light, through the shell to the central air, the *inward expansion* would be vastly heightened and increased

and would act more forcibly against the inner surface.[30] The crust would crack in many places, water would rush or be

---

[28] Catcott, *op. cit.,* Plate between pp. 56 and 57, pp. 57-61.

[29] *Ibid.,* pp. 61-63.

[30] *Ibid.,* p. 62.

pressed down and air would emerge. In the process the waters would furrow the land, which had previously formed a perfect sphere, and make mountains and valleys, the slopes of which would extend down into the depths of the sea and the openings into the abyss. Of course, some openings were on land; but there the waters did not cause such high mountains as near the sea because the locality where they subsided underground was not far below the summits. The waters would be united and form the great abyss mentioned so frequently in the Bible.[31] The abyss was the source of springs, and was connected with the lakes and seas by openings in their beds. The passage of the water through these openings caused a perpetual circulation of the water within the abyss itself. The form of the abyss was spherical since it was bounded by the concave surface of the earth's crust. It was not subdivided into caverns. Near the center was a ball of rather loose terrestrial matter, torn off by the waters in their withdrawal and carried down thither. This was the central body to which Halley attributed magnetic effects. The shell of the earth was not rent to pieces by the retreating waters because the ascending air impeded their descent and lessened their speed, so that they left gentle undulations of hills and valleys rather than precipices and broken rocks.[32] This state of the earth was represented by a second plate, opposite page 97, which showed fragments of earth, resting on water. The water broke through the crust in many places to form seas and lakes. In smaller channels the waters were shown rising to the tops of the mountains, whence they issued forth as rivers. Still more minute cracks represented the passages where "*vapours* principally ascend." Vegetation

---

[31] Gen. 49:25; Deut. 33:13; Eccles. 1:7; Ps. 24:1; 136; Prov. 8:27; Job 38:4; 26:10; Catcott, *op. cit.*, pp. 43-50, 62, 63, 89, 335-359.

[32] *Ibid.*, pp. 43-50, 63, 87-91, 168-246, 260, 280, 356, 357, 385-387, 394. *Cf.* also *supra*, p. 232.

on earth flourished only because of such cracks and vapors. The air surrounded the whole sphere; and the solid nucleus of earth, which had been torn off, was portrayed at the center.[33]

To cause the deluge the only necessary action was for God to increase the air pressure on the seas.   Then the air forced the ocean waters into the abyss.   It followed them thither, and expelled both the waters of the abyss and those of the ocean upon the surface of the land.   The waters in their tumultuous exit rent the crust, unquestionably with an earthquake, and dissolved everything, beginning with the central ball, which was less firm than the outer crust.   The cracks through which the water emerged were the windows of heaven that were opened at the deluge.   Though Catcott had declared the dissolution of the earth due to the waters, he also stated with no explanation of the inconsistency that it was largely caused by the passage of the air.   The air enlarged the pores through which it travelled.   Since organic matter offered no resistance to its passage, it demolished merely mineral and metallic bodies.   For this reason no antediluvian object of human construction was discoverable.   Another cause for the preservation of plant and animal structures was that their fibers were intertwined, while inorganic matter consisted of atoms whose surfaces were merely in apposition.   Besides, the organic debris was so small and light that it was easily moved and did not resist currents of air and of water, so that it was not pulverized.   The land and its products were not thrown into the sea because they were not dissolved until the waters had risen to their highest point and all was calm, so that the mineral and metallic parts, although they were reduced to atoms, the vegetables and the seeds did not move far laterally but only vertically, and later

[33] Catcott, *op. cit.*, especially pp. 43-50, 63, 326, 327.

settled again into nearly the same location.   The irregularity in the subsidence of the earth's strata, which were not
laid down wholly in accord with specific gravity, and the
position of crystals or spars, which formed horizontally or
even upwards while now they take shape only downwards,
were due to the upward pressure exerted by part of the air.
This pressure reduced greatly the gravity of bodies.[34]

At the appointed time, God changed the effects of the air,
so that it pressed solely upon the surfaces; and thus the earth
was re-formed.   The length of time that the retreat of the
waters lasted proved that the apertures in the sea were comparatively small.   The sole really important difference
between the formation of the earth at creation and its
re-formation in the days of Noah was that in the second case
the mountains contained fossils whereas those formed on the
third day of creation obviously could not enclose them.[35]

Catcott was strongly opposed to cosmologists who claimed
that all present mountains were raised on the third day of
creation, whether they attributed the eminences to the sea's
slow retreat, and to its heaping up masses of sand and mud,
as did Le Catt, Buffon and De Maillet, or agreed with the
Bishop of Clogher that the sea was caused by the excavation
and removal of an immense quantity of earth, which left a
hollow, and that then this earth was deposited on other
sections of the globe and formed mountains.   He also rejected the theories of Woodward, Burnet and Whiston,
because the regularity in shape of the mountains and the
valleys proved that they were not due to irregular elevation
or depression.[36]   However, he seemed to approve Woodward's thesis that the chief purpose of the flood was to

[34] Catcott, op. cit., pp. 3, 10, 65-79, 88, 374-401.
[35] Ibid., pp. 3, 86-91, 247-374, 401, 402; Catcott's father, ibid., p. 422.
[36] Ibid., pp. 14, 268-275, 328-332.

retrench the luxuriancy of the earth " and so take away the cause of the general corruption;" by making men labor more, and die earlier, so that they felt their weakness and dependence on God.[37]   The destruction of all except a few animals of each species was necessary lest they overwhelm the human survivors.   He agreed with Woodward also in the doctrine that since the flood no mountains had been formed.[38]

Catcott did not discuss the creation of plants, animals and man.   His interest was in the first half of the hexaemeron.   Nevertheless, he imitated his predecessors by his reference to the giving of names to the animals.   After the creation of man, for whose benefit all animate nature was formed, the various species were influenced by God to come to Adam for names, probably in the manner He used later in directing them to the ark.[39]

Catcott had only a few words to say on the final destruction of the earth by fire.   It would begin in the heavens above.   Either they would be cleft and streams of fire would be poured down on earth, or lightnings would come from the clouds.[40]

The work of Cockburn, Catcott and their coadjutors was a definite attempt to harmonize the Biblical narrative with the accumulations of scientific data that had been so busily gathered during the preceding half-century.   It was so far successful as to establish for many decades the orthodoxy of the doctrine that the Noachian deluge was universal rather than limited in extent.   That dogma outlived the various hypotheses by which the cause of the deluge and the constitution of the earth were related to the universality of the catastrophe.

[37] Catcott, *op. cit.*, p. 24.

[38] *Ibid.*, pp. 25, 82, 83, 275, 409, 410.

[39] *Ibid.*, pp. 41, 82.

[40] *Ibid.*, note p. 71.

CHAPTER XXIV

An Enlarging Universe and Genesis

Thomas Wright of Durham (1711-1786), of whom
little is known, was the first in a group of four writers [1] on
the universe who are often mentioned now, perhaps because
the second member of the quartette, Immanuel Kant, became
famous for his philosophical conceptions. Wright started
life as the son of a carpenter, and was in straitened circumstances for years. He gained a livelihood by varied
activities, including the construction of clocks and almanacs,
teaching and lecturing.[2] In 1750 he published a series of nine
letters entitled *The Universe and the Stars, Being an Original
theory on the visible Creation, founded on the laws of Nature.*
It was an attempt to solve the phenomena of the Milky Way.[3]
He had in addition a religious end to advance, " the adora-
tion of the Divine Being in his infinite creation of higher
works." [4]   He declared the manner, time and material of
creation at present unknowable to human philosophy.[5]
Moses's " elegant " account was written

only to the senses of a people who had not yet learnt to make use
of their reason any other way, but from the appearance of

---

[1] Wright, Kant, Lambert, Herschel.

[2] Clerke, *Modern Cosmogonies* (London, 1905), pp. 16, 20; Libby, *An
Introduction to the History of Science* (Boston, New York, Chicago,
1917), p. 143. Wright's work was discussed *ibid.*, pp. 143-145.

[3] Wright, *The Universe and the Stars* (Philadelphia, 1837), p. 9.

[4] *Ibid.*, p. 11, also pp. 12, 18, 19.

[5] *Ibid.*, pp. 12, 89, 90.

things, and upon a subject too sublime for vulgar capacities in any age, and had only been attempted in the deepest learning of *Egypt,* which, he though well acquainted with, the generality of them were totally strangers to.[6]

The universe was " a vast infinity of worlds, acted upon by an eternal agent, and crowded full of beings, all tending through their various states to a final perfection." [7]   It was a necessary corollary of God's infinite power that the stars were all suns, surrounded with planets, which were inhabited by beings not unlike men though they differed in conformity with their environment.[8]   There was " a universe of worlds, all decked with mountains, lakes, and seas, herbs, animals, and rivers, rocks, caves, and trees; and all the produce of in-dulgent wisdom, to cheer infinity with endless beings, to whom his omnipotence may give a variegated eternal life." [9] Wright described several of these worlds, which were dif-ferent from ours but all beautiful and fertile.   In some the air might be so dense that a traveller could fly in a chariot and water such that he could sleep thereon, or both might be so rare that he could not even sail a boat.   The inhabitants of others might be many degrees higher than man in reason, longevity and other qualities.   The beings who dwelt in all the planets of the same stellar system saw the same face of the heavens and the same constellations because of the great distances from star to star, but their sky differed from that in a different system.[10]

The sun and the stars were bodies of fire dispersed at great intervals through an infinite heaven by design, not

---

[6] Wright, *op. cit.,* p. 90.   [7] *Ibid.,* p. 15.

[8] *Ibid.,* pp. 20-27, 64, 65, 90, 128, 132.

[9] *Ibid.,* p. 85.

[10] *Ibid.,* pp. 85, 86, 139-141, 144.   He gave a scientific account of sun, planets and comets, *ibid.,* pp. 41-48.

by chance. The sun was not the center of the universe.
Since it and the stars were alike, they must all be movable or
all fixed. The second alternative was ridiculous and contrary
to our knowledge of the universe, which showed design and
the work of God. Hence all stars were or might be in
motion. The sun, as well as the planets, turned on its axis;
and its position in the sky seemed to have changed. Wright
attributed this change to its motion from one location to
another. Since, as he concluded, all the stars moved and did
not move in straight lines, they must do so in curves, either
in a plane as the planets did around the sun, or in different
directions around a concave orb. God was in the center and
those spheres nearer Him were more perfect. If all the
visible stars moved in a vast ring like Saturn's around some
opaque body, the phenomena of the Milky Way would be
produced. Its cloudy spots and the irregular distribution
of the stars, of which it had been proved to consist, would
be explained. Our own solar system was near the center of
this " Vortex Magnus." [11] Probably there was a central
body, " a globe of fire superior to the Sun, or otherwise a
vast terraqueous or terrestrial sphere, surrounded with an
Aether like our Earth, but more refined, transparent and
serene," presumably inhabited. A terraqueous sphere was
more likely since a fiery ball would be visible and besides no
beings who inhabited fire were known.[12]

Kant (1724-1804), who had seen a summary of this system, in 1755 accepted Wright's opinion about the Milky
Way as a congeries of stars in almost the same plane and
agreed that the different planets were inhabited, but enlarged
the hypothesis in various ways. He thought Sirius the center

[11] Wright, op. cit., pp. 55-67, 71-81, 88-102, 104, 105, 111-115, 118-128, 135.

[12] Ibid., p. 137, also note p. 152. An account of Wright was given
in Appendices B and C of Hastie, Kant's Cosmogony (Glasgow, 1900),
pp. 180-205.

of the stellar system called the Milky Way, while Wright believed that globe only the nearest of the stars. He differed from his predecessor because he attributed the highest types of life to the planets farthest from the center. The finer, or less dense, the matter of the planet, the greater was the freedom of spiritual development upon it. Hence the farther from the center of the universe we went, the more rational or spiritual the inhabitants. This was in accord with the doctrine that the denser central zone was first developed into systems.[13] Kant, unlike Wright, made an attempt to explain creation. There was originally a chaos of particles in an infinite universe. In accordance with the law of gravity they were mutually attracted. Especially were they drawn to centers of greater density. Thus the particles were divided into a great number of isolated masses, which were the germs of future stars. Then in each nebula occurred a central condensation of particles circulating in orbits. The repulsive or centrifugal force and the power of attraction were so balanced in some cases that the particles, especially since they were mutually deflected by collision, did not fall into the central bodies but revolved around them. Perfect balance would produce a circular orbit. The less the balance, the greater would be the eccentricity. Because their density was less, comets were clearly produced from the nebulous matter more distant from the center than that which formed the planets. The nebulae, which began in a condition of repose and of low temperature, became hot by compression. Nature was constantly making new systems farther from the center, and the inner ones were becoming old and breaking up.

[13] Hastie, *op. cit.*, pp. lxv-lxviii, *Universal Natural History and Theory of the Heavens,* by Kant, trans. by Hastie, pp. 30, 32, 43, 166, 167; Kant, *Allgemeine Naturgeschichte und Theorie des Himmels* (Leipzig, 1890) (1st ed., 1755), addition to ch. vii, pp. 76, 77, ch. viii, pp 86-90, pt. iii, omitted but summarized.

Gradually the exhaustion of the revolving movements in the universe would precipitate all planets and comets into the sun; but this would greatly increase its heat and fire, especially since the distant globes contained the lightest matter of nature, which was the matter most active in combustion. The increased fire would resolve everything into its smallest elements and scatter them by heat expansion to the wide regions of space occupied before the first formation of the universe. The heat would be reduced by the almost total dispersion of the mass, and then the forces of attraction and of repulsion would reproduce the system. Like the Phoenix, Nature reanimated itself indefinitely.[14]

In 1763 while writing on the existence of God, *Der einzig mögliche Beweisgrund zu einer Demonstration des Daseyns Gottes,* Kant repeated his ideas, and added his explanation of Saturn's ring as caused by the simple action of gravity. The atmosphere of the planet under the influence of heat extended far from its solid core. The atmosphere then gradually grew cold and shrank. From its unsuccessful efforts to fall into the planet it gained a circular motion. Those particles nearest to the central body had too little centrifugal force to balance the pull of gravity to the planet and fell into it. Those beyond this area revolved in a ring, the inner surface of which travelled faster than the outer. If the concentric circles that formed the ring had not been separated by lines of cleavage, they would have rubbed against one another and finally developed the same speed.

[14] Hastie, *op. cit.,* pp. lxxviii-lxxxi, trans. of *Universal Natural History and Theory of the Heavens,* ch. vii, pp. 152-154; Kant, *op. cit.,* pp. 68, 69, ch. viii, pp. 80, 81, 86-90. For Kant's account see also Arrhenius, *The Life of the Universe as conceived by man from the earliest ages to the present time* (London and New York, 1909), vol. i, pp. 6, 123, 124, vol. ii, pp. 137-145, 211-213, 231, 232, 258, 259; Clerke, *op. cit.,* pp. 20-28; Libby, *op. cit.,* pp. 142-148; Faye, *Sur l'origine du monde* (Paris, 1884), pp. 112-130.

This would have caused the outer portions to fly off into space and the inner to sink into the planet, or perhaps the whole ring would have formed satellites.[15]

Probably the most interesting of Kant's ideas as an attempted interpretation of the Biblical narrative was another hypothesis concerning the ring of Saturn. He suggested that the earth might once have had such a ring, composed of primitive matter, which was halted while falling obliquely, or of vapor, which had ascended from its surface.

What a beautiful sight for those who were created to inhabit the earth as a paradise! What a convenience for those on whom nature was designed to smile on all sides! But all this is still nothing compared with the confirmation which such an hypothesis may borrow from the record of the History of Creation, . . . The water of the firmament, which the Mosaic description mentions, has already caused not a little trouble to commentators. Might this ring not be used to help them out of this difficulty? This ring undoubtedly consisted of watery vapours. And besides the advantage which it might furnish to the first inhabitants of the earth, it had further this property of being able to be broken up on occasion, if need were, to punish the world which had made itself unworthy of such beauty, with a Deluge. Either a comet whose attraction brought the regular movements of its parts into confusion, or the cooling of the region in which it was situated, condensed its scattered vapour-particles, and precipitated them in one of the most awful deluges upon the earth. It is easy to understand what the consequences of this would be. The whole world was submerged under water. And, besides, it sucked in with the foreign and subtle vapours of this unnatural rain, that slow poison which brought all creatures nearer death and destruction. At the same time, the figure of that pale and light bow now disappeared from the horizon; and the new world, which could never recall its appearance without feeling

[15] Faye, *op. cit.*, pp. 124-126, which consisted chiefly of quotations from this treatise by Kant.

terror before this fearful instrument of Divine vengeance, saw
perhaps with no little consternation in the first rain that fell, that
coloured bow which seemed by its figure to be a copy of the
first, but which through the assurance of Heaven being reconciled, was to be a gracious sign and monument of the continuous
preservation of the now altered earth.[16]

Kant's and Wright's theses about the Milky Way were
further developed by Lambert and by Herschel, but their
work was rather scientific than theological.   By that epoch
the heliocentric theory had been accepted almost universally,
and astronomers were allowed to promulgate any doctrines
concerning the stars without accusations of atheism.   The
controversial emphasis had shifted to the date and the method
for the creation of the terrestrial globe.   Lambert's *Cosmologische Briefe* (1761) was not particularly influential;
and though Herschel's disc theory created a considerable
stir, the interest seems to have been chiefly scientific.   J.
Heinrich Lambert (1728-1777), who was the son of a poor
Swiss tailor, without knowledge of the work done by Wright
and Kant, declared the Milky Way to be " a disc of aggre-
gated stars, but with breaches and gaps indicating a multiplicity of systems circulating, . . . round a common center."
There were other Galaxies, grouped in a combination of a
higher order, and still further hierarchies of systems on an
ascending scale of magnitude and of grandeur.[17]

In April, 1784, in a paper on *The Construction of the
Heavens,* probably in ignorance of the suggestions offered

[16] This translation by Hastie is close to the original though idiomatic.
Hastie, *op. cit., Universal Natural History and Theory of the Heavens
by Kant,* pp. 129-131.   Kant, *op. cit.,* pt. ii, ch. v, pp. 52, 53.   Also
Arrhenius, *op. cit.,* vol. ii, pp. 143, 144; Libby, op. cit., pp. 145, 146;
Faye, *op. cit.,* p. 127.

[17] Clerke, *op. cit.,* pp. 17, 18; Libby, *op. cit.,* p. 149; Berry, *A Short
History of Astronomy* (London, 1898), p. 312; Lambert, *Cosmologische
Briefe über die Einrichtung des Weltbaues* (Augsburg?, 1761).

by Wright, by Kant and by Lambert, William Herschel [18] announced the same conclusion that the Milky Way was a disk or stratum of stars, with our sun not at but near the center. There were many similar disconnected stellar systems or nebulae, some of which were larger than ours. These were formed as the "result of the break-up of a greater stellar stratum." [19] Some stars, because of their close vicinity to one another, exerted an attraction which caused others to approach, and broke up large nebulae into several smaller groups. However, in 1791 he suggested that some nebulae, for example the nebula in Orion, were probably composed of a shining fluid rather than of separate stars; and in other ways after 1800 he modified his disc-theory. Herschel was another astronomer who believed in inhabitants of the other planets. He thought that even the sun might be inhabited, and that sun-spots were portions of the solid solar continent shining through the luminous solar clouds.

The countless patient observations with the new instruments, joined to the mathematical discoveries and calculations, removed astronomy during the last half of the eighteenth century from the arena where still strove ancient theological dogmas and recent scientific hypotheses.

[18] Accounts of his work may be found in many places, including the following: Macpherson, *Modern Cosmologies* (London, 1929), pp. 19-38; Arrhenius, *op. cit.*, vol. i, p. 118; Clerke, *op. cit.*, p. 29; Berry, *op. cit.*, p. 286.

[19] Macpherson, *op. cit.*, p. 27.

CHAPTER XXV

PIKE AND THE CLIMAX OF THE HARMONIZING THEORIES

PROBABLY the most successful attempt to harmonize the Biblical science with the discoveries of the last centuries was that of Samuel Pike (1717?-1773), an Independent minister, who in 1753 published *Philosophia Sacra: or, the Principles of Natural Philosophy. Extracted from Divine Revelation.* His theory showed traces of Hutchinson's influence but was much more coherent and better elaborated. Unfortunately, he was born a century too late, so that his work did not have the influence its logical development deserved. In fact, he himself is said to have changed his mind later in life and to have accepted the doctrine of John Glas that Biblical authority did not extend to such topics as physical science as well as to have adopted some usages of the church established by Glas and his son-in-law. However, in 1753 Pike asserted that all natural science could be deduced from texts in the Bible. The trouble in the past had been that the Hebrew terms had been erroneously translated, and so their real meanings had remained concealed.[1]

Pike's whole system rested on his idea of the heavens. They " dispose and keep every thing in nature, in its proper place." [2] By raising water vapor they caused the earth to

---

[1] Pike, *Philosophia Sacra* (London, 1753), pp. 11, 15, 17-19 and elsewhere. For example, he called the Bible "the only infallible guide both in natural and spiritual things". *Ibid.*, p. 105.

[2] *Ibid.*, p. 15. Pike's ideas show how great an alteration had taken place in thought during the preceding century. He was even more insistent than Fludd or Kircher on the influence of the heavens; but, though his theory was fantastic, it was far removed from the astrological concepts associated with the phrase by his predecessors.

produce food. By compression they effected the cohesion of matter; and their shining caused the revolution of the earth, which he accepted, together with its motion around the sun. God Himself created the matter of the heavens, the celestial ether, and then arranged it,[3] " putting the several parts together in such a manner and order, as to render it fit to operate, when he should be pleased to set it in motion . . . The heav'ns became a *machine,* a delegated agent, and then it is said, *God rested from it* [Creation]." [4] As they were "sufficiently clear, fine and pure, to operate with freedom, so they are sufficiently powerful to perform the work assign'd them." [5] After God had created and adjusted the heavens, He worked by means of this machine, but still upheld it, kept it together and governed it, accelerating or retarding its action or interposing to disturb the natural order. The ether was in continual circulation and commotion. It was constantly expanding, and the parts were continually striking against one another. Since the skies inclined more one way than another, any object placed in them did the same. Their prevailing pressure to the center of the world, the sun, caused gravitation toward that sphere. This force was nicely adjusted so that it retained the heavenly bodies in their places and made them travel in circles rather than in straight lines.[6]

The heavens contained matter in various shapes. That which was called in the Bible the darkness was ethereal matter in a state of inactivity, without " that regular and swift motion, whereby light is produc'd." [7] The heavens were created in this state and afterwards altered into a condition

[3] Pike, *op. cit.,* pp. 17-19, 22-25, 30, 31, 36, 42, 43, 55.

[4] *Ibid.,* p. 25.

[5] *Ibid.,* p. 27.

[6] *Ibid.,* pp. 27-33, 76-78.

[7] *Ibid.,* p. 34, also pp. 35-37.

of light.   The two were easily changed into each other, as was done in the beginning by giving the earth its diurnal motion.   The air that was dark became light by being turned to the sun and darkened again by being turned away.   The spirit, of which Moses spoke at creation, was obviously material, since he attributed motion to it.   The motion was tremulous in character.   The material spirit, which was proved by many passages to be air or wind, was the grosser part of the heaven, while the light or pure ether, which became visible whenever the spirit passed away, was the finest part. The light dispersed the denser air and helped to produce the rotation of the earth.[8]

In the heaven were suspended the moon and the planets, while the sun was located at the center of the universe.   The Bible employed three words for the sun and two for the moon, which were used in pairs.   The most common couple, Shemesh and Yara'h, together with Cocabim for the stars, meant not the celestial spheres but the light that came from them.   It was they which were said to rise and set, and they whom Joshua commanded to stand still, so that the miracle was in fact the retardation of the light.   They smote people (Isaiah 49:10; Ps. 121:6; Jonah 4:8) or were hot (1 Sam. 11:9; Neh. 7:3), statements obviously impossible with reference to the body of the sun.   Ecclesiastes 11:7 clearly meant the light of the sun in the expression that to see it is pleasant.   This would hardly be true of the solar body.[9]   These fluxes of light were " the fine aetherial matter that irradiates from the sun or moon, or stars; whether this aetherial matter be in such a motion to convey light to our eyes or no." [10]   The solar-light existed even in a dark

[8] Pike, *op. cit.*, pp. 34-42.
[9] *Ibid.*, pp. 28, 42-51, 76.
[10] *Ibid.*, p. 51.

dungeon and throughout the whole ball of the earth, but in such localities it was restrained from that free motion by which it made objects visible.   The light acted in a mechanical way like the rest of nature.   It was in constant motion from and to the body of the sun, from the center of the heavens to their circumference and back.   (Ps. 19: 5, 6). This motion, with that of the spirit, caused the regular return of day and of night, of winter and of summer (Eccles. 1 : 5, 6).   The earth was passive in these alternations; the active agents were obviously the light and the spirit.   Both the solar and the lunar light caused the growth of plants.   Since Shemesh and Yara'h were the words most frequently used in the Hebrew text, the light of the luminaries was generally meant when the English translation said sun and moon.[11] The second pair of terms did signify the bodies of the celestial globes.   It was seldom used and came from words meaning to be or to make hot and white.[12]   Thus the Bible never said that the sun moved.   The stars were called the head of Cocabim or stars' light (Job 22 : 12).[13]   The third word for sun, which was employed only thrice, meant the solar body or fire.[14]   Moses did not mention the fire as being in the heaven, though perhaps he included it under the term firmament; but other passages spoke of it as burning, dissolving, melting; and 2 Peter 3 : 12 talked of its effect on the heavens themselves.[15]   It meant the " vehement friction of the several parts of the aether, which dissolves and melts the grosser parts of the heav'ns and makes them become fine; that friction which tears the masses or denser parts to pieces, and dissolves them into loose atoms." [16]

[11] Pike, *op. cit.*, pp. 51-56, 60.

[12] Cant. 6: 10; Isa. 30: 26; 24: 23; Job 30: 28 were the only instances according to Pike.

[13] Pike, *op. cit.*, pp. 56-60.   [14] *Ibid.*, pp. 58-60.

[15] *Ibid.*, pp. 60, 61, 73, 75, 76.   [16] *Ibid.*, p. 61.

The " density " was a term applied to any parts of heaven so gross as to obstruct the passage of light, as the clouds. It meant also the dense, gross airs above the stars, at the very extremities of the heavens. It was said to be continually dissipated or unfolded,—that is, the finer or purer ether was continually worrying it and breaking it to pieces. When it was pulverized, it became the fine ether, which, on the other hand, continually assumed its form.[17] The farther from the sun at the center the sections of the heavens were, the grosser they were, so that perhaps at their outer extremity the heavens were " condensed into an immoveable solid." [18] By the motion of the solar light the denser airs were made to revolve towards the center. The greatest commotion and the strongest friction of the heavens were to be found at the center, and they gradually decreased till they were wholly absent at the circumference.[19] Except for the bodies of the luminaries, all the parts of the heavens were only

different states or conditions into which the aethereal fluid does or may occasionally pass. For the *darkness* is the fine atoms of the heav'n in a state of stagnation or inactivity, as at first created; or else the light prevented or stop'd in its enlightning motion. The *spirit* is the grosser parts of the heav'ns or masses compress'd together; while the *light* is the atoms, or finest part of heav'n in swift motion; which is sometimes so quick and free as to render objects visible. The light of the heav'ns is to be consider'd as distinguish'd into the *solar, lunar* and *stellar* lights, and these several lights being constantly attended with the spirit operate throughout nature: the *fire* is the *friction* of the parts of heav'n against one another, which melts or dissolves the heav'ns into the finest and purest aether. This friction is greatest at the center; and it gradually decreases towards the circum-

---

[17] Pike, *op. cit.*, p. 61.

[18] *Ibid.*, p. 64. Also pp. 63, 75.

[19] *Ibid.*, pp. 61, 63-65, 75.

ference; where the heav'ns are very much condens'd and this is call'd the *density*. All these parts of the heav'ns being in constant commotion, conflict, and revolution[20]

produced important results throughout the universe.

Since nature acted in a mechanical way only, and in a machine the parts touch one another and act only by contact, and since the influences of nature reached throughout the universe, the world must be so full of matter, which had all the foregoing names, that the particles were everywhere in contact.[21] As the Bible said, " nature acts by *expansion* and *compression*." [22] Moses declared that the spirit and the light, the grosser and the finer parts of the heavens, were in continual conflict and commotion. Where any place contained an unusual quantity of either one, the other tried to rush in and to expand it, so as to restore the balance. If it could not, it continuously pressed thither. This pressure was nature's powerful means of shaping and of preserving the universe. God in the beginning created a vast number of particles, the matter of the universe. The small and perfectly solid atoms were indivisible and dead. They lacked attractive, repulsive and elastic powers, and the power of creating, stopping or continuing motion. They were merely capable of being moved. These particles had definite shapes, but to know whether all were alike in size and shape surpassed human penetration.[23] They were placed in contact, but not so completely as to preclude motion, " in a very large sphere, confin'd at the extremities, and not permitted by the Creator to exceed those limits." [24] In this state of stagnation they

[20] Pike, *op. cit.*, p. 65.

[21] *Ibid.*, pp. 67-69, 98, 102, 103, 104.

[22] *Ibid.*, p. 69.

[23] *Ibid.*, pp. 69-72, 97, 99, 100, 102, 134, 136-138.

[24] *Ibid.*, p. 72. Also pp. 139, 148.

were the primitive darkness.   By the immediate power of
God they were put into commotion, rubbing, striking, sliding
by one another and causing universal stress and compression.
Such action made some atoms cleave together and form
masses of various sizes, which were named the spirit or air,
while others remained single, were in swift motion and
formed light.   Some after they had been compressed into
masses, were melted or dissolved again into atoms by friction or fire.   Meantime others were compressed into masses.
The localities with collections of single atoms made the least
resistance because they were in a state of most perfect
fluidity, and the collections of masses made the greatest.   In
either case the surrounding parts pressed in to expand,—that
is, to dilute, them.[25]   The greater the friction, the larger was
the proportion of single atoms and vice versa, " because it is
the nature of friction or fire to reduce the masses into
atoms." [26]   Because of the solar fire, the strongest friction
had always been at the center of the universe; and the heavens
in that section were the finest, since there existed the greatest number of single atoms.   The size or number of the
masses increased proportionately to the distance from the
center; hence the heavens were grossest at the circumference,
the density, where they perhaps even became congealed into an
immovable solid.   There was a pressure of the masses to
the center and of the atoms of light from it.   As the great
friction or fire at the heart of the universe dissolved the
masses to single atoms, a constant revolution was produced.
After completing this arrangement, God rested from His
work of creating and let secondary causes work as He had
foreseen and contrived in every particular, although still He
governed this machine of nature to execute all His will.[27]

[25] Pike, *op. cit.*, pp. 70, 72-74, 143-146.

[26] *Ibid.*, p. 74.

[27] *Ibid.*, pp. 61-64, 75-78, 101, 139.

Pike then applied his theory to explain various phenomena, *vis inertiae,* the attraction of cohesion, elasticity, gravity, magnetism and electricity, and said that it did explain fermentation, suction, the transmission, reflection and refraction of light, the formation of colors, the motions of the wind, the manner in which animal and vegetable life was sustained and numerous other phenomena. For example, he explained the gravity which attracted the planets to the sun by the constant inward flow of spirit or masses while the outward flow was merely the weaker one of light or atoms. The secondary planets were attracted towards the primary because the primary planets stopped some motions of the light and the spirit in the ether.[28] Both the light and the spirit were in constant motion, not only inward and outward but also, because of collisions, in all directions; and the primary planet " obstructs most of the motions that would otherwise have passed from the body outward all around it, and therefore the aether must have a prevailing pressure towards the body inward." [29] In other passages he attributed gravitation, to which he sometimes applied the name of cohesion, to the pressure of the ether surrounding two bodies, which was greater than that developed between the two.[30]

Then Pike affirmed that he would develop his theory by taking up " *Moses's* regular account in the first chapter of *Genesis*; and introduce what is said in other parts of scripture, by way of illustration or confirmation." [31] Moses's order was beautiful, for he mentioned first the matter of the earth as created, the atoms; second, the condition immediately thereafter; third, the spirit, the waters and the light; fourth, the division of waters above and below the expanse; fifth,

[28] Pike, *op. cit.*, pp. 80-97, 103-105, 138-149.
[29] *Ibid.*, p. 92.
[30] *Ibid.*, pp. 87-89, 142.   [31] *Ibid.*, p. 105.

the appearance of the dry land; sixth, the vegetation of the earth; seventh, the influence or government of the heavens over the earth; eighth, the "vegetation" of the waters; ninth, the production of animals; and tenth, the creation of man.   The earth was at first without form, a confused chaos of loose atoms, and void,—that is, empty or hollow.   It was a sphere or globe of loose atoms, empty in the middle.   Darkness, the heavens in their first state, was on the face of the deep, or the fluid condition of atoms, both outside and in the hollow at the center.   This darkness by commotion was formed into spirit.   The spirit by a tremulous motion separated the earthy and the watery particles, and produced a coating of water both within and without the crust of the earth.   Immediately thereafter began the diurnal revolution of the earth.   The division of the waters by the firmament or expansion meant their separation from the earth.   Those without the crust were below the firmament of the heavens, while those within were above the firmament at the center of the earth.[32]   On this occasion, the expanse received the name of heavens or placers because it had placed things in order and "sorted the different parts of the globe."[33]   The dry land appeared when the waters outside were gathered together into one place with those inside and formed the great deep.   The land rested on its surface.   This was proved by the account of the flood, when, by a miracle, the expanse rushed in and drove out the waters, which again covered the earth as at creation.   Later they "returned to their proper place, and there they are to this day."[34]

Besides these passages dealing with the condition of the earth, there were many "which seem to speak against, and . . . really speak for the globularity and the rotation of the

[32] Pike, *op. cit.*, pp. 106-111, 114.

[33] *Ibid.*, p. 111.

[34] *Ibid.*, pp. 111-115.

earth." [35]   The " foundations " seemed to imply immobility; but the term was used of the land, not of the whole globe, since it was said to be founded upon the seas or deep (Ps. 104: 5-9; 136: 6).   The psalmist referred to God's act in establishing the earth firmly after the deluge, not at creation.   Job 38: 6, in mentioning the sockets and corner stone of the earth, explained the cohesion of the crust, which was a vault over the waters and therefore had sockets and a key-stone to keep it from falling in.   The word translated pillars of the earth meant compressors in 1 Sam. 2: 8 and supporters in Job 9: 6 and elsewhere.   Both these well described the heavens. [36] In the passages asserting that the earth was established or made stable, the verb meant literally every part placed in the proper order; and the verb translated move or remove, denied of the earth, meant displace or dissolve, " that the parts of the earth are so machined or placed together, that they shall never be dissolved, as they were at the deluge." [37]   The ends of the earth were merely the extremities, borders or surface. The breadth of the earth, when used in the plural breadths, as in Job 38: 18, may have meant the two diameters.   When, in Job 11: 9, it was contrasted with the sea in the phrase longer than the earth and broader than the sea, the term was a very exact allusion to the fact shown by any globe that the land was long from pole to pole and the sea was broad from east to west. [38]   The annual and diurnal motion of our globe was implied in some passages, which gave also the cause. In two places in Job (37: 3 and 38: 12-14), the wings of the earth were mentioned.   The translators, who did not comprehend the meaning, put this translation into the margin

[35] Pike, *op. cit.*, p. 115.

[36] *Ibid.*, pp. 115-117.

[37] *Ibid.*, pp. 117, 118.

[38] *Ibid.*, pp. 118, 119.   The globe at which Pike looked seems to have misrepresented both Eurasia and the Atlantic Ocean.

and gave a non-literal rendering. Why the first reference should attribute wings to the earth " unless it did move or fly, is hard to conceive." [39] The second intimated that these wings carried the earth on its revolutions. God challenged Job, and asked him whether he caused the earth to revolve or could take hold of the wings of the earth and shake it out of its regular motions to the destruction of the wicked. He added that the morning dawn and the earth's wings were exactly fitted to it and that Job lacked power to alter them.[40] Psalm 96: 11 might be translated *"The heav'ns shall rejoice* or SHINE . . . *and the earth shall be glad or* REVOLVE." The shining of the heavens was the cause of the earth's revolutions.[41]

Where there is the greatest friction or heat, there must of necessity be the strongest pressure of the spirit. As the heav'ns therefore continually shine upon the earth, this actually produces, as the earth revolves, a greater heat in the afternoon than in the morning: consequently the spirit pushes in more strongly upon the afternoon than the morning part of the earth: and this being constantly the case, the pressure of the spirit is continually turning the evening edge away from the sun, and the morning edge towards it . . . Further, as there is a much greater heat at the evening, than at the morning edge of the earth, so the spirit will be continually pushing in against the evening edge, and drive the earth forward, as well as turn it round.[42]

Thus the heavens could move the earth on the suppositions " that God gave the motion to the earth at first, and placed the sun in the center of the system to shine continually upon it." [43] Moreover, the position of the earth was given in the

[39] Pike, *op. cit.*, pp. 119, 120.

[40] *Ibid.*, pp. 120, 121.

[41] *Ibid.*, pp. 121-123.

[42] *Ibid.*, pp. 122, 123.

[43] *Ibid.*, p. 123.

Bible. Job 26:7 meant " *He causes the north to lean aside over the loose atoms and hangs the earth upon that which binds it round* ",—that is, the expanse. " The earth then swims, as I may say, in the open expanse, and has its north part continually leaning aside." That passage denoted the inclination of the north pole.[44] Solomon in Eccles. 1:6 spoke of seasons, the solar light going south and turning again to the north and the light " as continually attended with and pursued by the spirit." [45] The same thought that explained the diurnal revolutions by the expanse " would lead us into the method of accounting for the returns of summer and winter: since the north part of the earth is most heated in summer, and the south part in winter." Obviously if all these things were true, the heavens might well " be said *to rule over the day and night;* and . . . *to have dominion over the earth.*" (Job 38:33).[46]

An interesting addition to Pike's treatise was a copper plate of the universe as visualized by him, with his explanation. He even gave smaller figures to represent the earth on various days of creation.[47] On the third day, for example, the airs within the earth rushed out, through the " more narrow and oblique fissures, . . . thro' which perhaps vapours and springs of water now ascend to form rivers, which run into the sea, and by that way return to the deep, from whence they are extracted." (Eccles. 1:7) [48] The water rushed in and was united to the interior waters to form the abyss or great deep. By this violent ingress and egress, part of the crust was broken off and sank to the center, where it formed a small globe within the earth and the

[44] Pike, *op. cit.*, pp. 123, 124.
[45] *Ibid.*, p. 124.
[46] *Ibid.*, p. 125.
[47] *Ibid., The Explanation of the Copper Plate*, pp. 1-8, and the plate.
[48] *Ibid., The Explanation of the Copper Plate*, pp. 6, 7.

abyss.   An opening in the crust on the plan " represents any sea or ocean that has a communication with the abyss." [49]

The first shining of the sun was on the equator at the first meridian at the time of the autumnal equinox.   " At that instant, the north pole lean'd aside, full east, the very way in which the earth proceeds in its annual orbit; and by an angle of twenty three degrees and a half." [50]

Pike did not believe that the stars were suns of other systems.   He asserted that this could not be proved by experiment or observation because of their great distance.   They were " either strong reflectors, at the verge of nature, placed there to prevent the *spirit* from being too much condensed to carry on the operations of nature; or else they are luminous bodies of themselves " [51] but probably without planets and incapable of dissolving the spirit into light to such an extent as the sun did.[52]   At the edge of the spherical universe was the density,

where the spirit is exceedingly dark and condensed into an immoveable solid: . . . the boundary of nature.   If the fix'd stars are only reflectors of light they touch the *density,* but if they are luminous bodies, 'tis possible they may be at some little distance within it: but which soever of these two they are, 'tis likely they are serviceable in nature to prevent a too great or too speedy condensation of the spirit into an entire density.[53]

Pike's copper plate engraving made them luminous bodies, for he placed them at equal intervals in a circle equidistant from the sun and at some distance from the circumference.

[49] Pike, *op. cit., The Explanation of the Copper Plate,* p. 6.
[50] *Ibid., The Explanation of the Copper Plate,* p. 8.
[51] *Ibid., The Explanation of the Copper Plate,* p. 4.
[52] *Ibid., The Explanation of the Copper Plate,* pp. 3, 4.
[53] *Ibid., The Explanation of the Copper Plate,* p. 4.

Pike's disquisition marked the culmination and conclusion to a period of development. No future author gave so convincing a reconciliation between the Scriptural picture of the universe and of the creation and the scientific discoveries of the seventeenth and the eighteenth centuries as Pike did. If his translations, which were certainly plausible, were accepted, the universe he portrayed seemed closely to fit the world as represented in the Bible and such phenomena as were generally accepted in the eighteenth century. The work of De Luc, the only important later exponent of the harmonization between the Biblical and the scientific doctrines, was so overbalanced with scientific data and theories that the Mosaic account appeared insignificant and was distorted. Despite sporadic outcroppings of earlier views, like the university dissertation of Peter Brouwer in the very year in which Pike published his treatise, the tendency after the middle of the eighteenth century was generally towards the doctrine, often indeed enunciated earlier, that the purpose of the Bible was to teach moral truths and not scientific. Brouwer declared that Adam must have received an account of creation from God and transmitted it to his descendants by word of mouth since human reason was too frail to explain such knowledge. Adam's offspring, as soon as they could, committed the record to writing. Brouwer's thesis was that Moses in composing Genesis used the monuments or so-called " schedulis " of the Patriarchs or other pious dead men.[54]

[54] Brouwer, *Dissertatio. Philologico-Theologica. Qua. Disquiritur. Unde. Moses. Res. in. Libro. Geneseos. Descriptas. Didicerit.* (Leyden, 1753), especially pp. 2, 11.

CHAPTER XXVI

DE LUC, THE MODERN SCIENTIST

THE modern scientific attitude was clearly shown in the work of Jean André De Luc (1727-1817), a Swiss geologist, who spent the last half of his life in England. There he became reader for Queen Charlotte and a fellow of the Royal Society. To him or to his contemporary, Saussure, belongs the credit for the first use of the terms geology and geologist.[1] He and his brother travelled extensively in the Alps and other mountains. They collected a notable museum of mineralogy and natural history in general, and an enormous mass of data on the present state of the earth. When he published his theories on the creation and the history of the earth,[2] a large portion of the five thick volumes presented detailed descriptions of the terrestrial strata, both in localities which he knew intimately and in others which he had visited, even more than once, to gather material. He was indefatigable in struggling through trackless territories and over cultivated fields, up innumerable mountain peaks and down mines, and in meeting all difficulties including the necessity for communication largely by signs with the illiterate peasantry, in search of facts to prove his theses or to suggest alternatives. With his sixty-five years' accumulation of data,[3] which must have

[1] Geikie, *The Founders of Geology* (London and New York, 1897), pp. 88, 89.

[2] De Luc, *Lettres physiques et morales sur l'histoire de la terre et de l'homme* (The Hague and Paris, 1779, 1780).

[3] De Luc, *Letters on the Physical History of the Earth* (London, 1831) (1st published, 1793-1795), introduction, p. 134 and note, letter vi, p. 270.

served as a basis as well as an inspiration for all later workers
in the field of geology, he was an exemplar of his dictum that
the Biblical narrative had led to the study of geology, physics
and chemistry, either to prove or to disprove Moses's account.[4] His decision that the flood was sufficiently recent to
be susceptible of proof, because the continents could not have
altered greatly since the date quite definitely assigned by the
Bible, had determined him to base his whole belief in the
authenticity of revelation upon a study of the phenomena pertaining to that event. Such a study included naturally a consideration of the terrestrial conditions which made such a
catastrophe the inevitable result of secondary causes, directed,
to be sure, by God. He eliminated miraculous interventions
in the event except for the preservation of the ark in the
tumult of waters.[5] Moreover he attempted again and again
to prove the brevity of time since our continents had emerged
from the waters. This was clear from the shallowness of
vegetable mould in uninhabited districts, from the existence
of cliffs both in mountains and on the sea-shore which had
not yet been worn down to a state of equilibrium, from the
quantity of ice, which was continually increasing, on Alpine
peaks and in polar regions, so that the later stages could be
dated and the time of the commencement estimated, from the
small size of terminal moraines to Alpine glaciers, from the
slight effects of rivers in the formation of alluvial plains and
deltas where the discovery of buried Roman relics showed
how recent was the accumulation, from the failure of streams
to fill with silt all mountain lakes through which they passed

[4] De Luc, *op. cit.*, letter iv, p. 158.

[5] *Ibid.*, introduction, pp. 4, 5, 35, 36, 131, letter ii, pp. 47-49, letter v,
p. 189, letter vi, pp. 240, 241; De Luc, *Lettres physiques et morales sur
l'histoire de la terre et de l'homme* (The Hague and Paris, 1779, 1780),
especially vol. i, pp. 8, 9, 242, 357, vol. ii, p. 87, vol. v, pp. 631, 632, 645-
660, 757, 759.

and the unfinished character of the beds they had carved out for themselves, from the comparatively perfect preservation of certain fossils as of elephants and rhinoceruses found in loose surface strata easily penetrated by rain water, from the thinness of peat deposits, from the insignificant development of the arts that proved their late inception, from the state of population which even yet left some lands uncultivated and from the comparatively modern names given to locations settled in early times.[6]

De Luc insisted on the study of the phenomena by naturalists before they composed theories. He declared that by the report of another a naturalist saw imperfectly and that he should explore places himself. He should not limit himself to one visit. Between visits he should consult the opinions of others in order that he might not fall into a rut or interpret the data falsely. He should then verify his conclusions.[7] With the encouragement, perhaps even the financial aid, of Queen Charlotte, De Luc seems to have followed this counsel of perfection on his numerous trips among the Alps and through the Low Countries and those sections of Germany and of France which border the Rhine. He studied the ideas of his predecessors and of his contemporaries, and arranged their systems into groups. In his great work, which consisted of his epistolatory reports to the queen, and which he wished might be read by everybody, specifically

[6] De Luc, *op. cit.*, vol. i, pp. 8-21, 398-400, vol. ii, pp. 20-61, 88-141, 383, 384, 483-486, vol. iii, pp. 8, 11, 26, 28, 29, 31-34, 41, 57-70, 100, 162, 180, 181, 262, 412, 416, 437, 438, 444-449, 477, 478, vol. iv, pp. 5-11, 14, 151, 152, 258, 286-289, 503, 504, vol. v, pp. 14-16, 81, 82, 104, 108, 109, 143, 153-155, 184, 185, 194, 195, 265, 303, 333-337, 463-466, 491-505, 622-624, 672, 673; De Luc, *Letters on the Physical History of the Earth* (London, 1831), introduction, pp. 4, 5, 9-22, 39, letter i, pp. 9-27, letter ii, pp. 47-54, letter iv, pp. 176, 177, letter v, pp. 196-229, letter vi, pp. 230, 233, 234, 249.

[7] De Luc, *Lettres physiques et morales sur l'histoire de la terre et de l'homme* (The Hague and Paris, 1779, 1780), vol. iv, pp. 16, 407, 408.

including women,[8] he gave a very fair presentation of the points of view and of the conclusions promulgated by other writers with his refutation. Finally in the fifth volume he elaborated his own ideas, which he had merely suggested earlier.

The phenomena that most impressed him were the stratification of the earth's crust, which was revealed both in plains when a well was dug and in mountains, and the fossils, especially the marine fossils, which these strata contained. The fact of the earth's rotation and its progress around the sun with the five other planets, together with Newton's law of gravity, he so took for granted as hardly to mention them, though later he denied that universal gravity caused the formation of those masses from which the globes of the universe developed, on the ground that it was preposterous to believe in any action of matter where it did not exist. His identification of the earth with the other planets went so far as to produce a casual reference to sensible inhabitants of the others, and the suggestion that perhaps the heat on each of the other planets was equal to the temperature on ours although they were not at the same distance from the sun. This would be due to such a difference in their atmosphere as would produce similar results in heat with different quantities of solar rays. This adaptation to their inhabitants of

[8] De Luc, *op. cit.*, vol. i, pp. 140-143. The letters were date 1775-1779. De Luc wrote many short papers, including some for the *Journal de Physique* and the *British Critic*, during the last decade of the century. By request, in 1792-1794, he wrote six letters to Professor Blumenbach on the physical history of the earth. They were published in the.*British Critic* 1793-1795 and republished in Paris in 1798. In 1831, after De Luc's death, they were translated into English and published in London with a long introduction. All De Luc's work is pleasant reading and reveals an interesting personality. His ideas seem to have developed during these dozen years; and in some respects the later work contradicted the earlier, notably in that he had become convinced that the strata in many or most of the mountains were tipped, even to a great angle.

the planetary constitutions and the size of their orbits he gave as proof of the necessity for an intelligent First Cause.[9] Man was the apparent end of the earth's creation, which was an act of God, not of chance. The globe was not a natural development of matter. Its origin was beyond man's discovery except by revelation. A true understanding of the change from non-existence to existence, or of the nature of all the beings formed including man, or of secondary causes and their actions, or of the relations of these matters to one another and their results was beyond the capabilities and organs of man. Therefore Moses gave merely the data that man could grasp, and only details of interest to man, much of which even Moses could know only by revelation.[10] For instance, while the strata of many mountains show their precipitation from the ocean, the cause for the formation of primordial mountains, especially those of granite, was unknown. Some solid bodies must have been formed in the original chaos, and perhaps these were they.[11]

De Luc, in accord with the practically universal opinion at his day, accepted fossils as the remains of real animals, and believed that their presence in the strata, together with the horizontal position of the rock layers, proved that our continents were once the bed of the ocean. He declared this belief to be held by all other naturalists as well. He denied the necessity for successive floodings of the land, though he attributed to such action of the sea the phenomena of

[9] De Luc, *op. cit.*, vol. i, pp. 115, 116, 193-195, vol. v, pp. 307-310, 543-548, 703-706; De Luc, *Letters on the Physical History of the Earth* (London, 1831), letter iii, p. 84.

[10] *Ibid.*, introduction, note p. 118, letter iii, p. 92; De Luc, *Lettres physiques et morales sur l'histoire de la terre et de l'homme* (The Hague and Paris, 1779, 1780), vol. i, pp. 103-109, 116-120, 273, 303, vol. v, pp. 633-642, 655-662, 669, 694, 735-738, 762, 763.

[11] *Ibid.*, vol. ii, pp. 200-224, vol. v, pp. 454, 455, 475. Nevertheless De Luc later attempted another explanation, *cf. infra*, pp. 271-273.

alternate layers of peat and stone. He apparently limited
these variations to small areas on islands. His fundamental
belief was in a great revolution, described by Moses as the
deluge, which bared our continents, while it submerged those
on which men, plants and animals had formerly flourished.
From this event De Luc worked back to creation and the
changes in the sea bottom that had converted it into our continents, and forward to a consideration of the changes the
land had undergone since it became dry. The retreat of the
sea, though preceded by successive slight recessions that were
really subsidences of the ocean level, occurred at one time,
but was gradual enough not to disorder the loose surface
strata.[12]

In the beginning the earth, like the other great bodies of
the universe, was a mass of particles in a state of rest. De
Luc named these pulvicules. In the course of six periods
of indefinite but great length all the stellar and planetary
masses were simultaneously formed into the shapes we see.
Moses called the periods days; but that term, as was shown
by its use in other texts, did not denote an interval of
twenty-four hours. Besides, our measure of days is the
earth's rotation before the sun, and the solar sphere was not
formed, or rather not luminous, until the fourth day. A
solar day was not meant by Moses till after the creation of
man, as was acknowledged by almost all Christian scientists.

[12] De Luc, *op. cit.*, vol. i, pp. 231, 344, 367-370, 379, 380, 408-411, vol. ii,
pp. 171, 172, 175, 264-267, 302-307, 513-532, vol. iii, pp. 162, 164, 180, 256,
257, 275, 276, 382-385, 465, vol. iv, pp. 113, 114, 125, 126, 131, 132, 134,
135, 263, 264, 289, 456, 457, 473, 543, 555-558, 566, 567, 582-592, 613, 630,
vol. v, pp. 103, 104, 216, 217, 224-227, 383, 388, 389, 453, 456-469, 475-477,
485-487 and note, 506-509, 612, 631, 632, 648-671; De Luc, *Letters on the
Physical History of the Earth* (London, 1831), introduction, pp. 9, 10,
29-76, 127, letter i, pp. 4-8, 15, 38-40, letter ii, pp. 52-69, letter iii, pp. 110,
111, 116-135, letter iv, pp. 151-166, 172, 173, 176-178, 180, 181, letter v,
pp. 182-190, letter vi, pp. 235-238, 241, 248, 249, 252-254, 262-264.

However, the order of creation was correctly given by Moses; and his later chronology was in solar years.[13]

As the Bible said, the first act was the creation of light by the word of God.   The action of light upon the pulvicules set in motion chemical operations which produced all geological phenomena.   This light was not from any luminous body, but completely penetrated both the earth and all the other great bodies in space.   Anything resembling the rays of the sun would have produced fire,—i. e., heat, only at the surface, and united with the elements there.   Lucidity and heat were the effects of two elastic fluids,[14] light and fire. When these were in some combinations with other elements, they temporarily ceased to produce such effects.   Fire necessarily contained light, but light could disengage itself from fire.   Light, which entered into the composition of most known substances of the earth and the atmosphere, was necessary for all action on our globe.   In the beginning the earth received a definite quantity of light that produced probably a greater heat in the whole than now.   The motion of light was so rapid that it darted into space notwithstanding gravity, unless it was retained by chemical combination. Both its escape and its combination, however, diminished the heat of the earth.   Therefore it must be constantly renewed, as was done by the sun's rays.   Fire on the contrary had weight, so that the lower layers of the atmosphere contained more of it than the upper, and the solar rays produced there a greater effect.   During the first period of creation the union of light with a particular element produced fire, and the

[13] De Luc, *op. cit.*, introduction, pp. 5, 46, 86-117, letter iii, pp. 82, 83; De Luc, *Lettres physiques et morales sur l'histoire de la terre et de l'homme* (The Hague and Paris, 1779, 1780), vol. i, pp. 356, 357, vol. v, pp. 637-644.

[14] De Luc explained elastic or expansible fluids as air, vapors, exhalations and emanations, *ibid.*, vol. v, p. 537.

union of that with water caused the water's liquefaction. Water existed only to a definite depth on the earth's surface, but was abundant in quantity and formed at first a heavy turbid liquid that contained all elements. From this by chemical operations all substances of the globe and of the atmosphere were successively separated. The center of the earth was still only pulvicules; but the liquid surface layer was deep enough to form the whole into a sphere, when it was rotated by a cause outside itself. Since the velocity of the rotation was about the same as now, the earth's equatorial diameter assumed its present dimensions.[15]

During the second period or day, solid particles were precipitated from the liquid, and, mixed with liquid, accumulated on the pulvicules in a thick bed of slime or mud. The superincumbent liquid from this era to an epoch shortly after the deluge passed through a series of stages with no possibility of reversal. The changes were due to new substances in the form of expansible fluids that rose from the bottom, both from the bed of mud and from the pulvicules below it when they were united with the superimposed liquid, and to other substances separated from the liquid by the union of its constituents with fire and light. The formation of the first atmosphere, which was in part water, coincided with the precipitation from the liquid of the first mineral strata. They covered the whole earth with a very thick crust of granite and similar rock. Local variations and interruptions produced differences in the size, the color and the proportion of crystals in the mass. There was no life on the earth, and therefore there were no organic remains in the granite. These strata

[15] De Luc, *op. cit.*, vol. v, pp. 536-542, 550-595, 704, 705; De Luc, *Letters on the Physical History of the Earth* (London, 1831), introduction, pp. 47-51, 58-61, letter ii, pp. 67-79, letter iii, pp. 81, 84-92, 101, 102, 111-113, letter iv, pp. 158, 180.

and all succeeding ones were horizontal when they were deposited.[16]

During the third period new kinds of expansible fluids were produced from the liquid that had now been emptied of granitic substances; and new precipitations resulted, though they still contained no organic bodies. The differences in strata resulted from the changes in the liquid produced by new expansible fluids and by the removal from it of constituents whose deposition produced a particular type of stone. During the later periods the variations in gases and liquid brought about alterations in the plant and animal life of the world, especially in the sea, but also on land since the atmosphere was affected by such expansible fluids as were exhaled. The variations were the chief reasons for the changes in fossils found in the different strata, and perhaps produced the complete extinction of some species.[17]

The causes of mountains commenced to act at this time. The liquid from the mud which underlay the granite gradually filtered into the mass of pulvicules, which therefore subsided as heaps of sand do now when flooded with water. The liquid formed various combinations with the pulvicules, depending upon the varying nature of both constituents. Sometimes solid parts were formed, which supported the crust for a time, while caverns were produced by the subsidence of neighboring pulvicules. By the chemical action involved, the caverns were filled with expansible fluids. As the pulvicules under the solid walls also subsided with a new accession of liquid, the crust broke and sank; and the liquid rushed in and expelled the expansible fluids. They combined

[16] De Luc, *op. cit.*, introduction, pp. 58, 59, letter i, p. 5, letter ii, pp. 61-68, letter iii, pp. 93-105.

[17] *Ibid.*, introduction, pp. 57, 58, 61, 64-67, 129, 130, letter ii, pp. 56, 57, letter iii, pp. 105-107, 130-135, letter iv, pp. 153, 154, 166-173, letter vi, pp. 238, 239.

with the water above to form a new medium from which a different type of stratum was precipitated. Part of the granitic crust was still supported by the walls of the original caverns and formed the cores of the great mountain chains, while the rest was shattered and tipped down on either side. The process, which continued until the time of the deluge, was the primary cause of mountains, and the reason why most of the strata were no longer horizontal and were so badly fractured.[18]

Some of the mountains remained under the sea; but a first general revolution, due to some great subsidence of pulvicules and hence of caverns, formed a hollow, into which the sea rushed and laid bare the first continents, which were much greater than ours, and the first islands,—that is, the summits of submerged mountains. The first continents lasted a long time because they were relieved from the weight of the water; and because, furthermore, the liquid could not pass directly and easily into the pulvicules beneath such sections of the crust and undermine partitions and caverns. Vegetation began at this epoch, but its nature was different from that of modern vegetable life since there was as yet no light from the sun. The plants of this era were the source of coal. Meantime, on the sea bed, our present continents were undergoing most of the catastrophes whose marks were still extant. The fissures made by the successive ruptures and subsidences of the strata in the production of mountains were filled with mineral and metallic substances. Apparently at this period took place most of those volcanic eruptions which, with earthquakes, disrupted the strata, and which formed some new layers of rock. De Luc thought that the majority of such eruptions took place under the sea, and that the expansible fluids liberated helped to

---

[18] De Luc, *op. cit.*, introduction, pp. 54-57, 59-61, letter i, pp. 6-8, 38, 39, letter ii, pp. 61-68, letter iii, pp. 107-111, 117-126, 128, 129, letter iv, p. 152.

shatter the vaults of the caverns. Many mountains were formerly volcanoes; but eruptions were local, and slight in their effects compared with those produced by chemical precipitations from a liquid, to which he attributed most of our strata. Lava came from the mud between the solid strata and the pulvicules. This was of varied character but was mixed with ingredients which prevented its petrifaction in that location. The formation of expansible fluids in its mass, or their entrance from without, produced new combinations that caused the evolution of heat and the incandescence of the whole. Then any water that approached it was changed to steam and raised the whole lava until it found an outlet. The spaces left by its emergence were intercommunicating caverns or galleries and served to transmit the force of earthquakes.[19]

The important event in the fourth period was that then the sun became luminous. The earth constantly lost its light by radiation into space; hence it was essential that additional supplies should be acquired from an external source. The sun, like the earth, was in the beginning a mere mass of pulvicules in space, but received an immense quantity of light. The chemical operations thus inaugurated differed from those on earth since the original matter of the solar body was different. Nevertheless, as with the other celestial spheres, liquidity was introduced; and this, upon the rotation of the sun, formed the solar mass into a sphere. Its body later became solid and opaque as might be observed through

<hr>

[19] De Luc, op. cit., introduction, p. 62, letter iii, pp. 109-111, 126, letter iv, pp. 137-152, 155-166, letter v, pp. 184-186; De Luc, Lettres physiques et morales sur l'histoire de la terre et de l'homme (The Hague and Paris, 1779, 1780), vol. ii, pp. 399, 400, 412-445, 447-452, 476-483, 504-509, vol. iii, pp. 323-328, 505, 506, 509-511, 548-552, vol. iv, pp. 134, 135, 147-150, 152-223, 226-229, 232-264, 283, 290, 291, 299, 301-319, 322-335, 380-406, 408-415, 418-425, 427-436, 439-476, 479, 481-532, vol. v, pp. 26, 27, 356, 358-369, 383, 452, 453, 460-462, 475-482, 642-644.

the sun-spots, which were transparent parts of its atmosphere. They were places which had temporarily ceased to emit light or perhaps had not yet been decomposed into light. There was no reason to surmise that the sun was intensely hot. Like phosphoric substances it was decomposed by chemical reactions, and formed an atmosphere, which was in turn decomposed to produce light.[20]

The effect on the earth of the light from the new source was marked during the fifth period by precipitation of a new mineralogical type. The strata contained the first traces of animals. Only marine creatures flourished. At the same era, a period of extensive disruption in the sea bed resulted from the undermining of enormous caverns. The alteration produced by the combination of water and the new expansible fluids caused striking changes in precipitations and in animals. The mountains that had risen from the sea bed were further enlarged and the strata twisted. The liquid by filling the caverns was so reduced in level that some of the volcanoes and other submarine mountains were above or near the surface, so that their summits did not receive the new precipitations.[21] Perhaps some fossils of fish between strata of copper pyrites showed poisoning by submarine volcanic eruptions. At this period and later occurred total extinction of certain animal groups, whose previous existence was proved by their remains. The most notable cases of such disappearances, however, happened later at the revolution that brought to light our continents. Possibly no representatives at that epoch escaped to new lands, or changes in atmosphere and other conditions proved too great for their survival, or

[20] De Luc, *Letters on the Physical History of the Earth* (London, 1831), letter iii, pp. 111-115.

[21] *Ibid.*, letter iii, pp. 116-135, letter v, pp. 184, 185; De Luc, *Lettres physiques et morales sur l'histoire de la terre et de l'homme* (The Hague and Paris, 1779, 1780), vol. iv, pp. 263, 264, 456, 457.

they were so altered by the new environment as to be un-recognizable. In the new state of the earth they, at least in their earlier forms, had become useless. There also ex-isted innumerable examples of fossils whose modern repre-sentatives were no longer found in the same locality. Besides all the other changes in atmosphere, land surface and water, the lowering of the ocean level would decrease the temperature of those places lately at sea level so that they would no longer form suitable habitats for warmth-loving animals and plants.[22]

The sixth period began " when the greater part of the stony strata, after having been produced, had already suf-fered the catastrophes . . . described in the preceding periods." [23] The precipitations in this period left almost no hard rock but merely sand and other loose surface strata. They contained the earliest traces of terrestrial animals but none of man. Some of these fossils were carried down to the sea by rivers; others resulted from the submergence of islands on which the plants and animals dwelt. The strata on the sea bed were still subject to subsidences that broke and tipped them. In addition, the currents and the tides helped to shape the mountains. Their force had increased since the bottom was so irregular. The old continents were inhabited by plants, animals and men. De Luc's most radical divergence from Genesis except for his transformation of days into periods, occurred here, for he asserted that this sixth period lasted until the deluge.[24] The sand layer, which

[22] De Luc, *op. cit.*, vol. ii, pp. 141, 247-258, 310, 311, 531, 532, vol. iii, pp. 24-26, 382, 383, 408, 432, 441, vol. iv, p. 122, vol. v, pp. 260-262, 264, 458, 459, 466, 467, 507-509, 513-518, 612-616, 620-623, 663-665; De Luc, *Letters on the Physical History of the Earth* (London, 1831), letter i, pp. 10-15, letter iii, pp. 132, 133, letter v, pp. 190-194, 212, 213, 215, 216.

[23] *Ibid.*, letter iv, pp. 173, 174.

[24] *Ibid.*, introduction, pp. 70-74, letter iv, pp. 174-181, letter v, p. 195; De Luc, *Lettres physiques et morales sur l'histoire de la terre et de l'homme*

he mentioned, was the work of a peaceful sea, and everywhere covered our continents. Even after the flood, the ocean continued to precipitate sand, so that the present sea bed resembled our continents in its surface layer. After the sixth era there were no more caverns to be invaded, from which might escape new expansible fluids to alter the water and the atmosphere and to produce new and different precipitations. For this reason the water, after it had deposited all its sandy constituents, no longer formed new strata. The retreat of the sea at the time of the deluge and its quiescence ever since in its own place had involved at the same period the almost complete cessation of volcanic eruptions, although they might recommence if water penetrated anew those magazines of fermentable matter below the surfaces of the old craters.[25]

The cause of the catastrophe that ended the sixth period was a slow infiltration by liquid under the crust of the continents. It increased the size and number of the caverns, so that finally the foundations of the dry land were almost wholly layers of caverns. At last a sudden rush of liquid into the lowest of these layers, perhaps preceded by subterranean fires which opened passages, undermined the supports and caused the lowest vaults to collapse. This brought about the demolition of all the layers successively. Since, when all animals on the old continents, including man, were drowned, their bones were left at the bottom of the sea, it was not strange that human fossils were not found in the strata of our dry land. Winds, violent agitations of the

(The Hague and Paris, 1779, 1780), vol. i, pp. 408, 409, vol. iv, p. 473, vol. v, pp. 388, 389, 466, 467, 469, 475-477, 479-484, 642-644.

[25] *Ibid.*, vol. iv, pp. 473, 474, vol. v, pp. 333, 334, 353 and note pp. 353 and 354, pp. 463-465, 483-485, 506, 507, 655; De Luc, *Letters on the Physical History of the Earth* (London, 1831), introduction, pp. 29, 66-70, letter ii, p. 57, letter v, pp. 183, 184, 186-189.

ocean and probably volcanic eruptions, as the matter of the sunken continents fermented, added to the confusion.   Probably the outer edges of the old continents fell first.   The weight of the water upon the top produced still further breakage of the cavern vaults and greater subsidence of the continents.   The water rushed impetuously thither and left bare its original bed, which became our modern continents. Moses portrayed the conclusion of the catastrophe when the sea approached the center of the continent because that alone was observed by Noah.   The only parts once dry still unsubmerged were the islands of the ancient sea that became mountain peaks.   The plants and animals that lived there migrated down their slopes, and together with the domesticated organisms saved in the ark repeopled the earth.[26]

Many facts showed that Moses did not invent the account, and their agreement with what had been discovered by ages of study of the phenomena proved the truth of the revelation he received.   The olives growing on Mt. Ararat, which is now too cold to support such fruits, as well as the other vegetation which supplied the Noachians with food upon their emergence from the ark, the omission of all horrors, such as piles of corpses on the land after the flood, the rivers of Eden, which fitted the old continent but have no pertinence to the new, the longevity of the antediluvians, which was due to great salubrity of air and food and decreased in the new world when it would be injurious, the importance of the rainbow, a new phenomenon, the result of a change in atmosphere which produced the tempestuous and local rains that were its cause—all these showed Moses's knowledge of the truth from tradition and revelation before the study of nat-

[26] De Luc, op. cit., introduction, pp. 62-64, 75, 76 and note, letter v, pp. 186, 187, 195, 196, letter vi, pp. 235-241, 243-250, 256, 257; De Luc, Lettres physiques et morales sur l'histoire de la terre et de l'homme (The Hague and Paris, 1779, 1780), vol. v, pp. 469, 485-488, 649-669.

ural history had revealed its reasons to mankind. As a final response to Buffon's theory that the successive cooling of the earth caused the migration of some species to the tropics and the extinction of others, De Luc elaborated the idea that the sinking of the continents and the displacement of the sea must have altered the earth's center of gravity and therefore slightly affected its rotary motion and the inclination of its axis. In addition, changes in the atmosphere because of the final release of expansible fluids would certainly cause differences in the heat aroused by the solar rays. A probable effect was the decreased retention of heat outside the torrid zone so that great differences in temperature appeared between summer and winter, night and day. The new earth was superior in that it was better adapted to man, who had become corrupted by his ennui of simple things. Such weariness resulted from the fertility of the soil and his own longevity.[27]

Not only did plants and animals survive on the ancient islands to repopulate the earth but even men, such as the ancestors of " the good Incas ", who had escaped the corruption of the continentals. However, here De Luc seemed rather unsure of his ground and refused to discuss the matter further. He even weakened and said that America and the islands might have been filled with men in some other manner after the deluge. The heresy was not repeated in his later book.[28]

Interesting was the suggestion that angels inhabited the earth before man was created, since both angels and the earth existed before the human race. The first education of man,

[27] De Luc, *Letters on the Physical History of the Earth* (London, 1831), introduction, p. 29, letter v, pp. 190-195, 212, 213, 215, 216, letter vi, pp. 234, 235, 238-250, 252-270; De Luc, *Lettres physiques et morales sur l'histoire de la terre et de l'homme* (The Hague and Paris, 1779-1780), vol. v, pp. 616-621, 646, 676, 686, 687, 735-738.

[28] *Ibid.*, vol. v, pp. 491, 665, 666.

for example in language, and the incitement which caused
Adam to name the animals, were by angels. Man's own
faculties could not have enabled him to develop this knowledge.[29] De Luc explained the flaming sword that guarded
the gate of Paradise without reference to angels. He
thought that it was a volcanic eruption, and added that
then the whole garden sank to the bottom of the sea, even
before the destruction of the ancient continents.[30]

De Luc's collection of specimens,[31] together with his choice
of an audience, illustrates anew the extent to which the new
ideas and the new interest in science had spread through
the upper ranks of society. In his truly scientific emphasis
on exhaustive accumulations of data and on theories to fit
natural phenomena even when the examples contradicted
his preliminary hypotheses, as with regard to the inclination
of mountainous strata, he is a striking example of the increasing dependence upon observation rather than upon
authority which characterized the seventeenth and the
eighteenth centuries and which has proved the guide for
modern scientists to such comprehension of the world as
we have acquired. In another respect he was in line with
the best tradition. He broke away from the vulgar abuse

[29] De Luc, *op. cit.*, vol. v, pp. 690-697.

[30] De Luc, *Letters on the Physical History of the Earth* (London,
1831), letter vi, p. 264.

[31] A common activity of gentlemen amateurs in that day was the formation of such collections, as is shown among other places by the many
references to them in De Luc's own work, for instance De Luc, *Lettres
physiques et morales sur l'histoire de la terre et de l'homme* (The Hague
and Paris, 1779, 1780), vol. ii, pp. 202, 246, 247, 258, vol. iii, pp. 377-381,
533, vol. iv, pp. 144, 145, vol. v, pp. 33, 223, 260, 322, 350. Buffon spoke of
the same custom in his *Époques de la nature* and elsewhere. Buffon,
Oeuvres complètes (Paris, 1831-2), vol. v, pp. 52, 54, 55, 57, 59, 60, 64,
66, 175, 176, 229, 295. Woodward's remarkable collection a half century
earlier was mentioned by Harris (John), *Remarks On some Late Papers,
Relating to the Universal Deluge* (London, 1697), pp. 164, 165.

of his contemporaries that stained much of the scientific writings of the time as it did the political. Though he criticized, he did so with dignity, justice and kindness, and often expressed appreciation. He never descended to railing, and his objections were leveled against the doctrines rather than against their champions.

CHAPTER XXVII

THE END OF AN ERA

In France meantime had arisen a sceptical spirit, which was evinced by *Le systeme de la nature,* published anonymously in 1770 or 1771 [1] by Baron d'Holbach (1723-1789). Holbach, who had been born in Germany, was a friend of Diderot and the Encyclopedists. Probably Diderot assisted him in this open attack on Christianity and religion. He certainly contributed notes. It was a diffuse and declamatory book, which asserted rather than proved its statements. It rejected the creation of matter from nothing by a spiritual being, and said that the creation mentioned in the Bible was merely a formation. The annihilation of matter was as impossible as its creation. Matter was eternal, as was also motion, which was the necessary consequence of its existence, because matter was naturally and constantly in motion and apparent rest was only relative. All the phenomena of nature were ascribable to the diverse motions of its varied matter. The four elements were continually interacting. The sun was at the center of the solar system, and the planets revolved around it.[2] Though probably man was not also eternal, the first of the human race were not created by God; and man was not a superior and privileged being. The origin of man Holbach felt was a kind of evolution, peculiar to our planet and probably a necessary consequence of its formation or of the energies produced thereby. He seemed willing to be-

[1] Holbach, *The System of Nature* (New York, 1835), advertisement, p. v.

[2] *Ibid.,* especially pp. 18-23, 34, 208, 240-242.

282

lieve that the other planets were inhabited, but felt that their inhabitants must be unlike man in many ways, such as ability to endure temperatures fatal to human life.[3] The planet itself might be a mass detached from some other celestial body, or the result of incrustations similar to sun-spots, or it might be an extinguished or displaced comet. Probably he meant star.[4] As a corollary to his idea that life was produced by mechanical forces, he asserted the generation of " insects " from flour and water, from fermentation and from putrefaction, though the theory had been discarded by most authors for a century.[5] In discussing the flood, he and Diderot declared that the presence of fossil shells and the traditions of all nations proved that the whole earth had at various times been flooded, but that probably the Biblical flood was not universal, though it might have been produced by the contact of a comet with the earth, a perfectly natural cause.[6]

Holbach's unhesitating acceptance of the four elements and the exploded hypothesis concerning the spontaneous generation of small animals shows that his scientific knowledge was not profound and that he was more interested in anti-religious propaganda than in the discovery of the truth. In a period dedicated to experiment and the accumulation of data, he neither searched nature for the truth himself nor accepted the results of investigations by others.

Late in the eighteenth century the increased knowledge produced new and more scientifically fruitful hypotheses. To France belongs the credit for having promulgated the theory which swayed the thought of the nineteenth century. In 1796 Laplace, in his *Exposition du système du monde,*

[3] Holbach, *op. cit.*, pp. 43-47, 241.   [4] *Ibid.*, p. 44.

[5] *Ibid.*, p. 20.

[6] *Ibid.*, p. 176 and notes pp. 167, 176.

announced his famous nebular hypothesis, which he enlarged and of which he offered the proofs during the earlier years of the next century. With him may be said to have come to an end the tentative cosmogonies of which the preceding centuries were so prolific.

Germany during the same period was the home of that Abraham Gottlob Werner (1749 or 1750-1817) who by his lectures on geology in the Freiberg Mining Academy for nearly forty years after 1775, though he wrote little, inspired a more scientific study of geology. Werner's personality was so attractive and his teaching so inspiring that students flocked to him from all Europe and spread his doctrines and methods far and wide. He attempted to substitute for the wild theories of the earth current in his day a methodical classification of minerals and of their strata by which any new bed or rock might be recognized and its relation in time to others discovered. According to him, the strata were deposited at a period when the whole earth was submerged under an ocean deep enough to cover all present mountains. The earliest strata of granite, basalt and some other types of mineral were produced by chemical precipitation and everywhere underlay the later beds of limestone, sandstone, coal, salt and more recent basalt. Some of the later rocks resulted from chemical precipitation, but others were solidified from mere mechanical sediments. Still later and higher were the alluvial deposits of clay, sand, peat and other unconsolidated minerals. The cause which removed enough of this primitive ocean to permit the gradual appearance of the dry land was not explained either by himself or by his followers. The interpretation was especially difficult since the process of removal was interrupted by periods of increased height in the sea level, as was clear from the location of late strata on hills that were apparently dry during the period when earlier beds were laid down. Werner seemed to think that the excessive water was stolen by some celestial body which removed from the earth part of its ocean and of its atmosphere. He gave no clear reason for the formation of mountains, though he felt that some of their phenomena were due to the slipping of the upper strata down from their peaks.[7]   Werner was a protagonist in the great Wernerian-Huttonian controversy on the origin of the rocks.   His theory resembled Woodward's inasmuch as it connected the rock formations with the deluge when the whole earth was dissolved in the waters of an all-embracing ocean and re-formed by subsidence into strata as the sea receded or evaporated.   Werner found no place in his theory, however, for Woodward's central heat, but thought the interior of the earth cold.   Volcanoes, which were unknown in earlier ages, and similar phenomena were due to the spontaneous ignition of coal beds.[8]   James Hutton (1726-1797) of Edinburgh in 1785 read and subsequently published his *Theory of the Earth; or an Investigation of the Laws observable in the Composition, Dissolution, and Restoration of Land upon the Globe.*[9]   Two volumes containing part of the theory in enlarged form were published in 1795, and a portion of the rest in 1899.[10] His style was so obscure that his work did not attract the attention it deserved until in 1802 his friend, John Playfair,

---

[7] The first sketch of his theory appeared in a pamphlet of twenty-eight pages, Werner, *Kurze Klassification und Beschreibung der verschiedener Gebirgsarten* (Dresden, 1787).   It gave the essence of the whole.   Geikie, *The Founders of Geology* (London and New York, 1897), especially pp. 102-137.

[8] Mayer, *The Seven Seals of Science* (New York and London, 1927), pp. 185-187.   The *Encyclopedia Britannica*, art. "Werner," seems to imply that the ocean out of which the strata were precipitated was the body of water at creation.   *Cf.* also Geikie, *loc. cit.*

[9] In the *Transactions of the Royal Society of Edinburgh*, vol. i, Geikie, *op. cit.*, pp. 158, 159, 163-165.   In 1790, 1791, the account was assailed by De Luc, who leaned to Werner's views.

[10] Hutton, *Theory of the Earth, with Proofs and Illustrations* (1795).

published his *Illustrations of the Huttonian Theory of the Earth*.   Hutton did not attempt to promulgate a theory of creation but limited himself to a discussion of the contemporary state of the earth and felt that its present composition must be explained by causes active at present or recently. He declared for the modern view that contemporary rocks were in great measure formed from the waste of older ones, laid down under the sea.   Subsequently, with the interpolation of veins and masses of molten rock, that were liquefied by the interior warmth of the earth, the strata were disrupted and raised by subterranean heat.   By means of this high internal temperature of the globe the horizontal strata had been tipped and folded in great confusion.   After they were above the surface of the water, they in turn were worn down. The process of eroding the whole land surface, depositing the debris on the bed of the sea and upheaving new continents never ceased.   Hutton asserted the igneous origin of both basalt and granite.   Werner, however, the chief authority in geology of the day, was upheld by most, especially by "ecclesiastics, who denounced Hutton as an atheist and a meddler." [11]   In the end, nevertheless, Werner's mistaken attribution of basalt to oceanic precipitation rather than to volcanic action produced a vigorous controversy and resulted in the gradual secession from his views of his most intelligent and skilful disciples.[12]

Meanwhile hypotheses derived from Biblical data were still current in many fields of interest.   Even so late as 1788 appeared a new and enlarged edition of James Beattie's work, *The Theory of Language,* which declared that mankind had speech from the beginning as a choice gift of the Creator,

[11] Mayer, *op. cit.,* p. 186, also p. 187; Geikie, *op. cit.,* especially pp. 150-197.

[12] *Ibid.,* pp. 137-149, 197.

and was inclined to the opinion that writing as well as language was taught by God to Adam. On the ground that hieroglyphic characters implied quaintness and witticism, Beattie believed that " the wisdom and simple manners of the first men " made them employ alphabetical writing.[13]

Nevertheless, the knowledge of science became constantly more wide-spread so that no gentleman could afford to be ignorant of its conspicuous doctrines. Compendia continued to be written for the general public. George Adams (1750-1795), a London instrument maker and optician for royalty, in 1794 published five volumes of *Lectures on Natural and Experimental Philosophy*.[14] The last volume consisted of plates to illustrate the others. The lectures, which purported to give the principal phenomena of nature and to show that they displayed the goodness, wisdom and power of God, were in a popular vein. Volume IV on astronomy, electricity, magnetism and meteorology affirmed that the heliocentric system was generally received and gave a summary thereof, together with a proof of its truth and of the absurdity which Adams declared was inherent in the Ptolemaic. He said that the heavens were unbounded in extent. Through them moved not merely the planets but also the sun and the stars, though their motion was relatively slight. The sun was not the center of the universe but part of the sidereal stratum which we name the Milky Way. The center of gravity in the solar system was some distance from the center of the sun, sometimes even near its surface. The movement of all the planets, including the satellites, was due to gravity. Adams apparently accepted the theory of Descartes and Leibnitz that the heavenly bodies were moved

[13] Beattie, *The Theory of Language* (London, 1788), especially pp. 99, 110, 315, 316.

[14] He was the author of numerous elementary scientific works and treatises on the use of mathematical instruments.

by a circulating fluid, and that there was no vacuum in nature, though he also said that the celestial motions were like those of electricity and of magnetism, where objects seemed to act upon one another at a distance without any intervening impulse.   Adams was another of the advocates for a plurality of inhabited worlds.[15]

The book criticized those who pretended to believe the Bible but said that God did not " know how to accommodate his doctrines to the capacities of the vulgar, without speaking with philosophical impropriety of his own works." [16] His actions and interpositions showed that He governed the universe as well as that He formed it.[17]   The natural Mosaic account of creation " when rightly understood, may be found to be most accurate, philosophical, and just." [18]   On the first day was formed light,—that is, " the matter of light, by the means of pure original motion," [19] which came directly from God.   This matter was obviously elementary fire.   The fire

produces that rapid *motion* of light from the sun or stars to the earth . . . *Fire* and *light* combined, produced air or the first and purest etherial particles; and, therefore, in the Mosaical account, the firmament, the expanse, or the atmosphere of the AIR, was the *second* day's work, or the *second* state of things in their progress to perfection and fulness.[20]

Air was not so subtle and active as fire and light but more so than water or vapor and formed the intermediate link between fire and water.   When " condensed, exposed to obstruc-

---

[15] Adams, *Lectures on Natural and Experimental Philosophy* (London, 1794), vol. iv, pp. 1, 2, 6-47, 53-56, 61, 62, 80-131, 177-179, 213, 216, 218-222, 231, 232, 239-257, 263-279.

[16] *Ibid.*, vol. iv, p. 571.   [17] *Ibid.*, vol. iv, p. 293.
[18] *Ibid.*, vol. iv, p. 431.
[19] *Ibid.*, vol. iv, p. 432.
[20] *Ibid.*, vol. iv, p. 432.

tions, and thus deprived of the greatest portion of it's etherial fire," it became vapor and then water in its various forms " as the fire dissipates, and the motion ceases." Since it was then almost deprived of its original motion, it was less subtle and more gross, and became an object of the senses and subject to the laws of gravitation.[21]

Water is the great support of animal and vegetable substances, which at length are reduced to earth in their various changes, from the first principles of active nature, down to the lowest, grossest material form; from the fountain of life, from the architypal ideas of the Divine Mind, through spirits to fire, light, ether, air, water, earth, down to sluggish inert matter.[22]

Even at this late date Oriental and neo-Platonic ideas of emanations and a chain of creation were current with some whose daily tasks would seem to label them as prosaic and exact materialists. Fire, light, air and water were " the grand agents in nature " ; the earth was " a basis for them to rest and to work upon ". In the former group of elements was " the circulation of motion in it's descent and degrees ", a descent " regular and beautiful . . . from the spiritual to the natural world, from motion to rest " [23] in the earth where they manifested their effects. Each part was preparatory to the succeeding, a link in the chain, and an instrumental cause. Finally " creation was no longer all fire, light, air, or water; but each retained it's respective rank " [24] and the world was ready for plants, animals and men. The earth as well as the sun was a source of heat, either from a central fire or from a heat diffused through the whole planet from the epoch of creation. The terrestrial warmth

[21] Adams, *op. cit.*, vol. iv, p. 432.

[22] *Ibid.*, vol. iv, p. 433.

[23] *Ibid.*, vol. iv, p. 433.

[24] *Ibid.*, vol. iv, p. 433, also p. 431.

was renewed and preserved by the sun, and moderated the cold of winter.[25]

America did not lack an interest in cosmology and in the relation of scientific to Biblical doctrines.   The belief in the heliocentric system was firmly established in the New World by the second half of the eighteenth century.   Besides the reprints of European books, America produced some of her own.   In Philadelphia during 1785 was printed the beginning of *A General Compendium; or, Abstract of Chemical, Experimental and Natural Philosophy* by Charles Vancouver, which was based on the earth's revolution around the sun.   It broke off abruptly on page forty-eight after the enunciation of the following theses among others.   The body of the sun was not solid but consisted of elementary fire or light, a fluid.   At creation God operated by secondary causes, having endued matter with the quality of attraction. To each planet at its formation He gave also a counterbalancing progressive force.   The combination of the two impulses produced a circular motion.[26]

In 1798 the Commencement oration at New Haven, which was afterwards printed, was delivered by Ebenezer Grant Marsh (1777-1803) *On the Truth of the Mosaic History of the Creation*.   The treatise was composed as his Master's Oration; and it, together with his work as graduate student, was so esteemed that he was immediately given the post of instructor in Hebrew in spite of his youth.   He had graduated from Yale in 1795 when he was only eighteen; and by the time he was twenty-four, after three years during which he had taught and studied theology, he was licensed to preach. His sermons gave general satisfaction.   A year later he was

[25] Adams, *op. cit.*, vol. iv, pp. 433, 434, 545.

[26] Vancouver, *A General Compendium; or, Abstract of Chemical, Experimental, & Natural Philosophy* (Philadelphia, 1785), pp. 2-4, 10, 11, 31.

appointed Professor of Languages and Ecclesiastical History, although his entrance upon his new duties was postponed until the university was able to collect funds for his salary. Unfortunately the time never arrived, since he died of cancer at twenty-six years of age. Naturally his views on cosmogony were neither profound philosophy nor startling innovation, but for that very reason they illustrate current intellectual opinion.

Marsh was another interpreter who identified Noah with the " Indian Bacchus ", the Chinese Fohi and the Hindu seventh Menu and said that this concept proved Noah's settlement in Persia and the close relationship of all these Oriental races. Moses's account of early events was the oldest in the world, for he lived several centuries before any other historian. Probably the manner of creation was revealed to Adam and transmitted by tradition to Moses. In the process the narrative would pass through only seven hands. Had his version not agreed with the general tradition, the Israelites would immediately have discovered the fact and have proclaimed him an imposter. In addition, the account was confirmed by many heathen fragments, chiefly about Chaos, about an intelligent principle or God, Who formed all things therefrom, and about the creation of man from mud by God. The heathen did not deduce these doctrines by the use of reason but acknowledged that they had received them from their wiser ancestors. Sometimes they affirmed a divine source for their dogmas. Many pagan philosophers suggested barbarian and even Hebrew traditions as the basis of their opinions.[27] The most rational answer as to the source whence these celebrated ancestors drew their facts was " from Moses or Adam, to whom they must have been revealed by God. *They,* certainly, were as unable to discover them by

---

[27] Marsh, *An Oration, on the Truth of the Mosaic History of the Creation* (Hartford, 1798), pp. 22-39, 53-58.

the power of reason, as all succeeding philosophers." [28]
Moses and Adam did not have even enough learning to " tell
the true meaning of many of them." [29]   The earth could not
have been formed by natural causes, such as those suggested
by Burnet, Woodward, Hutchinson, Whiston, Buffon or
Hutton, because of the ages necessary for the process.
Buffon, Hutton and De Luc, who claimed a great antiquity
for the earth on geological grounds, were wrong.   Marsh
called De Luc's arguments too contemptible to deserve an
answer.   The fossil shells, of which Hutton talked, came
from the deluge.   It lasted long enough for many shell-fish to
grow after they had been brought on the land and fastened on
new beds.   Only a few could have followed the water in its retreat.   So great a pressure of water, five or six miles deep,
would have made the earth very soft and pressed shell-fish to
great depths.   It would have forced both them and the
remains of terrestrial animals into clefts of rocks and petrified them.[30]   Marsh was apparently a trifle hazy as to the
results of so great a volume of water and offered inconsistent
and unscientific hypotheses.

Probably Marsh agreed with Usher, who was " generally
considered as the most accurate chronologer ", in the belief
that the world was created October 23, 4004 B. C.[31]   The
length of time God took was probably chosen for the instruction of men and angels.   Unquestionably angels had
been created earlier.   The deliberation and detail of the action
made both terrestrial and celestial philosophers appreciate
it more completely, and gave a " ' divine example of weekly
labor and sabbath rest ' " the more effectually to inculcate
the doctrine.[32]

---

[28] March, *op. cit.*, p. 39.   [29] *Ibid.*, p. 40.

[30] *Ibid.*, pp. 40-45.   [31] *Ibid.*, p. 58 note.

[32] *Ibid.*, p. 21.   The quotation was from Stackhouse, l. i, c. i.   Marsh
was addicted to quotations, especially from the *Universal History*.

The stellar systems were perhaps formed many thousands of years before the solar system, and the mention of stars on the fourth day was probably an interpolation from the margin. Presumably the globes of the solar system were all created simultaneously from different chaotic masses.[33] The doctrine that the planets were developed from one chaos would make us " reject the laws of gravitation and place the earth in the center of the system." [34] By heaven Moses unquestionably meant " the space circumscribed by the path of Herschell, or that of the most distant comet in our system, or, which is most likely, the upper region of the air." [35] Marsh did not attempt to decide whether the spirit which moved on the waters was a violent wind to dry them up, the Holy Spirit or plastic nature. With regard to the creation of light he was more dogmatic. He affirmed that it clearly existed in the darkness but could not be seen unless it was " excited ".[36] A lighted candle was visible three miles, but so small a body obviously could not " furnish a sufficient quantity of light to fill a spherical space six miles in diameter. It is more probable, that the particles, in that space, are excited by the candle." [37] Without such a previous supply of light throughout the world, many solar spheres could not produce illumination. Ordinarily these particles were excited by the sun, but before the creation of the sun God might have been the exciter.[38] But it was

more rational to conclude, from the connexion between all the bodies in the solar system, that the sun and moon were in ex-

[33] Marsh, *op. cit.*, pp. 11, 12, 17.
[34] *Ibid.*, p. 12 note.
[35] *Ibid.*, p. 12.
[36] *Ibid.*, pp. 13, 14.
[37] *Ibid.*, p. 14 note.
[38] *Ibid.*, p. 14.

istence from the commencement of the creation, but could not be seen the three first days, on account of the vapours, and heterogeneous particles, with which the air was filled.[39]

Probably the light gradually increased as the foreign particles in the air subsided, so that the sun and the moon appeared on the fourth day. The atmosphere was somewhat cleared on the first day so that light could pierce it. By the second it was so far perfected as to be capable of supporting clouds. These were probably the waters over the firmament, while those below were the waters on the earth's surface.[40] The first method suggested by Marsh for drying the earth was the hypothesis upheld by Bishop Patrick (*Com. on Gen.* 1:9), that the land was raised by an earthquake. Into the caverns produced by the same force the waters could flow. Then, with no hint of his own opinion, he added Whiston's statement that the terrestrial columns of different density sank into the subterranean abyss for different distances.[41]

Since the spontaneous generation of plants and animals was fully disproved, all living creatures must have been formed by a supernatural power; and the earth and the water were merely the matter used. Their rapid production was a miracle rather than the result of any fecundity in the earth. Fowl and fish were so much alike in their methods of moving and of producing young in quantity that they clearly had a single original. The creation of man differed from that of the animals because it had a degree of solemnity and was preceded by a consultation of the Trinity. The variety of races was generally conceded to be due to climate and state of society, and not to descent from other than the original pair.[42] For his peroration, Marsh summarized his point of view. He felt the

[39] Marsh, *op. cit.*, p. 15.
[41] *Ibid.*, p. 16.
[40] *Ibid.*, pp. 15, 17.
[42] *Ibid.*, pp. 18-21.

truth of Christianity . . . intimately connected with that of this part of the history of Moses. If the world was formed previously to the creation of man, it follows, that our knowledge of its formation must have come originally from God. If, therefore, we are convinced that the Mosaic account is true, we must allow it to be a revelation, and, of course, admit the truth of the scriptures both of the Old and New-Testament. And such is the evidence with which it is supported, that they, who refuse to believe it, *would not be persuaded though one should rise from the dead.*[43]

Marsh was rather a compiler than an innovator. He revived the ancient custom of listing various contradictory theses with absolute impartiality. He seemed unwilling to antagonize any auditors except the scientists. His work was in no way noteworthy save as an expression of the rising interest in scientific topics among the citizens of the new republic. It formed a fitting conclusion to a discussion that had ceased to engross the leaders of thought.

[43] Marsh, *op. cit.*, p. 59.

PART II
TOPICAL REVIEW

CHAPTER I

The Heavens

THE preceding chapters have attempted to summarize many of the cosmological systems current during the seventeenth and the eighteenth centuries. There is, however, another angle from which they might be discussed. Instead of a presentation of the complete cosmological scheme developed by an author, it is possible to group related ideas propounded by various philosophers and scientists on some of the topics treated. Although such a recapitulation would involve repetition, it should show the correlations of doctrines with one another and the dependence of each author upon many of his predecessors. Logically the first questions to be considered should deal with the universe as a whole, the heavens and the celestial spheres. Then should follow those connected with the elements, the earth and its formation. Last of all should be mentioned the problems connected with organic nature, plants, animals and men. Continually the conflict will be evident between the orthodox doctrines derived from Aristotle, Ptolemy and the Scriptures and the new scientific knowledge promulgated by Galileo, Kepler, Newton and a host of less well-known investigators and theorists.

Among the most influential new scientific theories were Descartes's, which presented an intelligible, plausible and comprehensive picture of the present cosmic phenomena and of their history.[1] The Cartesian vortices were wholly ac-

[1] Descartes, *Oeuvres* (Paris, 1824), vol. iii, *Les principes de la philosophie.*

cepted or even taken for granted by Glanvill,[2] Gadroys,[3] Mallement de Messange,[4] Fontenelle,[5] Burnet,[6] Dickinson,[7] Catoir,[8] Horrebow,[9] Swedenborg,[10] Le Catt and De Maillet [11] among others. M. de Castelet in a letter to Mallement de Messange, which accused the recipient of plagiarism from his theory, accepted the vortices with the emendation that the bodies at their cores were planets and not suns, in other words that all or most of the stars were planets, and were carried with their satellites around a distant center. He and the anonymous author of the *Essay d'un nouveau systeme du monde* mentioned Descartes's minor vortices that

[2] Glanvill, *Scepsis Scientifica* (London, 1665), pt. i, pp. 129, 142, 143.

[3] Gadroys, *Le systeme du monde* (Paris, 1675), pp. 132, 133, 143, 153, 156-189, 198-200, 203-209, 224-228, 270-274, 277, 288-299, 304, 318-322, 373-376, 385, 393.

[4] Mallement de Messange, *Nouveau systheme du monde* (Paris, 1678), p. 5.

[5] Fontenelle, *Entretiens sur la pluralité des mondes* (Paris, 1821), pp. 95-99, 113-130.

[6] Burnet, *Doctrina Antiqua de Rerum Originibus* (London, 1729, 1736), *Archaeologiae Philosophicae*, pt. i, p. 179, pt. i, critique, p. 36.

[7] Dickinson, *Physica Vetus et Vera* (Rotterdam, 1703), especially p. 82, although the effects he assigned to such a motion did not coincide with those accepted by Descartes.

[8] Catoir, *Disputatio Theologica de Arca Noachi et Diluvio* (Gröningen, 1704), sec. xviii.

[9] Horrebow, *Clavis Astronomiae* in *Operum mathematico-physicorum, etc.* (1740), quoted by Delambre, *Histoire de l'astronomie au dix-huitième siècle* (Paris, 1827), p. 140.

[10] Swedenborg, quoted by Arrhenius, *The Life of the Universe as conceived by man from the earliest ages to the present time* (London and New York, 1909), vol. i, pp. 111-117, and by Clerke, *Modern Cosmogonies* (London, 1905), p. 15.

[11] Le Catt and De Maillet, quoted by De Luc, *Lettres physiques et morales sur l'histoire de la terre et de l'homme* (The Hague and Paris, 1779, 1780), vol. ii, pp. 180, 326-334.

drag around the earth, Jupiter and Saturn their satellites.[12] The author of the *Essay* and Kircher thought that the globes carried the matter of the vortices around with them as they whirled instead of attributing the motion of the spheres to the vortices.[13] Kircher believed that the atmospheres were effluvia of the various globes and were kept distinct from one another because they differed as the globes did.[14] The last hypothesis was Swedenborg's opinion as well.[15] In opposition to Descartes's thesis that the vortices touched one another, Kircher thought of them as separated by a considerable space, through which comets wandered.[16] Huygens said that they were little islands in the expanse of the universe. They were surrounded by air which moved more slowly.[17] Warren displayed his customary inconsistency by an apparent acceptance of Descartes's vortices, an exposition of the Cartesian theory and a declaration that the Biblical account was literally true and that Descartes himself denied the verity of his own hypotheses.[18] Swinden propounded the interesting suggestion that all the vortices were perhaps enveloped by the empyreum. Since he believed the solar vortex to be central, such a location for the empyreum would remove the

[12] De Castelet, *Lettre à Monsieur Mallement de Messange* (?, 1679), pp. 3-6; *Essay d'un nouveau systeme du monde* (Paris, 1691), pp. 8-11. The author felt that the rotation of the earth and of the supplementary vortex was caused by the unequal pressure of the sun's rays on various parts of the surface.

[13] *Ibid.*, pp. 2, 8, 11; Kircher, *Itinerarivm Exstaticvm* (Rome, 1656), pp. 175-177.

[14] *Ibid.*, pp. 176, 177.

[15] Swedenborg, *Miscellaneous Theological Works* (New York, 1863), *The Earths in the Universe*, secs. 20, 61, 64, 86, 89, 128, 148.

[16] Kircher, *op. cit.*, pp. 175, 177, 178.

[17] Huygens, *Nouveau traité de la pluralité des mondes* (Amsterdam, 1718), pp. 269-275. (First published with the title *Cosmotheoros*.)

[18] Warren, *Geologia* (London, 1690), pp. 51-54, 92-96.

sun or hell as far as possible from the dwelling-place of God
and the blessed. Perhaps our vortex limited the activities
of the devil. In spite of this supposition, he neither definitely accepted nor rejected the theory of vortices, which he
attributed to Huygens.[19] Swedenborg's suggestion that
each planet had its own hell and that the spirits from the
different celestial spheres had difficulty in mingling or in
communicating with one another showed an affinity for this
point of view.[20] On the other hand, the Cartesian doctrine
of vortices was sometimes rejected on the ground that it was
atheistic, as for example by Cudworth, who during the seventeenth century planned and partly executed a monumental
work against atheism.[21] Newton and his adherents, including Whiston,[22] rejected the Cartesian vortices on scientific
grounds; and after about fifty years their theories as to the
causes of planetary motions triumphed even upon the continent.

Definitions of Biblical terms caused disputes. Alsted [23]
and Le Clerc [24] maintained that the word " firmament " as
used in the *Book of Genesis* had a twofold meaning, though
Le Clerc limited its significance in the sixth and seventh verses

[19] Swinden, *An Enquiry into the Nature and Place of Hell* (London,
1727), pp. 226-232, 249, 250.

[20] Swedenborg, *op. cit., The Earths in the Universe*, secs. 109, 137.

[21] Cudworth, *The True Intellectual System of the Universe* (London,
1743) (1st ed., 1678), vol. ii, pp. 683, 684. He apparently favored the
supposition that the other stars were surrounded by planets, most or all
of which were inhabited by intelligent beings who might glorify God,
though earlier he had called the belief " extravagant ", *ibid.*, vol. ii, pp.
675, 882, 883.

[22] Whiston, *A Vindication of the New Theory of the Earth from the
Exceptions of Mr. Keill and Others* (London, 1698), p. 22.

[23] Alsted, *Physica Harmonica* (Herborn, 1642), pp. 29, 32, 33.

[24] Le Clerc, *Mosis Prophetae Libri Quinque* (Amsterdam, 1735),
(1st ed. of Genesis, 1693), pp. 7-11.

of the first chapter to the air below the clouds. Duguet and d'Asfeld called it both the space between the earth and the stars and that containing the stars and the planets.[25] In the *Itinerarivm Exstaticvm* Kircher upheld the thesis that the firmament was the ethereal expanse from the moon to the bounds of the universe, but some pages earlier and in the *Mundus Subterraneus* eight years later he used the term as equivalent to the sphere of the fixed stars.[26] The opinion that it was the stellar sphere was held also by Hakewill,[27] by Blancanus, who believed it to be a solid sphere with a diameter equal to twenty-eight thousand semi-diameters of the earth and with the stars fastened to its swiftly whirling form,[28] and by Pfleumer, who arrived at the conclusion after a consideration of all the other interpretations, especially those of the early Fathers. He listed six other definitions, among which he included the thesis that the firmament denoted the good angels or good men.[29] Fludd believed that it included both the planetary and the stellar heavens.[30] Riccioli apparently accepted in the end the identity of the

[25] Duguet and d'Asfeld, *Explication de l'ouvrage des six jours* (Paris, 1740), pp. 53-60, 346.

[26] Kircher, *Itinerarivm Exstaticvm* (Rome, 1656), pp. 258, 297-299; Kircher, *Mundus Subterraneus* (Amsterdam, 1664-5), t. i, p. 37.

[27] Hakewill, *An Apologie or Declaration of the Power and Providence of God in the Gouernment of the World* (Oxford, 1635), pt. i, p. 87.

[28] Blancanus, *Sphaera Mvndi* (Bologna, 1620), pp. 130, 132, 133, 307-312, 336, 351-353, 356-358. The same opinion was expressed by Mersenne, who cited Tycho Brahe as his authority. Mersenne, *Qvaestiones Celeberrimae in Genesim* (Paris, 1623), cols. 79, 80, 811-826, 828-840, 845, 872.

[29] Pfleumer, *Dissertatio Theologico-Critica, de Aqvis Svpracoelestibvs* (Jena, 1733) (Delivered 1663), pp. 5-7, 10-13. Mersenne similarly had given eleven or more different interpretations of the word firmament, as if the mystical and spiritual definitions were just as probable as the corporeal. Mersenne, *op. cit.*, cols. 681-684, 799-804, 809-826.

[30] Fludd, *Utriusque Cosmi Maioris scilicet et Minoris Metaphysica, Physica atque Technica Historia* (Oppenheim, 1617), p. 53.

firmament and the stellar heaven; but he wavered for some time, both over the solidity of this heaven and over the inclusion of the ethereal planetary heaven as part of the firmament. Although he finally located the stars there and accepted its solidity, he also affirmed that, according to the Bible, not heaven but the things contained therein moved. At last he decided that there were five heavens, the empyreum, the aqueous or crystalline, the firmament or stellar, the ethereal or planetary and the airy. Then he immediately added that perhaps the last was no heaven at all and that the fourth possibly was united with the third.[31] Besides these more ordinary interpretations, two or three were evolved that showed considerable ingenuity. Hutchinson thought that the earth was shaped from chaos in the form of a hollow sphere. Both within and without was air, and this he termed the firmament. Obviously, as the waters were pressed out on either surface of the hollow earth, those within the earth were above the central firmament and those without were below the outer.[32] The opinion was adopted by Pike [33] and by Catcott.[34] Burnet in the first edition of his theory seems to have advanced the suggestion that the firmament was the earth crust itself, which separated the waters of the abyss from those on the surface; but he receded from this position in later editions and said that there was no solid firmament.[35]

[31] Riccioli, *Almagestvm Novvm Astronomiam Veterem Novamqve Complectens* (Bologna, 1651), vol. ii, pp. 216-225, 238-244, 271-276.

[32] Hutchinson, *Moses's Principia* (London, 1724), pp. 22-34.

[33] Pike, *Philosophia Sacra* (London, 1753), pp. 69-71, 107-111, *The Explanation of the Copper Plate,* pp. 5, 6.

[34] Catcott, *A Treatise on the Deluge* (London, 1768), pp. 55-60.

[35] Warren, *Geologia* (London, 1690), pp. 226-228; Warren, *A Defence of the Discourse Concerning the Earth Before the Flood* (London, 1691), pp. 119, 120; Warren, *Some Reflections upon the Short Consideration Of the Defence of the Exceptions against the Theory of the Earth* (London, 1692), p. 43; Burnet, "Latin Theory", pp. 124, 254, cited by Warren; Burnet, *The Sacred Theory of the Earth* (London, 1722) (5th ed.), vol. ii, bk. iii, p. 41.

Several authors, in consideration of the fact that each of the planets and other celestial bodies was composed of water as well as of the other elements, decided that the water on all except the earth was the water above the firmament, which was the interplanetary space or perhaps the interval between solar systems.[36] Descartes had thought that the firmament was the outer boundary of the solar vortex.[37]

In the heavens were located stars, planets and comets, their inhabitants, as Comenius called them.[38] Even through the time of Kepler the stars were believed to be approximately equidistant from the earth or from the sun if that was the center of the universe. Fludd [39] and Schott [40] upheld the doctrine, but Blancanus was doubtful.[41] On the other hand, Kircher asserted firmly that the stars were at varying distances from the earth, to which he assigned a central location.[42] Descartes's theory clearly was inconsistent with the supposition that the stars were equally remote, as he himself recognized.[43] Although the belief that the stars were equi-

---

[36] Witty, *An Essay toward a Vindication of the Vulgar Exposition of the Mosaic History of the Creation of the World* (London, 1705), pp. 70, 71, though he added that perhaps the superior waters were the clouds, *ibid.*, pp. 72, 73; *cf.* also *infra*, pp. 368, 369.

[37] Descartes, *op. cit.*, vol. iii, *Les principes de la philosophie*, pt. iii, sec. 131.

[38] Comenius, *Naturall Philosophie Reformed by Divine Light* (London, 1651), p. 15.

[39] Fludd, *op. cit.*, pp. 44, 127.

[40] Schott, remarks in Kircher, *Iter Extaticum Coeleste* (Würzburg, 1660), p. 342.

[41] Blancanus, *op. cit.*, p. 307.

[42] Kircher, *Itinerarivm Exstaticvm* (Rome, 1656), pp. 259, 260 and elsewhere.

[43] Descartes, *op. cit.*, vol. iii, *Les principes de la philosophie*, especially pt. iii, sec. 23. Some who agreed with Descartes on this point were the following: Mallet, *Description de l'univers* (Paris, 1683), vol. i, pp. 90, 102, 104; Burnet, *op. cit.*, vol. ii, bk. iii, p. 41; Burnet, *Doctrina Antiqua*

distant from the center of the universe was generally denied
or ignored after the time of Descartes, it was affirmed a
century later by Pike.[44]   In an attempt to establish some
order in the location of the stars Comenius asserted that they
differed in distance according to their density, as did the
clouds, so that the densest were closest to the earth at the
center, though he may have meant the planets, since he was
discussing them on the same page.   Earlier in his treatise
he located the stellar sphere more than 720,000,000 miles
from the earth and divided stars into numerable and innumerable according to their size.   The Milky Way consisted of
countless very small stars.[45]   His thesis concerning the relation between stellar density and distance resembled the common opinion that the distance of the planets from the sun
varied according to their density and that the celestial spheres,
both stellar and planetary, varied in perfection according to
their distance from the center of the universe.   The only
difficulty seemed to be the decision as to whether the inner
spheres were more or less dense, more or less spiritual and
perfect.[46]

de Rerum Originibus (London, 1729, 1736), Archaeologiae Philosophicae,
pt. i, p. 217; Huygens, op. cit., pp. 249-256; Huygens, cited by Macpherson,
Modern Cosmologies (London, 1929), pp. 18, 20; Witty, op. cit., pp. 170,
171; Harris (Joseph), The Description and Use of the Globes and the
Orrery (London, 1740), p. 34; Duguet and d'Asfeld, op. cit., p. 115;
Wright, The Universe and the Stars (Philadelphia, 1837), pp. 119-128;
Adams, Lectures on Natural and Experimental Philosophy (London,
1794), vol. iv, pp. 45, 46, 221-223, 240 and elsewhere.

[44] Pike, op. cit., The Explanation of the Copper Plate, pp. 3, 4, and the
plate itself.

[45] Comenius, op. cit., pp. 117-119, 121, 122.

[46] Those who thought the inner planets the densest were as follows:
Newton, cited with approval of the statement but for different reasons
by Buffon, Oeuvres complètes (Paris, 1831-2), vol. i, pp. 185-190; Kant,
Allgemeine Naturgeschichte und Theorie des Himmels (Leipzig, 1890),
pp. 68, 76, 77 and pt. iii, where he applied the doctrine also to the inhabitants

According to Jéhan, in the first half of the seventeenth century, almost all astronomers believed that the stars were self-luminous and moved with the eighth or sidereal heaven. Biblical commentators added that they had been formed from condensed water, the abyss, on the fourth day.[47] Fludd explained their production as the result of the conflict on the second day between light or *forma* and the shadows. During the struggle some light was entangled in masses of the shadows, and together they were raised to the concave surface of the crystalline sphere. To this they were frozen; and, like other opaque bodies, they reflected the light. Though he denominated as stars also those spheres formed after the sun on the fourth day, in that case he probably meant the planets. They, as well as the stars, were incorruptible, at least until the end of the world. The production of the sun and the

of the planets and declared that those more remote from the center were more rational or more spiritual. Wright had perhaps the same idea, Wright, *op. cit.*, especially pp. 113, 135, 136, 139-141. The belief in the inferior density of the outer planets was upheld by Swedenborg, cited by Arrhenius, *op. cit.*, vol. i, pp. 114, 123, 124, who cited Kant also, *ibid.*, vol. i, pp. 123, 124. Comenius also thought that the inner planets were the densest, although he was discussing their distance from the earth rather than from the sun. Comenius, *op. cit.*, pp. 121, 122. The opposite opinion, that the density increased with the distance from the central sphere, was held by Descartes, *op. cit.*, vol. iii, *Les principes de la philosophie*, pt. iii, sec. 147; by Gadroys, *op. cit.*, pp. 182-184; and by Warren, *Geologia* (London, 1690), p. 86. Descartes had previously declared that centrifugal force would drive farthest from the center the largest particles in a rotating mass, though he realized that Mars was both more remote from the sun than the earth and smaller. Dickinson asserted that the smallest particles would be driven farthest from the center. Descartes, *op. cit.*, vol. iii, *Les principes de la philosophie*, pt. iii, secs. 54, 82, 85, 147; Dickinson, *op. cit.*, especially pp. 68, 70-72, 205. Wilkins believed in a successive increase in size of the planets from Mercury to Saturn. Wilkins, *The Mathematical and Philosophical Works* (London, 1707-8), bk. ii, *A Discourse Concerning A New Planet*, p. 219.

[47] Jéhan, *Dictionnaire de cosmogonie et de paléontologie* (Paris, 1854), art. "Cosmogonie aux XVIe et XVIIe siècles," col. 306.

other planets differed from that of the stars and the Milky Way, although they were all composed of the same matter, as were also comets and falling stars.   The Milky Way was an opaque band, fastened to the concave surface of the crystalline heaven between it and the stars.   The heavenly bodies varied in density and in amount of *forma*.[48]

Some other scientists, like Fludd, held that the stars as well as the planets shone by light reflected from the sun; but this opinion was increasingly difficult to accept as the century progressed and especially after the era of Descartes.[49]   Their assimilation to the sun, which had been a thesis of Giordano Bruno at the close of the sixteenth century, proceeded apace.[50] Many authors, like Bruno, went so far as to assign to the stars planetary attendants invisible to us but the abode of intelligent beings.[51]   The opinion gradually developed that the stars were made of ether, which was identified with fire. This view was held by many, including Schroeder,[52] Gad-

[48] Fludd, *op. cit.*, pp. 44, 127-132, 134-145. For a complete account of planetary genesis according to Fludd, *cf. supra*, pp. 28-30.

[49] Some who asserted that the stars were not self-luminous were Blancanus, *op. cit.*, p. 342; Hakewill, *op. cit.*, pt. i, p. 99; Mallement de Messange, *op. cit.*, pp. 5, 6, 9-12, 18-21, who believed it of most stars and went so far as to say that our earth might be a sun to some other globe, though perhaps he called the stars planets because of the circular motion around a central spot that he attributed to them rather than because of any doctrine concerning their luminosity; M. De la Jonchere, Abstract of a projected work, *A New System of the Universe*, p. 32, printed in Burnet, *op. cit.*   Pike affirmed that they were perhaps reflectors but more probably self-luminous, though they were not the centers of other systems and were not mobile.   Pike, *op. cit.*, *The Explanation of the Copper Plate*, pp. 3, 4, and the plate.

[50] Macpherson, *op. cit.*, pp. 18, 20, 26 note.

[51] This doctrine was popularized by Fontenelle, *op. cit.*; Huygens, *op. cit.*; and was upheld anonymously by Bishop Wilkins in two often reprinted books, *The Discovery of a New World* and *A Discourse Concerning A New Planet*, Wilkins, *op. cit.*, pp. 1-274.

[52] Schroeder, *Aqvas Supracoelestes à multis hactenus Doctoribus Supra Coelum Sidereum locatas* (Kiel, 1671), cap. iv, art. xi, who thought them made of primeval light.

roys,[53] Milton,[54] Burnet [55] and Swinden.[56]   Gale said that
they were formed of primogenial light or fire.[57]   Bacon,[58]
Comenius [59] and Alsted [60] taught that all the celestial bodies
were true flames or fires.   Comenius, who excepted the moon
but included the other planets, declared that they were the
present shape assumed by the primeval light, although in accordance with his general doctrines he believed also that they
were made of matter, spirit and light;[61] Alsted considered
that they were formed of condensed light,—i. e., that they
were the denser parts of their orbs.[62]   Wright said that they
and the sun were composed of fire.[63]   Mallet thought them
self-luminous and composed of a different matter from the
planets; but he declared that each planet, including the sun,
differed from the others.[64]   Hale thought that the planets
differed both from the stars and from one another because of
the " greater proportion of more gross and feculent Matter

[53] Gadroys, *op. cit.*, pp. 161, 166, 174, 213, 214.

[54] Milton, *The Poetical Works* (London, 1862), *Paradise Lost*, bk. iii,
ll. 715-719.

[55] Burnet, *op. cit., Archaeologiae Philosophicae*, pt. i, critique, p. 36;
Burnet, *The Sacred Theory of the Earth* (London, 1722), vol. ii, bk. iv,
pp. 317-320.

[56] Swinden, *op. cit.*, pp. 230, 231.

[57] Gale, *The Covrt of the Gentiles* (Oxford and London, 1670-77),
vol. i, pt. i, bk. iii, p. 48, pt. ii, bk. iii, pp. 338-342.

[58] Bacon, *Works* (Boston, ?), vol. iv, *Sylva Sylvarum*, cent. i, no. 31,
p. 179.

[59] Comenius, *op. cit.*, pp. 13, 14, 116, 119, 121, 124.

[60] Alsted, *op. cit.*, pp. 34, 38, 39.

[61] Comenius, *op. cit.*, pp. 13, 14, 25-27, 119, 121, 124, 126.

[62] Alsted, *op. cit.*, p. 34. That was Mersenne's opinion as well. Mersenne, *op. cit.*, col. 831.

[63] Wright, *op. cit.*, pp. 55-57, 61, 67, 77.

[64] Mallet, *op. cit.*, vol. i, pp. 90, 91, 112.

added " to the fiery primitive light and ether of which the
stars and the sun were made.[65]

Descartes introduced into the mass of fluctuating and
vague opinions a concrete theory dealing with the birth and
the death of suns or stars.[66]   It captured the imaginations of
his contemporaries.   Gadroys accepted it in its entirety,[67]
as did many others.   Burnet adopted it so far as to talk
about vortices and dead stars that became planets and comets
but might be resuscitated.[68]   Descartes affirmed that as the
vortex rotated, there collected in a central sphere the minute
particles of a first element.   This sun or star was a necessary
center for each vortex.   Its incrustation with sun-spots
would darken it until its force decreased to such a point that
it lost its vortex and was swallowed up in a neighboring
vortex as a planet or wandered from one to another as a
comet.[69]   Obviously he was one of the earlier proponents
of the thesis, which constantly became more popular, that
the creation of sun and stars, if not of planets, far antedated
the Mosaic history of the terrestrial creation.   The doctrine
was implicit if not explicit in most accounts after his time.
Le Clerc, who was frequently considered radical, said, however, that sun and stars were formed on the fourth day.[70]
Kircher assimilated the stars to the sun in many respects but
denied inhabitants to any planets that might surround them.
He declared that all the celestial spheres were composed of

[65] Hale, *The Primitive Origination of Mankind* (London, 1677), pp.
301, 302.

[66] Descartes, *op. cit.*, vol. iii, *Les principes de la philosophie*, pt. iii.

[67] Gadroys, *op. cit.*, pp. 166, 173, 174, 278-282.

[68] Burnet, *op. cit.*, vol. ii, bk. iii, p. 141, bk. iv, p. 317; Burnet, *Doctrina
Antiqua de Rerum Originibus* (London, 1729, 1736), *Archaeologiae Philosophicae*, pt. i, critique, pp. 36, 37, 51.

[69] Descartes, *op. cit.*, vol. iii, *Les principes de la philosophie*, pt. iii.

[70] Le Clerc, *op. cit.*, paraphrase, p. 6.

the same four elements as the earth, but that the elements of each so differed from those of the others that they could not mix. If removed by force, they must return to their own sphere.[71]

Most authorities, including even Blancanus,[72] believed in a spherical form for the stars; but Maupertuis declared that some were flattened like millstones, so that they could be seen only when their disks were turned towards the observer.[73] An idea, expressed by Hakewill, gained some currency. He thought that the stars and the sun were not themselves fiery and hot but merely produced heat in such matter as possessed the appropriate tendency. The heat was the effect of the solar light and not of the motion. Otherwise it would cease when the motion stopped as when Joshua commanded the sun to stand still; it would be uniform because it would resemble the uniform motion of the celestial bodies; and the higher regions of the air, which were nearer to the motion, would be warmer than those near the earth.[74]

Comenius endeavored to give a cause for the creation of so many stars, including those that were not even visible. They heated the earth and lighted it on every side; by their burning and swiftly travelling light they moved the whole heavens and carried their sphere about in twenty-four hours. They differentiated times and gave great variety to things on earth.[75] The last argument, which asserted their astrological influence, as well as that of the planets, appealed to Kircher and to many others, although his insistence upon the vain folly of astrologers was constant. He compromised by the

[71] Kircher, *op. cit.*

[72] Blancanus, *op. cit.*, pp. 342, 343.

[73] Maupertuis, *Essay de cosmologie* (Paris? or Amsterdam?, 1750), pp. 135, 136, and as quoted by Delambre, *op. cit.*, p. 364.

[74] Hakewill, *op. cit.*, pt. i, pp. 103, 104.

[75] Comenius, *op. cit.*, pp. 90, 116-118.

ancient declaration that the stars inclined men to various actions but did not compel them.[76]   Sir Thomas Browne declared that stars were differentiated astrologically because of their color, so that the white planets and stars like Jupiter, Venus and Arcturus were regarded as benignant and the red as portentous.   He suggested that in the same way the white comets might be beneficient and only the red be ominous.[77] Other reasons were added through the centuries for the production of such numbers of stars, among which was the help they afforded to navigation in general and to the discovery of longitude in particular; but a chief argument for planetary inhabitants was the belief that the service of the earth was too insignificant and mean for their splendor and that so scattered a light was not well adapted to such a service.

The agreement that the stars were of great size was practically universal, although the dimensions suggested would seem insignificant to a modern astronomer.   Blancanus quoted with approval Tycho Brahe's estimate that the stars of the sixth magnitude were a little smaller than the earth, while those of the first were seventy times as large or about four-fifths of the solar size.[78] Comenius held that all stars were from eighteen to one hundred and seven times the size of the earth.[79]

In 1572 the sudden appearance of a new star in Cassiopeia and its disappearance after two years startled the astronomers.   Another appeared in Septenarius in 1604.   Since orthodox opinion at that epoch denied both the possibility of new creations and the corruptibility of the heavens, astronomers were greatly perturbed; and many theories were

[76] Kircher, *op. cit.*, especially pp. 84-86, 96-103, 108-116, 131-136, 158, 160-164, 193-197, 203, 210-215, 230, 231, 238-242, 283, 328-330.

[77] Browne, *Works* (London, 1888-1890), vol. ii, *Vulgar Errors*, p. 209.

[78] Blancanus, *op. cit.*, p. 344.

[79] Comenius, *op. cit.*, p. 117.

advanced during the succeeding centuries to explain new, variable and vanishing stars, which clearly were parts of the same problem.[80]   Tycho Brahe and Kepler thought them as well as comets "temporary conglomerations of a cosmical vapour filling space";[81] and Galileo declared them both perhaps "products of terrestrial exhalations of extreme tenuity, at immense distances from the earth, and reflecting the sun's rays."[82]   Because of their absence of parallaxes, they could not be below the moon.   In three public lectures, which antagonized the Aristotelians, he called public attention to the new star of 1604.[83]   Hakewill found no better explanation of the one in Cassiopeia than to say that it was the miraculous work of God.   He thought also miraculous the oft-cited change in Venus during the reign of Ogyges, mentioned by St. Augustine on the authority of Varro, who claimed that the information was given in Castor.[84]   Fontenelle tried to avoid the heresy of a new creation or an annihilation of matter by the supposition that dispersed matter might from time to time unite to form a new world; but he was inconsistent and also accepted the popular theory of the day, that of Descartes.[85]   In the end most scientists agreed with Gadroys that the new stars were not newly generated but like comets had long existed and merely appeared

[80] Fahie, *Galileo His Life and Work* (New York, 1903), pp. 53, 54.

[81] *Ibid.*, p. 55.

[82] *Ibid.*, p. 55, also p. 181.

[83] *Ibid.*, pp. 55, 56, 181, 182.

[84] Hakewill, *op. cit.*, pt. i, pp. 87, 88. Raleigh, *The History of the World* (Edinburgh, 1820), vol. i, pp. 209, 210, attempted to formulate a scientific explanation of the Ogygian alteration in Venus, and Burnet considered it a proof of his theory. The quotation from St. Augustine was *De Civitate Dei*, l. 21, c. 8, and from Varro, *De gente populi Romani*. *Cf. supra*, p. 71.

[85] Fontenelle, *op. cit.*, pp. 128-135.

suddenly.[86] Maupertuis grouped them with nebulous stars
to prove that there was more than one variety of stars.
Perhaps their temporary invisibility was due to planets that
revolved around them or to their own shape. According to
his hypothesis many stars were disk-like and visible only
when their faces were turned towards the earth. The empty
spaces in the sky were localities where the stars were less
luminous and much smaller or perhaps more flattened.[87]

However, the most widely accepted theory was that of
Descartes. He asserted that new stars were originally suns,
on which sun-spots had accumulated until they were eclipsed.
Sometimes the luminous first element within broke through
the crust and flooded the surface with matter which glowed
even more brilliantly than at first since it was more agitated.
Then mankind would observe a new star. If spots accumulated again on the surface, the star would disappear. Variable stars resulted from such alternations of darkness and
light. Comets and planets represented merely a further
stage when the imprisoned first element failed to break the
crust.[88] Gadroys,[89] Burnet,[90] Ray [91] and Swedenborg [92]
were among those who adopted Descartes's explanations.

[86] Gadroys, op. cit., pp. 280-282; Burnet, op. cit., Archaeologiae Philosophicae, pt. i, critique, p. 50.

[87] Maupertuis, op. cit., pp. 134-136, and as quoted by Delambre, op. cit.,
p. 364.

[88] Descartes, op. cit., vol. iii, Les principes de la philosophie, pt. iii,
secs. 101-104, 110-119.

[89] Gadroys, op. cit., pp. 278-282, 287-294, 313, who mentioned specific
instances of new stars, pp. 31-33.

[90] Burnet, op. cit., Archaeologiae Philosophicae, pt. i, critique, pp. 36,
37, 51; Burnet, The Sacred Theory of the Earth (London, 1722), vol. ii,
bk. iii, p. 141, bk. iv, pp. 317-320.

[91] Ray, op. cit., pp. 314-316, 322, except for the doctrine, which he asserted was denied by Descartes also, that the earth was an extinguished
sun or star, ibid., pp. 317, 318.

[92] Swedenborg, quoted by Arrhenius, op. cit., vol. i, pp. 111, 114.

Kircher agreed in associating the phenomena with those of comets, and called new stars tailless comets. They seemed fixed because of their distance. His theory of their cause resembled his hypothesis about the production of comets. He declared that they were exhalations from the planets and the stars, perhaps particularly from the pole star, and, like clouds, reflected stellar light to us. Perhaps the new stars were not the effluvia themselves but were opaque, hidden, lunar globes, which reflected anew the light cast upon them from the exhalations.[93]

Apparently to avoid an asseveration of changes in the heavens, the star at the birth of Christ, which Grew thought a probable instance of a new star,[94] Hakewill explained rather as " a *blazing light* created in the Region of the Aire, . . . then [than] a new and true *created starre, seated in the firmament.*" [95] Elsewhere he called it a comet.[96] On the whole, however, scientists agreed that such phenomena proved the corruptibility of the heavens, as was explicitly stated by Riccioli,[97] Kircher,[98] Schott [99] and Planer.[100] Colbert accepted stellar birth, motion and death as a proof of the permeability of the planetary region, though he probably meant comets instead of new stars.[101] Alsted's

[93] Kircher, *op. cit.*, pp. 173, 278-282; Kircher, *Mundus Subterraneus* (Amsterdam, 1664-5), t. i, p. 62.

[94] Grew, *Cosmologia Sacra* (London, 1701), p. 318.

[95] Hakewill, *op. cit.*, pt. i, p. 87.   [96] *Ibid.*, pt. i, p. 136.

[97] Riccioli, *op. cit.*, vol. ii, pp. 237, 238, where he mentioned sun-spots as another proof of celestial corruptibility.

[98] Kircher, *Itinerarivm Exstaticvm* (Rome, 1656), p. 280.

[99] Schott, in Kircher, *Iter Extaticum Coeleste* (Würzburg, 1660), pp. 26, 35.

[100] Planer, *Cometa. Coeli Pars et Partus* (Tübingen, 1682), p. 13.

[101] Colbert, *Regi Armis Omnia Expugnanti Architecturam Militarem Sapientia Omnia Constituenti Totius Mundi Constitutionem Belli Pacisque Arbitro Bellatricem Pacificam Mathesin* (?, 1668), p. 13.

most notable contribution to the discussion on new stars was the declaration that they portended and brought about unusual events.[102]

Planetary theory produced fewer problems than stellar, though it gave rise to a bitterer dispute over the major question concerning the correct classification of the sun and of the earth. After astronomers had decided that planets were solid spheres and were not made of some fifth element or attached to orbs which carried them around, it was generally agreed that they were composed of the same matter as the earth and consisted of the four elements, though possibly the elements varied a trifle from globe to globe so that each planet would retain its identity. Their motion was attributed to various causes. Descartes and the Cartesians believed that they were carried by the vortices, in which they were engulfed, as leaves are carried by a stream.[103] Newton's opinion that their motion was started by God and was continued by the force of gravity is well known. Perhaps the simplest explanation was the ancient belief that to each sphere was assigned an angel or possibly several angels, who guided its course and performed any other appropriate tasks. Even Kepler believed in the presence on the sun of such celestial beings and in their influence, although he gave another reason for planetary motion. He thought that if intelligences did move the planets, their orbits would be circular.[104] Hakewill, on the other hand, considered that

[102] Alsted, *Methodus Admirandorum Mathematicorum Novem libris exhibens universam Mathesin* (Herborn, 1641), p. 245. New stars, etc., were discussed by Mallet, *op. cit.*, vol. i, pp. 102-106; Adams, *op. cit.*, vol. iv, pp. 213-217.

[103] Descartes, *op. cit.*, vol. iii, *Les principes de la philosophie*, pt. iii, secs. 18, 19, 26-31.

[104] Kepler, *Epitome of the Copernican Astronomy* (1618-1621), bk. iv, pt. 2, 3, pp. 499-530, especially p. 508, quoted by Berry, *A Short History of Astronomy* (London, 1898), p. 196; by Riccioli, *op. cit.*, vol. ii, pp.

natural motion of such bodies as were neither light nor heavy would be circular, and therefore that the elliptical planetary motion was not natural. Angels had been appointed by God to assist and to perpetuate the motion of the planets. Though he did not insist on his view, he apparently believed that stars and planets were fastened to their spheres and thus enabled to execute their varied motions, including the diurnal rotation around the earth.[105] Riccioli, who quoted Kepler, denied that the circle was the only perfect figure. He affirmed that seven principal angels moved the major planets, and that less important spirits presided over the lesser motion of the satellites. Probably four, twelve or twenty-four were required to move the orb of the fixed stars; and perhaps they were stationed in one locality as in Palestine, while the other angels accompanied their charges. They moved the spheres by intellect and will, not by corporeal organs.[106] The satellites and the sphere of the fixed stars were carried in a spiral.[107] Fludd believed that an angel presided over each heavenly body, but was not needed to move it.[108] Kircher and perhaps Schott assigned more than one angel to each sphere and differentiated them in rank. The angels of the sun, for example, were seraphs. The classification of angels adopted by Kircher was naturally that of Dionysius.[109] Postel, writing in the previous century, had

---

247, 249; and by Arrhenius, *op. cit.*, vol. i, p. 103, who erroneously stated that Kepler believed the planets to be guided by angels. The pages are the same in Kepler, *Epitome Astronomiae Copernicanae* (Frankfurt, 1635), pt. ii, secs. 1-3.

[105] Hakewill, *op. cit.*, pt. i, pp. 92, 93.

[106] Riccioli, *op. cit.*, vol. ii, pp. 247-251, 289, 315. Riccioli said of the belief that angels needed corporeal instruments to move a planet " quid potest esse stolidius ", *ibid.*, vol. ii, p. 250.

[107] *Ibid.*, vol. ii, p. 289.   [108] Fludd, *op. cit.*, pp. 150, 151.

[109] Kircher, *op. cit.*, pp. 35, 60, 152-154; Kircher, *Itinerarivm Exstaticvm* (Rome, 1656), especially pp. 25, 26, 96-98, 116-118, 181-183, 203, 227, 254, 255, 276, 277, 357, 361-365, 373.

accepted the hypothesis that each of the ten orbs had a separate genus of intelligences who moved it. The celestial influences on bodies and on irrational *animae* were the acts of these intelligences through the medium of ethereal matter.[110] Burton sapiently limited himself to the remark that some believed every " star " had a soul or angel to animate and to move it.[111] Dr. Ozorio of Portugal called the belief that the motion of the thirteen heavens was caused by angels the more probable one.[112] Dickinson said that the movement of the stars was governed by them.[113]

By others, several strange materialistic hypotheses were evolved to explain planetary movements. Kepler and Wilkins thought that the spheres were moved by magnetic rays, which left the sun in straight lines and carried the planets along as if they were cogs catching on to a wheel. The sun itself revolved on its axis in approximately twenty-five days.[114] This was a variation of the Copernican view as presented by Mallet. He declared that according to Copernicus the planets of themselves were neither heavy nor light and that they had a round shape suited to motion. The rays of the sun drew them through the Zodiac. The nearer planets moved more swiftly because the rays which acted upon them were more powerful and active than those which affected

[110] Postel, *De Universitate* (Leyden, 1635), pp. 11-14, 40. Though the first edition of his work had appeared during the sixteenth century, its continued popularity was evinced by the publication of this third edition.

[111] Burton, *The Anatomy of Melancholy* (London, 1920), vol ii, p. 60.

[112] Ozorio, *Theologie cvrievse. Contenant la naissance du monde* (Dijon, 1666), pp. 133-141, 148. This seems to have been Mersenne's conclusion, though he added that perhaps they moved themselves. Mersenne, *op. cit.*, col. 844.

[113] Dickinson, *op. cit.*, pp. 125, 126, 224-227.

[114] Kepler, *op. cit.*, pt. ii, secs. 1-3, pp. 499-530, quoted by Berry, *op. cit.*, p. 196; by Riccioli, *op. cit.*, vol. ii, p. 247; and by Wilkins, *op. cit.*, bk. ii, p. 259.

the remoter spheres. Mallet himself may have accepted this view or may have preferred the Cartesian vortical theory.[115] The author of the *Nouveau systeme du monde* apparently attempted to combine the two theories. He affirmed that the rays consisted of material particles, which left the sun and passed through celestial matter by regular paths. They pressed upon the earth and drove it from its position of equilibrium with reference to the celestial matter. Its return as it was repulsed by the surrounding matter caused oscillations, which were diminishing so that in time a circular orbit might replace the present elliptical course. The earth travelled more slowly when it was in aphelion than when it was in perihelion because the celestial matter farther from the sun was thicker and moved more slowly while the rays were weaker. The earth's rotation was due to the motion of the supplementary vortex in which it and the moon were located. The rays of the sun caused this motion as well.[116] Pike thought that the planets were driven about the sun by the heat produced by the shining of the sun. The heat or friction at the center of the universe pulverized the masses into atoms, and therefore the spirit or masses pressed towards the center to restore the equilibrium. The initial rotation of the earth came from God; but later, since the heat was greater in the afternoon than in the morning, the spirit pressed in more strongly upon the afternoon part of the earth and continually turned the evening edge of the earth away from the sun. In addition, since the heat was much greater at that edge than at the morning one, the spirit continually pressed against it and drove the earth forward

[115] Mallet, *op. cit.*, vol. i, pp. 68-84.

[116] *Essay d'un nouveau systeme du monde* (Paris, 1691), pp. 1, 2, 5, 7-11, 13.

as well as around. A similar explanation accounted for
seasonal variations.[117]

The invention of the telescope made it possible to discern
spots on the sun. Johann Fabricius in northern Europe
was the first one to publish his observations on spots in
1611,[118] but it is generally believed that during or before
November of the preceding year Galileo had seen them. Unfortunately he and Christopher Scheiner, a Jesuit who was
professor of mathematics at Ingolstadt, disputed as to priority in their discovery. This was the beginning of personal
controversy between the Jesuits and Galileo. Scheiner's
famous book, *Rosa Ursina*, 1630, was a fierce personal attack on Galileo. Galileo gave the correct interpretation of
the sun-spots while Scheiner thought that they were little
planets.[119] Perhaps Scheiner's was the theory denied by
Blancanus [120] and by Kircher,[121] who attributed to some
astronomers the erroneous belief that sun-spots were little
stars carried around the sun. This hypothesis would not
explain their appearance and disappearance. The most common deduction from the spots and their phenomena was
that the heavens were not incorruptible; [122] but they were
also used to prove the rotation of the sun, as by Gadroys [123]

[117] Pike, *op. cit.*, pp. 22, 40-42, 53-55, 60-65, 121-123, 125. *Cf.* also
supra, pp. 253-256, 259-261.

[118] Johannis Fabricii Phrysii *de Maculis in Sole Observatis* (Wittenberg, 1611).

[119] Berry, *op. cit.*, pp. 157, 199; Grant, *History of Physical Astronomy,
from the Earliest Ages to the Middle of the Nineteenth Century* (London,
1852?), pp. 213-228; Fahie, *op. cit.*, pp. 128-132 and notes pp. 132, 266.

[120] Blancanus, *op. cit.*, p. 253.

[121] Kircher, *op. cit.*, p. 154.

[122] Wilkins, *op. cit.*, bk. i, p. 26; Riccioli, *op. cit.*, vol. ii, pp. 237, 238;
Kircher, *Iter Extaticum Coeleste* (Würzburg, 1660), p. 35; Planer,
op. cit., pp. 13, 14; Wolf, *Cosmologia Generalis* (Frankfurt and Leipzig,
1737), pp. 75, 76.

[123] Gadroys, *op. cit.*, p. 39.

and Mallet.[124]   The explanation by Descartes of their cause
was, like his other hypotheses, the most logical and the most
influential.   He stated that particles of the third element
were carried into the body of the sun.   Some were pulverized and assumed the form of the first element; but others,
which were more awkward in shape and slow in motion, were
expelled to the surface of the solar sphere and floated there
like scum.   Gradually they increased in size by becoming
entangled with one another.   While some were dissolved by
the constant friction of the first element below them and at
their edges, others remained for months or even longer.
The same series of events occurred on the stars.   When
the spots increased until the surface was nearly or completely covered, the light of the sun was reduced or extinguished.   The crust might be dissolved or merely cracked
and flooded by the imprisoned first element.   Later another
crust might form outside the thin coating of the first element
and it in turn might be cracked and covered with a coat of
the fiery matter.   By the alternations of this process, the
whole crust would become so thick that it could no longer
be fractured.[125]   Glanvill,[126] Gadroys,[127] Fontenelle [128] and
Burnet [129] were among those who accepted the whole account.
Holbach gave it as one possible method of planetary genesis,
together with the suggestion that the earth might have been
detached " from some other celestial body." [130]   Leibnitz

[124] Mallet, *op. cit.*, vol. i, p. 68.

[125] Descartes, *op. cit.*, vol. iii, *Les principes de la philosophie*, pt. iii,
especially secs. 94-104, 110-118, pt. iv, sec. 2.

[126] Glanvill, *op. cit.*, pt. i, p. 145.

[127] Gadroys, *op. cit.*, pp. 278-289.

[128] Fontenelle, *op. cit.*, pp. 128-134.

[129] Burnet, *op. cit.*, vol. ii, bk. iii, pp. 139, 142, bk. iv, p. 317; Burnet,
Doctrina Antiqua de Rerum Originibus (London, 1729, 1736), *Archaeologiae Philosophicae*, pt. i, critique, pp. 36, 37, 51.

[130] Holbach, *The System of Nature* (New York, 1835), p. 44.

associated his doctrine of the congelation and solidification on the part of a surface layer over an igneous earth with Descartes's explanation of such a layer as due to sun-spots with no apparent realization of the fundamental difference in source between the two types of opaque matter.[131] In addition Buffon called the spots a kind of scum;[132] and Ray adopted the hypothesis as possibly the cause for new and variable stars, for the future fate of the sun and therefore of the earth, for a possible destructive eruption of the central terrestrial fire and for the obliteration of the sun mentioned in the Bible as a preliminary to the final conflagration, although he denied its validity as a cause for the formation of planets, and asserted that Descartes himself denied it.[133] Thomas White thought that sun-spots were clouds of cinders and such wastes, and considered them a proof that at least the outer part of the sun consisted of bitumen and sulphur.[134] Swedenborg believed that the imprisoned fire in its efforts to escape from the shell of sun-spots strained and broke it. The shell then gathered into a belt around the solar equator, and by the rotation of the vortex was broken into masses, which became planets and satellites.[135] The *Essay d'un nouveau systeme du monde* expressed an idea somewhat similar to Descartes's. As the rays of the sun, which were subtle material particles, traversed the celestial matter by paths they had made there, they broke off particles of opposing bodies and carried them back to the sun. Since these foreign bodies were incapable of following the rapid motion of the sun, they were soon cast out like scum. The finer ones

[131] Leibnitz, *Opera Omnia* (Geneva, 1768), vol. ii, *Protogaea*, p. 202.

[132] Buffon, *op. cit.*, vol. v, p. 75.

[133] Ray, *op. cit.*, pp. 314-318, 322, 338, 339.

[134] White (Thomas), *Institutionum Peripateticarum Libri Quinque* (Frankfurt, 1664), p. 65.

[135] Swedenborg, quoted by Arrhenius, *op. cit.*, vol. i, pp. 111-114.

made a solar atmosphere, and the coarser were united by the agitation of the sun to form spots. If they were detached from the sun by its agitation, they became comets.[136]

Kircher's explanation of sun-spots was totally different. He considered them a kind of cloud, which was formed from the vapors of the boiling solar ocean, and which hid the surface from terrestrial observation. The sea burst out through holes in the land with such force as to be thrown high into the atmosphere as vapor. The spots disappeared by falling to the surface as fiery rain. The agitation of the solar atmosphere was the cause of their brief duration. The planets affected the sun. When because of their position the influences of water and cold were most powerful, the surface of the solar sea calmed down; and there were no eruptions or spots. On the other hand, the planets of a contrary nature produced great disturbances. If the spots increased or were thrown far into space, they broke free and were carried hither and thither as comets, which invariably followed the appearance of numerous sun-spots. Excess in size or numbers, which produced pallor of the sun, caused sterility, pestilence, famine and other evils on the earth, since the virtue of the sun was impeded by the curtailment of its rays. The purpose of the spots was both to purify the fiery ocean, so that it might acquire fresh strength for illumination and for heat, and to moderate its influence and warmth by the interposition of clouds. As Kircher said in the *Mundus Subterraneus,* sun-spots are diseases of the sun like fevers in man.[137] De Luc had still another explanation for them, part of which he declared that he had taken from Herschel. He asserted that the sun con-

[136] *Essay d'un nouveau systeme du monde* (Paris, 1691), pp. 13, 14.

[137] Kircher, *Mundus Subterraneus* (Amsterdam, 1664-5), t. i, pp. 58, 62; Kircher, *Itinerarivm Exstaticvm* (Rome, 1656), pp. 125, 151-155, 158-165, 180.

tained a great quantity of light and resembled phosphoric substances in that it emitted light as it decomposed. This process constantly renewed the sun's atmosphere, from which light was detached by a further decomposition. Sun-spots were transparent parts of the atmosphere which were not yet decomposed or which had temporarily ceased to emit light. Through them appeared the opaque body of the sun. There was no reason to believe that globe intensely hot.[138] Herschel also was of the opinion that the spots were parts of the solid solar continent at times shining " through the luminous solar clouds," and added the suggestion that even the sun might be inhabited.[139]

[138] De Luc, *Letters on the Physical History of the Earth* (London, 1831), letter iii, pp. 113, 114.

[139] Herschel, quoted by Arrhenius, *op. cit.*, vol. i, p. 118.

CHAPTER II

Celestial Influences

It is hardly necessary to mention the fact that throughout the seventeenth century belief in astrology flourished. Galileo was considered by the Grand Duchess of Tuscany the greatest of astrologers, and in 1609 worked on the horoscope of the duke. He incidentally reached an erroneous conclusion. When Kepler's salary at Prague was not paid, he supported himself by casting horoscopes and by publishing an almanac.[1] The vogue of almanacs spread far and lasted long, since a century and a half later Franklin with his flair for the popular demand published *Poor Richard's Almanac* during several years. Even yet almanacs of the traditional type with their mixture of astrological and astronomical data, their miscellaneous scraps of information and entertaining epigrams and anecdotes have not ceased to predict the weather day by day; and strangely enough, even yet their blunders have not destroyed the confidence of their readers.

Riccioli rejected astrology as an abuse of the study of the stars,[2] as did Sir Christopher Wren in his annotations on Sir Thomas Browne's *Vulgar Errors,* while Sir Thomas himself,[3] like Hale,[4] spoke on both sides; but until the last decade of the

[1] Fahie, *Galileo His Life and Work* (New York, 1903), pp. 64, 65 and note. However, Galileo rejected the moon as cause of tides.

[2] Riccioli, *Almagestvm Novvm Astronomiam Veterem Novamqve Complectens* (Bologna, 1651), vol. i, preface, pp. vi, vii.

[3] Browne, *Works* (London, 1888-1890), vol. i, pp. 461, 462, and note p. 453, vol. ii, pp. 209, 462, vol. iii, pp. 125, 126.

[4] Hale, *The Primitive Origination of Mankind* (London, 1677), pp. 247, 256, 262-265, 285, 286, although his final conclusion seems to be opposed to a belief in the effects of the stars and their conjunctions in the production of men and animals.

seventeenth century most scientists and philosophers as well
as the common people seem to have accepted the classic dicta
of astrology. Although Bacon, for example, criticized
much of the astrological literature of his day as " full of
superstition," [5] he elaborated a " Sane Astrology," [6] which
apparently differed from the other in that the stars affected
only large groups of people and large areas and that the influences must be continuous for some time, not instantaneous
and evanescent. Hobbes, a leading iconoclast of the century,
may have doubted the claims of astrology, since he grouped
it with other methods of foretelling the future, many of
which he slurred; but nevertheless he classified it among
the sciences.[7] Since he defined it as the influence of the
stars, and mentioned astronomy in addition, he did not follow the example of Heylyn [8] and probably of Sir Walter
Raleigh.[9] They sometimes employed the term astrology for
astronomy, although they did not doubt the influences of the
celestial spheres. Blancanus [10] and Alsted,[11] however,
clearly meant astrology when they called it a subdivision of
mathematics, and accepted its dogmas as a whole despite

[5] Bacon, *Works* (Boston, ?), vol. viii, *De Augmentis Scientiarum*, p.
489. Also pp. 487-491, 516.

[6] *Ibid.*, vol. viii, p. 492. Also pp. 489-497.

[7] Hobbes, *Leviathan* (Cambridge, 1904) (1st ed., 1651), pp. 53, 76.

[8] Heylyn, *Mikρόκοσμος a Little Description of the Great World*
(Oxford, 1633) (1st ed., 1621), pp. 14, 15, 659, 782; Heylyn, *Cosmography in Four Books* (London, 1674) (1st ed., 1648?), bk. i, p. 15, bk.
iii, pp. 153, 174, 183.

[9] Raleigh, *The History of the World* (Edinburgh, 1820) (1st ed., 1614),
vol. i, pp. 32-38, 66, 67, 166, 186, 220, 221, vol. ii, pp. 149, 153, 154, 162,
165, vol. vi, p. 352.

[10] Blancanus, *Sphaera Mvndi* (Bologna, 1620), p. 399.

[11] Alsted, *Methodus Admirandorum Mathematicorum Novem libris
exhibens universam Mathesin* (Herborn, 1641), pp. 214, 220, 228-230, 244-
248; Alsted, *Physica Harmonica* (Herborn, 1642), p. 113.

the rejection by Alsted of the astrological division of the heavens into left and right on the ground that it was absurd.[12] Hakewill proved the truth of astrology from the Bible, though he denied the common belief in the disastrous effects of eclipses.[13] Postel, who had no scepticism concerning the doctrine, felt that the pagan names assigned to the heavenly bodies should not be used by Christians and in a treatise republished in 1636 redesignated the symbols of the Zodiac in accordance with the parts of the body governed by each, as *Capitale* or *Capitarium* for instance, and replaced the constellations by geometrical groupings.[14] Rationalism as to other matters was not necessarily linked with rationalism in rejection of astrology. Webster, who by his vigorous opposition to the belief in witchcraft assisted in its downfall, accepted astrology,[15] while Glanvill, a leading exponent of witchcraft, ridiculed astrology and declared that there were six different ways, all according to rule, of "*erecting* a *Scheme*," [16] by which contradictory results were obtainable, though on the next page he spoke of studying astrology to see "*how far it will honestly go.*" [17] Though many believed in the influences exerted by the celestial spheres,[18] perhaps the most elaborate account was presented by

[12] Alsted, *op. cit.*, p. 111.

[13] Hakewill, *An Apologie or Declaration of the Power and Providence of God in the Gouernment of the World* (Oxford, 1635), pt. i, pp. 111-114, 167-169, 173, 174.

[14] Postel, *De Signorum coelestium vera configuratione* (Leyden, 1636), pp. 6-8, 12, 13, 19, 20, 28-32, 34-59; Postel, *De Universitate* (Leyden, 1635), pp. 11-14, 18, 40, 43, 48, 71.

[15] Potts, *Discovery of Witches* (Manchester, 1845) (1st ed., 1613), introduction, p. xli.

[16] Glanvill, *Saducismus Triumphatus* (London, 1681), p. 68.

[17] *Ibid.*, p. 69.

[18] Among them were Jordan, *The Creation of the World, with Noah's Flood* (London, 1827) (Written 1611), pp. 156, 157; Lilly, *An Intro-*

Kircher in his various books.[19] Fludd [20] and Dickinson [21] were close seconds.

The celestial virtue was supposed to affect either solely or chiefly those sublunar objects whose nature was akin to theirs. Perhaps for that reason a common belief asserted

duction to Astrology (London, 1887) (1st ed., 1647) ; Comenius, Naturall Philosophie Reformed by Divine Light (London, 1651), pp. 113, 116, 121 ; Butler, Hudibras (London and New York, 1886) (1st ed., 1663-1678), pt. ii, canto iii, pp. 148-150, 155, 156, unless he was merely presenting the common opinion; Bochart, Opera Omnia (Leyden, 1712) (1st ed., 1663), vol. ii, cols. 463, 464; Ozorio, Theologie cvrievse (Dijon, 1666), pp. 136, 137 ; Van Helmont, Opera Omnia (Frankfurt, 1682), p. 112; Milton, The Poetical Works (London, 1862), Paradise Lost, bk. iii, ll. 583-585, bk. iv, ll. 660-672, bk. v, ll. 414-426, bk. x, ll. 657-664, Paradise Regained, bk. iv, ll. 382-393; probably Mallet, Description de l'univers (Paris, 1683), vol. i, pp. 122, 124, 126, 128, 130, 134, 136, 142, 160; Gadbury, Thesaurus Astrologiae (London, 1674) ; probably Gadroys, Le systeme du monde (Paris, 1675), pp. 392-394, although his master Descartes ignored the topic in his Principia; some philosophers who, according to Beaumont, attributed earthquakes to "certain Conjunctions of the Planets", Beaumont, Considerations On a Book, Entituled The Theory of the Earth (London, 1692-3), p. 28; Grew, Cosmologia Sacra (London, 1701), pp. 88-91 ; M. de la Jonchere, abstract by J. M. of Jonchere's projected book, A New System of the Universe, 1728, p. 31, in Burnet, Doctrina Antiqua de Rerum Originibus (London, 1729, 1736).

[19] Kircher, Mundus Subterraneus (Amsterdam, 1664-5), t. i, pp. 56, 57, 59-64, 103-106, 108, 109, 128-137, 145, 151, 153, t. ii, pp. 165-167, 381, though on page 283 he called astrology vain and false and on pages 283 and 304 said that men were attracted to it and to its "sister", alchemy, by the devil; Kircher and Schott, Kircher, Iter Extaticum Coeleste Würzburg, 1660), pp. 35, 241, 243, 244, 283-289, 312-315; Kircher, Arca Noë (Amsterdam, 1675), pp. 74, 95, 128, 130, 131, 210, 211, 213, though on pages 174 and 211 he again referred to the devil as instructor in astrology; Kircher, Itinerarivm Exstaticvm (Rome, 1656), pp. 52, 53, 58-61, 98-101, 104, 105, 108-115, 132, 133, 193, 195, 203, 205, 210-215, 231, 235-242, 255, 326-330.

[20] Fludd, Utriusque Cosmi Maioris scilicet et Minoris Metaphysica, Physica atque Technica Historia (Oppenheim, 1617), pp. 38, 105, 106, 145-149, 187, 193, 196-198 and elsewhere.

[21] Dickinson, Physica Vetus et Vera (Rotterdam, 1703), pp. 123, 126-133, 135-139, 188-190, 223, 228-230, 250, 270, 301-303, 309, 310, 322, 329-333.

that man was a miniature reproduction of the macrocosmos or great world. Some authors, like Swedenborg,[22] emphasized the reverse thesis and called the universe an enlarged man. The various planets, for example, corresponded to the organs of the body.[23]

Although all the tenets of astrology were widely held, perhaps the most frequently mentioned were those dealing with the portentous aspect of comets. Kircher called the comet " dirum mortalibus omen." [24] It was supposed to prophesy or to produce wind, famine, plague, war, earthquakes, floods and death to great men, especially to kings.[25]

[22] Swedenborg, *Miscellaneous Theological Works* (New York, 1863) (1st published in Latin in London, 1758), *The Earths in the Universe*, secs. 5, 9, 10, 86, 88; Swedenborg, *The Heavenly Arcana* (London and Boston, 1839-48), n. 2996, 2998, 3624-3649, 3741-3750, 3883-3896, 4039-4055, 4218-4228, 4318-4331, 4403-4421, 4523-4534, 4622-4634, 4652-4660, 4791-4806, 4931-4953, 5050-5062, 5171-5190, 5377-5396, 5552-5573, 5711-5727, 10030.

[23] A few instances of belief in man as a microcosm were as follows: Sir Walter Raleigh, *The History of the World* (Edinburgh, 1820) (1st ed., 1614), vol. i, pp. 64-66; Fludd, *op. cit.*, frontispiece, pp. 8, 19, 28, 33, 34, 44, 172, 183 *etc.*; Mersenne, *Qvaestiones Celeberrimae in Genesim* (Paris, 1623), cols. 208-210, 886, 937, 1131, 1132, 1739; Alsted, *Physica Harmonica* (Herborn, 1642), pp. 224, 265-268; Comenius, *Naturall Philosophie Reformed by Divine Light* (London, 1651), pp. 16, 46, 47, 226, 227; Browne, *Works* (London, 1888-1890), vol. ii, p. 400; Beaumont, *Considerations On a Book, Entituled The Theory of the Earth* (London, 1692, 1693), p. 54; Dickinson, *Physica Vetus et Vera* (Rotterdam, 1703), pp. 165, 188-190, 253; Kircher, *Itinerarivm Exstaticvm* (Rome, 1656), pp. 77, 78, 114, 229, 236-238, 240, 242, 371, 394, 395. On the other hand, the resemblance was rejected as a mere analogy by Spencer, *A Discourse concerning Prodigies* (London, 1665), pp. 70, 71, 279, 280.

[24] Kircher, *op. cit.*, p. 167. Also pp. 3, 154.

[25] Fludd, *op. cit.*, pp. 183, 185, 197, who declared that comets partook of the nature of Mars and of Mercury; Hakewill, *op. cit.*, pt. i, p. 135; White (Andrew), *A History of the Warfare of Science with Theology in Christendom* (New York and London, 1910), vol. i, pp. 181-183, 188, 189, 191-196, quoting several including Büttner, *Cometen Stundbüchlein*

The poets, including Shakespeare,[26] Samuel Butler,[27] Milton [28] and so late an author as Thomson in the *Seasons*,[29] mentioned these evil effects both directly and in similes. The courtiers of the dying Cardinal Mazarin asserted that the comet of 1680-81 portended his decease, although he, and Madame de Sevigné, who reported it, ridiculed the idea.[30] In connection with the same celestial visitor the Town Council of Baden, Switzerland, decreed that all inhabitants should attend every religious service unless prevented by a good

(Leipzig, 1605), who from eighty-six Biblical texts proved God's purpose to use the heavenly bodies for man's instruction and then gave tables to deduce the comet's significance from the time and place of its first appearance, and some doggerel rhymes for peasants and children by two pastors and doctors of theology at Basle, Grasser and Gross, *Christenliches Bedencken...von dem erschrockenlichen Cometen* (Zürich, 1664); Spencer, *A Discourse concerning Prodigies* (London, 1665), preface and pp. 12, 13, 98-105, who rejected it but called it the opinion of the commonalty and quoted Grotius as an adherent of the belief; Mentelle, *Cosmographie élémentaire* (Paris, 1781), p. 216 note, who attributed the fear to the people though he denied its validity; apparently Raleigh, *op. cit.*, vol. vi, p. 352. Kunstmann in Heyn, *Specimen Cometologiae Sacrae* (Leipzig, 1742), pp. 11-13 quoted two authors who proved the ominous character of comets by Greek and Latin verses and by examples respectively, Ioannes Mavricivs Polzivs, concionator rostchiensis, *Mnemosynon sacrum*, and Ioannes Boedikervs, rector of the Cologne gymnasium, *Christlicher Bericht von Cometen*, but he himself felt that they were ministers of divine justice and signified instead the end of the world, *ibid.*, p. 32, as did Heyn's other pupil, Werder. Werder added that the belief in them as prophecies of pest and of death was common, *ibid.*, pp. 36, 37.

[26] Shakespeare, *History of King Henry the Sixth* (New York, 1882), pt. i, act i, sc. i, ll. 2-5; Shakespeare, *Tragedy of Hamlet, Prince of Denmark* (New York, 1879) (both ed. by Rolfe), act i, sc. i, ll. 117-125.

[27] Butler, *op. cit.*, pt. ii, canto iii, p. 149.

[28] Milton, *op. cit.*, *Paradise Lost*, bk. ii, ll. 707-710.

[29] Thomson, *The Poetical Works* (London, 1860?), vol. i, *The Seasons: Summer*, ll. 1706-1716.

[30] Madame de Sevigné, letter to the Comte de Bussy, Jan. 2, 1681, quoted by Olivier, *Comets* (Baltimore, 1930), pp. 12, 13.

reason and should abstain from merrymakings and late hours.[31] The Protestants associated the appearance of comets with the death of leaders in the church or with great persecutions. In America, Danforth proved their portentous nature by many examples, including the death of Mr. Cotton and the poor crops of 1663 and of 1664, as well as by Scriptural quotations. He used these facts to induce the people to repent.[32]

Attempts were made at pseudo-scientific explanations of these effects. Droughts, poor harvests and famines, winds, earthquakes and pestilences were the natural effects of comets upon the elements of earth and air, while wars and the death of princes were produced because comets dried up the natural humors of the body and increased the gall. Therefore they caused emotions that led to violence and quarrels, especially with princes, who were more delicate and arrogant than other men and lived in luxury with little restraint from such things as were particularly injurious when dryness predominated in the heavens.[33] Mallet affirmed that moderns rejected comets as causes for the fall of empires, the death of great men, pestilences and famines, but asserted that, like the other celestial spheres, they could naturally announce and even cause alterations in the air and could act upon bodies and upon the fruits of the earth.[34] Grew adopted another compromise. He said that they did not cause but were merely coincident with major catastrophes.[35] Derham was

[31] Jr. B. A. A., 37, 241, 1927, quoted by Olivier, *op. cit.*, p. 13.

[32] Danforth, *An Astronomical Description of the late Comet or Blazing Star As it appeared in New-England in the 9th, 10th, 11th, and in the beginning of the 12th Moneth, 1664. Together With a brief Theological Application thereof* (Cambridge, 1665), pp. 16-21.

[33] Reinzer, *Meteorologia Philosophico-Politica* (Augsburg, 1712), pp. 101-103, quoted by White (Andrew), *op. cit.*, vol. i, p. 189.

[34] Mallet, *op. cit.*, vol. i, p. 160.   [35] Grew, *op. cit.*, pp. 95, 96.

doubtful concerning their astrological effects;[36] and some authors, like Glanvill,[37] definitely rejected the idea. Hakewill, who himself disagreed, said that the evil effects of comets were generally accepted.[38] In spite of his attempt at scepticism, he immediately thereafter called the rainbow which appeared upside down in Mary Tudor's reign "a prodigious and supernatural signe indeed of those miserable and bloudy times which quickly followed after."[39] Even so late as 1746, Hervey repeated the assertion that the common people still believed in the portentous nature of comets, although he repudiated the thesis.[40]

Astrology influenced practice as well as theory. By means of it pious shepherds, especially Jacob and his sons, were supposed to have increased their flocks; and Noah constructed a talisman which lighted the ark and preserved the health of the inhabitants.[41] The first knowledge of the science was attributed to various Biblical characters, Seth, Enoch and Adam,[42] while great proficiency in the art was assigned to Noah, Abraham, Moses, Amos and others, as well as to the Chaldeans and to mythical African kings, such as Uranus and Atlas.[43] In more modern times a large pro-

[36] Derham, *Astro-Theology* (London, 1721), pp. 54, 55.

[37] Glanvill, *Scepsis Scientifica* (London, 1665), p. 129.

[38] Hakewill, *op. cit.*, pt. i, pp. 135, 136.

[39] *Ibid.*, pt. i, p. 137.

[40] Hervey, *Meditations and Contemplations* (Dublin, 1767) (1st ed., probably 1746), vol. ii, pp. 62, 63, 66, 92, 93.

[41] Dickinson, *op. cit.*, pp. 301-303, 309, 310, 322, 329-333.

[42] Jordan, *op. cit.*, pp. 102, 103, 156, 157; Gale, *The Covrt of the Gentiles* (Oxford and London, 1670-1677), vol. i, pt. ii, bk. i, pp. 6-9.

[43] *Ibid.*, vol. ii, pt. iii, bk. i, p. 33; Raleigh, *op. cit.*, vol. i, pp. 189, 190, vol. ii, pp. 149, 165; Duguet and d'Asfeld, *Explication de l'ouvrage des six jours* (Paris, 1740), pp. 121, 122; Burnet, *op. cit.*, *Archaeologiae Philosophicae*, pt. i, p. 25; Dickinson, *op. cit.*, pp. 270, 301-303, 309, 310, 322, 329-333; Bentley, *The Folly and Unreasonableness of Atheism Demonstrated* (London, 1699), p. 91.

portion of the practices indulged in by witches and by others who employed magic for healing or for harming were assisted by or wholly dependent upon the aspects of the stars. In Scotland attempts at healing based on astrological principles were punished by both church and state, but to no avail.[44] The choice of a mate in marriage and a physician in disease was governed by a consideration of their horoscopes. Unlucky "Egyptian" days were still shunned and lucky ones sought for the commencement of an undertaking or the application of medicine.[45] Gadbury wrote a book which gave all possible directions for the choice and conduct of a physician.[46] It based its argument for the importance of astrology in the cure of disease on the following theses: all natural diseases not the result of accident come from the four humors, which are directly affected by the moon; since diseases are more than four in number, their diversity must be due to some influence upon these four humors; this influence is the effect of the planets both singly and in relation to one another upon the moon, and its position with reference to the zodiacal signs.[47] Rothius, the scion of a medical family, felt that this belief was so dangerous as well as so false that he composed a refutation.[48] In the preceding

[44] Dalyell, *The Darker Superstitions of Scotland* (Edinburgh, 1834), pp. 28, 89, 121, 257, 285, 286, 368, 369 and elsewhere mentioned applications of astrology to life during the seventeenth and the eighteenth centuries and quoted many books of that epoch, including Gaffarel, *Curiositez Inouyes*, c. 6, pp. 106, 110, and Symson, *Description of Galloway* (1684), p. 95, as well as accounts of clerical and lay trials and laws.

[45] Arthur Hopton, *A Concordancie of Yeares* (1612), chapter entitled "Of the infortunate and fatall dayes of the yeare", quoted by Elworthy, *The Evil Eye an Account of this Ancient & Widespread Superstition* (London, 1895), p. 408. Also Gadbury, Rothius, Burton and others, *cf. infra*.

[46] Gadbury, *op. cit.*   [47] *Ibid.*, p. 261.

[48] Rothius, *Astrorum Influentias in Humana Corpora Dissertatione Astronomico-Physica* (Delivered Ulm, 1703), especially secs. 29-33, 56,

century Blancanus was emphatic in his affirmation of stellar assistance in the cure of disease and considered laudable that part of astrology which treated of the topic.[49]   Postel [50] and Grew [51] also believed that the stars influenced disease; Mallet reported that the hypothesis was current; [52] and Burton was inclined to the doctrine, although he declared that there was a difference of opinion upon the subject.   He asserted the necessity for choice of a period suited astrologically to various activities.[53]   Besides its value in medicine, astrology was of importance in the construction and use of talismans and such aids to humanity.   They were very popular, although Gale named them all, together with the Agnus Dei, " Magick trumperies "; [54] and they were shaped under auspicious constellations or stamped with them.   For the production of divining rods or the choice of those who by their means could discover concealed water, treasures, criminals and other secrets, the appropriate combinations of celestial spheres were requisite.[55]

Thus astrology was generally accepted during the seventeenth century, except for the so-called judicial astrology,

65, 66. Mersenne nearly a century earlier had upheld the same views. Mersenne, *op. cit.*, cols. 554, 571-574, 593, 594.

[49] Blancanus, *op. cit.*, pp. 339, 399.

[50] Postel, *De Signorum coelestium vera configuratione* (Leyden, 1636), pp. 12, 13.

[51] Grew, *op. cit.*, p. 89.

[52] Mallet, *op. cit.*, vol. i, p. 142.

[53] Burton, *The Anatomy of Melancholy* (London, 1920), vol. ii, p. 17, vol. iii, pp. 356, 357.

[54] Gale, *op. cit.*, vol. i, pt. ii, bk. i, p. 67. Mersenne thought such talismans ridiculous. Mersenne, *Les qvestions theologiqves, physiqves, morales, et mathematiqves* (Paris, 1634), pp. 84-89.

[55] Le Brun, *Histoire critique des practiques superstitieuses* (Paris, 1702), especially pp. 54, 55, 57-60, 63, 108, 119, 120, 123, 125, 208-211. He discussed the effect of the stars on divining rods and the like in great detail, and quoted many authors, including Fludd and Gadrois, *Des influences des astres*, c. 7.

which purported to prophesy the future. This was opposed as an interference with the free-will of men and of God. Raleigh rejected it, though in his second volume he seemed less positive;[56] Blancanus called it an unworthy study, forbidden by human and divine laws, although possibly he did not deny its truth;[57] Thomasius declared it unchristian,[58] and Gale a " Black Art " whose source was hell;[59] Duguet and d'Asfeld denominated it and its parts frivolous and idolatrous;[60] and Le Brun, who was heartily opposed to all of astrology, affirmed that the errors of judicial astrology had been exposed in the Bull of Sixtus V.[61] Mersenne rejected judicial astrology, though he spent some time discussing alternative horoscopes for the perfect musician. In addition, in his opinion the belief that God had inscribed all future events in the book of the stars was not heretical since it had not been condemned by a council.[62] Alsted, on the other hand, who believed in astrological prophecies, explained how to make prognostications.[63] Often however, it was asserted that the stars inclined men to certain courses but did not compel them. Sometimes the addition of Kircher, that they did compel animals and inferior types of matter, was explicitly offered.[64] Nevertheless the negative opinion was

[56] Raleigh, op. cit., vol. i, pp. 33-38, vol. ii, pp. 149, 153, 162.

[57] Blancanus, op. cit., p. 399.

[58] Thomasius, Exercitatio de Stoica Mundi Exustione (Leipzig, 1676), dissertatio xx, Fatum sidereum.

[59] Gale, op. cit., vol. i, pt. ii, bk. i, p. 66. Also vol. ii, pt. iii, bk. i, p. 33.

[60] Duguet and d'Asfeld, op. cit., pp. 118-122.

[61] Le Brun, op. cit., pp. 194-210, 291, 295-297.

[62] Mersenne, Les prelvdes de l'harmonie vniverselle (Paris, 1634), pp. 1-26, 34-109; Mersenne, Qvaestiones Celeberrimae in Genesim (Paris, 1623), cols. 379-390, 957-1012.

[63] Alsted, Methodus Admirandorum Mathematicorum Novem libris exhibens universam Mathesin (Herborn, 1641), pp. 246, 247.

[64] Kircher, op. cit., pp. 112, 113, 193.

also in evidence. Mirabaud called the principles ridiculous and the results vain;[65] and with him agreed Burton,[66] Hakewill,[67] Browne,[68] Schott[69] and Rothius.[70] Many went further. Rothius, because of the distance of the stars and the physical characteristics of the planets, rejected the effects of all the heavenly bodies except the sun;[71] and Christian Ludovic Scheidt in 1749 denied the suggestion that fossils were due to the influences of the stars and their silent commerce with earthly things.[72] Burnet rejected astrology and declared that it and magic were probably taught men by evil spirits " for they . . . seem . . . more than human Contrivances or Dotages." [73] Warren,[74] Huygens[75] and Donck[76] denied the truth of astrology. In addition its opponents employed a stronger weapon than argument, in the shape of ridicule. Sporadic examples of this occurred during the seventeenth century,[77] and early in the eighteenth century

[65] Mirabaud, *Le monde, son origine, et son antiquité* (London, 1778) (2d ed.), pt. i, p. 10.

[66] Burton, *op. cit.*, vol. iii, pp. 279, 441, 442.

[67] Hakewill, *op. cit.*, pt. i, pp. 112-114.

[68] Browne, *op. cit.*, vol. i, p. 461, who, however, did not reject " a sober and regulated astrology."

[69] Schott, in Kircher, *Iter Extaticum Coeleste* (Würzburg, 1660), p. 285.

[70] Rothius, *op. cit.*, secs. 57-64.

[71] *Ibid.*, secs. 3-19, 21-35, 46-49, 58-66.

[72] Leibnitz, *Opera Omnia* (Geneva, 1768), vol. ii, *Protogaea*, p. 188.

[73] Burnet, *op. cit.*, *Archaeologiae Philosophicae*, pt. i, p. 132. Also pp. 25, 131; Burnet, *The Sacred Theory of the Earth* (London, 1722), vol. ii, bk. iii, pp. 38-41.

[74] Warren, *Geologia* (London, 1690), pp. 6, 7.

[75] Huygens, *Nouveau traité de la pluralité des mondes* (Amsterdam, 1718), pp. 171, 172.

[76] Donck, *Disputatio Theologica, de Divina Creatione Coelorum et Terrae in Principio* (Leyden, 1713), thesis vi.

[77] Fontenelle, *Entretiens sur la pluralité des mondes* (Paris, 1821) (Written 1686), p. 44; Bentley, *op. cit.*, pp. 91-98, 100, especially pp. 93-95.

the attitude of polite society in London had become one of scepticism and ridicule, as was shown by two papers in the *Spectator,* one by Addison and one anonymous.[78]

[78] *The Spectator* (London and New York, 1898), vol. vii, no. 505, Oct. 9, 1712, especially p. 150, vol. viii, no. 604, Oct. 8, 1714, especially pp. 206, 207.

CHAPTER III

Primeval Light

The Biblical account of the creation began with the creation of the heaven and the earth, without form and covered with darkness. Then by His word God produced light on the first day. He divided it from darkness, and called the two respectively day and night. The explanation of the first act presented only slight difficulties to commentators, and the Scriptural version was accepted as narrating the creation of matter out of nothing. The portrayal of this matter as formless coincided with the ideas transmitted to posterity by the Greek natural philosophers, and the agreement was often used to prove both the scientific accuracy of Moses and the doctrine that the pagans borrowed their culture and wisdom from the Jews. It was far otherwise with the second episode. The belief that light antedated sun, moon and stars by three days, and that there were days at all before the sun existed, demanded and obtained exegesis. Some of the interpretations during the seventeenth and the eighteenth centuries had long histories and had been evolved by the Jewish Rabbis or by the Fathers of the early church, but others of considerable popularity were apparently modern. Seldom did a commentator shirk the duty of exposition altogether, although Le Clerc[1] refused to philosophize on the cause and nature of this light on the ground that sufficient data were lacking. He denied that by light and darkness self-

---

[1] Le Clerc, *Mosis Prophetae Libri Quinque* (Amsterdam, 1735) (1st ed., 1693), p. 6.

338

existent entities were meant [2] because no one could attribute such an idea to the sacred writer. Therefore the division of the two meant that by their means time was divided. He also denied that the creation of light meant the creation of angels.[3] This time-worn suggestion was generally ignored during the seventeenth and the eighteenth centuries, although perhaps Riccioli had it in mind when he declared that the light was corporeal, not spiritual, and rejected as of no importance to us the idea that the preceding night was the period of the fight between good and bad angels while light came when the good " were confirmed in grace and raised to the light of glory." [4] An interesting variant was the unique statement of the Cornish poet, Jordan, that light was created on the second day together with the sea, while the angels of nine orders were created on the first.[5]

The Aristotelian doctrine that all things were divided into actives and passives lent itself to the dogma that the secondary cause of creation was the combination of the active principle of light with the passive one of inert matter, or the action of the light upon the matter. Matter was generally conceived to be a chaos of particles. Sometimes a third principle was added, the spirit, which was also active, though

[2] Fludd was almost alone in the attribution of real existence to darkness, Fludd, *Utriusque Cosmi Maioris scilicet et Minoris Metaphysica, Physica atque Technica Historia* (Oppenheim, 1617), pp. 26, 27. However, Shuckford thought that both light and darkness consisted of material particles, the former fiery, the latter opaque. Both were in the original chaos. Shuckford, *The Sacred and Profane History of the World Connected* (Philadelphia, 1824), vol. i, p. 21.

[3] Belief mentioned by Pfleumer, *Dissertatio Theologico-Critica, de Aqvis Svpracoelestibvs* (Jena, 1733), pp. 10, 11.

[4] "Confirmati sunt in gratia, & eleuati ad lumen gloriae", Riccioli, *Almagestvm Novvm Astronomiam Veterem Novamqve Complectens* (Bologna, 1651), vol. ii, p. 216. Also pp. 209-211.

[5] Jordan, *The Creation of the World, with Noah's Flood* (London, 1827) (Written 1611), pp. 4-9.

perhaps in an inferior degree.   Therefore it was natural
that the second step in creation should be the production of
light or the active element.[6]

This light was generally identified with fire;[7] but sometimes it was called the result of fire;[8] sometimes it and fire

[6] Fludd, *op. cit.*, pp. 14, 16, 27, 28, 30-32 *etc.*; perhaps Mersenne, *Qvaestiones Celeberrimae in Genesim* (Paris, 1623), cols. 712, 713; Comenius,
Naturall Philosophie Reformed by Divine Light (London, 1651), pp. 10-15,
20, 23, 25-27, 30-37, 46, 98, 99; Kircher, *Itinerarivm Exstaticvm* (Rome,
1656), pp. 292, 293, 300, 301, 370, 371; Leibnitz, *Opera Omnia* (Geneva,
1768), vol. ii, *Protogaea*, pp. 201, 202; Horrebow, *Clavis Astronomiae*, in
Operum mathematico-physicorum, etc. (1740), discussed by Delambre,
Histoire de l'astronomie au dix-huitième siècle (Paris, 1827), p. 140;
Pike, *Philosophia Sacra* (London, 1753), pp. 40-42, 52-56, 65, 69-76;
Catcott, *A Treatise on the Deluge* (London, 1768), pp. 51-60, 88, 89;
Wallerius (John G.), *Meditationes Physico-Chemicae de origine Mundi*
(Stockholm, 1779), circa p. 109, cited in De Luc, *Letters on the Physical
History of the Earth* (London, 1831), introduction, note p. 49; Vancouver,
*A General Compendium; or, Abstract of Chemical, Experimental, &
Natural Philosophy* (Philadelphia, 1785), pp. 31-33; De Luc, *op. cit.*,
intro., pp. 47, 49-51, letter ii, pp. 67-79, letter iii, pp. 81, 112.

[7] Apparently Riccioli, *op. cit.*, vol. ii, pp. 225-231, especially pp. 210,
230, though his clearest statement affirmed merely its corporeality;
Dickinson, *Physica Vetus et Vera* (Rotterdam, 1703), pp. 68-76, 206-216,
220, who also called light an efflux or a by-product of fire, as well as
attenuated fire, *ibid.*, pp. 72, 74, 75, 206, 221, 248; Kircher, *op. cit.*, pp.
300-302; Catcott, *op. cit.*, pp. 55, 56, 58, 88, 200, especially note p. 201,
who also suggested that possibly light was from fire; Fludd, *op. cit.*, pp.
27, 72; Vancouver, *op. cit.*, pp. 10, 11, 31; Gale, *The Covrt of the Gentiles* (Oxford and London, 1670-77), vol. i, pt. i, bk. iii, pp. 46, 47, pt. ii,
bk. iii, pp. 338-342, vol. ii, pt. iv, bk. ii, p. 452; Grotius (Hugo), *Annotations on 2 Pet. 3: 7*, quoted with approval by Gale, *op. cit.*, vol. i, pt. ii,
bk. iii, pp4338, 339; Hale, *The Primitive Origination of Mankind* (London,
1677), pp. 294, 298, 302, who also called light an effect of fire; Alsted,
Physica Harmonica (Herborn, 1642), pp. 26-28, 38, 39, who thought
fire one variety of light; Comenius, *op. cit.*, pp. 11-13, 36, 37; Leibnitz,
op. cit., vol. ii, *Protogaea*, p. 201.

[8] Adams, *Lectures on Natural and Experimental Philosophy* (London,
1794), vol. iv, p. 432; perhaps Pike, *op. cit.*, pp. 65, 73-76. As mentioned
in the preceding note, many authors were inconsistent. Dickinson, Catcott
and Hale not only identified fire and light but also declared fire to be the

were the effects of a third cause;[9] and sometimes as with De Luc's theory, it was the cause of fire.[10] The question whether light was the substance of the sun [11] or something

cause of light. Probably the idea was not clear in their own minds. Descartes and his followers, who felt that light resulted from the pressure of the first element upon the balls of the second, may also be grouped with those who felt that light was the result of fire.

[9] All those, to be mentioned later, who believed that the sun was created in the beginning, either in full strength or in gradually increasing power, or that there was some sort of primitive body to which the light was attached, considered light and fire as two manifestations of a common antecedent.

[10] Wallerius, *op. cit.,* quoted in De Luc, *op. cit.,* introduction, p. 49 note; De Luc, *ibid.,* introduction, pp. 49, 50, letter ii, pp. 75-79, letter iii, pp. 81, 84-87, 111-115. In spite of his statement that fire and light were the same, Fludd declared that heat was caused by the motion of the light, Fludd, *op. cit.,* pp. 33, 34, 68.

[11] Apparently the opinion of Hakewill, *An Apologie or Declaration of the Power and Providence of God in the Gouernment of the World* (Oxford, 1635), pt. ii, p. 39; and of Hutchinson, *Moses's Principia* (London, 1724), p. 45, who said that the sun issued from light, not light from the sun. Also Alsted, *op. cit.,* pp. 20, 34, 38, 39; Kircher, *op. cit.,* pp. 292, 293, though he also declared it composed of all four elements, including light, *ibid.,* pp. 269, 300-302; Comenius, *op. cit.,* pp. 11, 13, 14, 27, 116, 119, 231, though he sometimes added matter as a constituent of the sun; Schroeder, *Aqvas Supracoelestes à multis hactenus Doctoribus Supra Coelum Sidereum locatas* (Kiel, 1671), cap. iv, art. xi; Bossuet, *Discours sur l'histoire universelle* (Paris, 1850), p. 121; Gale, *op. cit.,* vol. i, pt. i, bk. iii, p. 46, pt. ii, bk. iii, pp. 338-342, vol. ii, pt. iv, bk. ii, p. 452; Grotius, *op. cit.,* quoted by Gale, *op. cit.,* vol. i, pt. ii, bk. iii, pp. 338, 339; Swinden, *An Enquiry into the Nature and Place of Hell* (London, 1727), pp. 178-183; Dr. Nichols, *Conferences with a Theist,* vol. i, pt. i, quoted by Swinden, *op. cit.,* p. 219, and by *An Universal History, from the Earliest Account of Time to the Present* (Dublin, 1744), vol. i, p. 42, though by the author of the *History* without approval. Buffon, *Oeuvres complètes* (Paris, 1831-2), vol. i, *Théorie de la terre,* p. 184, thought that light was the substance of the sun, or perhaps part of its substance. With this view agreed Maupertuis, *Essay de cosmologie* (Paris? or Amsterdam? 1750), p. 113; and Vancouver, *op. cit.,* pp. 10, 11, 31. Witty, *An Essay towards a Vindication of the Vulgar Exposition of the Mosaic History of the Creation of the World* (London, 1705),

added to a previously non-luminous body to form the radiant
orb [12] divided the pundits into two groups. It was often
stated that light was intrinsically invisible, permeated all
things [13] and needed excitation by an exterior stimulus to
become visible. Marsh put the idea most strongly when he
declared that obviously a small candle could not furnish a
quantity of light sufficient to fill a sphere six miles in diameter,
whereas a lighted candle could be seen three miles. Therefore the space must be full of particles which were excited by
the light, as generally by the sun. Without these, no number
of suns could cause light. Before the creation of the sun
perhaps God excited the particles directly.[14] De Luc asserted
that the primitive light must have been different from the

pp. 62, 63, on the other hand, apparently rejected this view that light was
the substance of the sun which was later collected into the luminary.
Though he mentioned the hypothesis, and failed to decide among the
various theories of light, he said slightingly that it was at the time believed by few.

[12] Clearly the opinion of Fludd, *op. cit.*, pp. 30, 134-141; Hale, *op. cit.*,
pp. 295, 302, 303; Milton, *The Poetical Works* (London, 1862), *Paradise
Lost*, bk. vii, ll. 243-249, 353-362; De Luc, *op. cit.*, letter iii, pp. 113-115;
and apparently of Duguet and d'Asfeld, *Explication de l'ouvrage des six
jours* (Paris, 1740), pp. 38, 39, 99; and of Riccioli, op. cit., vol. ii, pp.
210, 211, 225-231. Raleigh, *The History of the World* (Edinburgh,
1820) (1st ed., 1614), vol. i, pp. 18, 21, 22, asserted both doctrines,
seemingly without realization of any antagonism between the two thoughts,
and added the possibility that the primeval light ceased to exist after
the sun's creation together with the proposition that till the fourth day it
did not move since such motion was unnecessary before the creation of
plants. Dickinson, *op. cit.*, pp. 60, 69-76, 117, 118, 121, 122, 126, 129,
205-207, 220, 221, declared that light was added to an unluminous body
to form the sun, that light was the substance of the sun and that the
material of the future sun was fire, the cause of light.

[13] Fludd, *op. cit.*, pp. 28, 70, 125, 128, 130, 180, 181; Kircher, *op. cit.*, pp.
293, 300-302, 370, 371, who, however, sometimes spoke as if it were
visible; Catcott, *op. cit.*, pp. 55, 56, 88, 200, 201 and note; Pike, *op. cit.*,
pp. 51, 52, 83, 84, 87, 88.

[14] Marsh, *An Oration, on the Truth of the Mosaic History of the
Creation* (Hartford, 1798), p. 14.

illumination now poured out by the sun, since it completely
penetrated the great bodies of space and the elements and
acted at great depths, not merely at the surface as would
have been the case had it been emitted by any luminous
body.[15]

Jéhan declared that the belief current in the first half of
the seventeenth century was that God by the condensation
of water formed a globe, "attached to it the expansion of
the light and entrusted to an angel the care of moving this
globe in twenty-four hours, from East to West, around the
earth till the creation of the sun." [16] Fludd said that light
travelled around the universe in the path of the spirit each
of the first three days, but he did not specify what form it
had save that it was invisible.[17] That the primitive light
journeyed three times around the world before the creation
of the sun seemed to be the opinion adopted by Postel,[18] by
Riccioli,[19] who added that it shone first on Palestine or Paradise, and by Le Clerc.[20] Most writers believed it was attached to or formed a luminous body. Duguet and d'Asfeld
declared that the body to which it was attached was not revealed in order to teach us that nothing was luminous by
nature but everything when and so long as God willed.[21] A
similar purpose for the production of light before the sun

[15] De Luc, *op. cit.*, letter iii, pp. 84-86.

[16] " Y attacha l'expansion de la lumière et confia à un ange le soin de
mouvoir ce globe en 24 heures, d'Orient en Occident, autour de la terre
jusqu'à la création du soleil ", Jéhan, *Dictionnaire de cosmogonie et de
paléontologie* (Paris, 1854), art. " Cosmogonie aux XVIe et XVIIe
siècles," col. 305.

[17] Fludd, *op. cit.*, pp. 30, 49-51, 151, 152.

[18] Postel, *De Universitate* (Leyden, 1635), p. 40.

[19] Riccioli, *op. cit.*, vol. ii, pp. 212, 213, 215.

[20] Le Clerc, *op. cit.*, p. 6.

[21] Duguet and d'Asfeld, *op. cit.*, pp. 38, 39.

was given by Heylyn,[22] and Riccioli asserted that the reason
was to prevent idolatry of the sun and the stars.[23]   Alsted
thought that this light was in part formed into a globular
body, in part unformed as the matter of heaven and fire;[24]
Comenius concluded that it was created in a mass, as were
also the other two principles, matter and spirit, and that as it
moved around the world it rarefied and purified the matter
near itself and condensed the matter at the center and at the
outer extremity of the universe;[25] Hale affirmed that light
was lodged in a fit vehicle, which encircled the chaos once
during every twenty-four hours.[26]   Witty quoted Bishop
Patrick to the effect that light was a portion of luminous
matter moving about the earth on the first three days to
hasten its perfection.[27]   He himself did not disagree,
although elsewhere he spoke of the planets as revolving on
their axes.   Certainly he rejected the Cartesian doctrine.[28]
Milton gave perhaps as clear and attractive a picture as any.
In *Paradise Lost* he wrote that light sprang from the deep and

> " ' from her native east,
> To journey through the airy gloom began,
> Sphered in a radiant cloud, for yet the sun
> Was not; she in a cloudy tabernacle
> Sojourn'd the while.' "

[22] Heylyn, *Cosmography in Four Books* (London, 1674), introduction,
p. 3.

[23] Riccioli, *op. cit.*, vol. ii, pp. 209, 210; also Mersenne, *op. cit.*, col. 736.

[24] Alsted, *op. cit.*, pp. 20, 25-28, 38, 39.

[25] Comenius, *op. cit.*, pp. 11, 12, 20, 23, 25, 36, 37, 46, 98.

[26] Hale, *op. cit.*, pp. 294, 295, 298, 302, 303.

[27] Bishop Patrick, *On Genesis*, cap. i, p. 6 (or 9), quoted by Witty,
op. cit., pp. 181, 182.

[28] *Ibid.*, pp. 65, 139, 141, 142, 151-156.   Witty tried so hard to cover
all possible arguments and points of view that his own opinions were
frequently indecipherable.

Somewhat later God formed of dark though ethereal matter the sun, moon and stars, and transplanted to the solar globe the greater part of this light.[29]   As is evident, most of these authors wrote during the seventeenth century.   In the later years of that century and throughout the following the belief gained ground that the sun was created before the events mentioned in Genesis, or at least that the creation of light betokened that of the sun.   Burnet [30] and Whiston [31] propounded the doctrine of the sun's preexistence and stated that it was invisible at first because of the solid particles in the atmosphere.   Light was said to be created

when the superior Regions of the Chaos were become so far clear and defecate, that the Rays of the Sun in some degree could penetrate the same, enough to render a sensible Distinction between Night and Day, or that space the Sun was above, and that it was beneath the Horizon.[32]

By the fourth day the air was cleared to such a point that the sun and the moon became distinctly visible.   In the *Archaeologiae Philosophicae* Burnet went so far as to reject the doctrine that light antedated the sun as impossible, and declared that the statement was made by Moses only because of Israelitish stupidity to prevent the theory that God worked three days in the dark.[33]   As usual, the author of the *Universal History* accepted the explanation of Burnet and

[29] Milton, *op. cit., Paradise Lost*, bk. vii, ll. 243-249, 353-367.

[30] Burnet, *The Sacred Theory of the Earth* (London, 1722), especially vol. i, bk. i, pp. 2, 3, 7, bk. ii, pp. 447-453.

[31] Whiston, *A New Theory of the Earth* (Cambridge, 1708), introduction, pp. 67, 68, also pp. 24, 300-302, 305-308, 316-318.

[32] *Ibid.*, p. 24.

[33] Burnet, *Doctrina Antiqua de Rerum Originibus* (London, 1729, 1736), *Archaeologiae Philosophicae*, pt. i, critique, pp. 41, 42.

Whiston,[34] though it had been disputed by Warren [35] and by
Keill [36] as contrary to the plain sense of the Bible and to the
natural effects of light in such a chaos. Swinden felt that the
creation of light meant the production of the sun and that on
the fourth day God merely gave it another use for the division
of seasons. In other words the earth was then started on
its course around the sun. So intricate an operation resembled the assembling of the wheels in a watch and took a
whole day. Dr. Nichols, though he called the creation of
light merely the production of a tendency toward light, asserted a doctrine concerning the other planets similar to
Swinden's belief about the sun.[37] Even Marsh after his interesting suggestion based upon the light of a candle declared
the belief in the existence of the heavenly bodies from the
beginning and in their obscuration by vapors and solid particles in the air to be more rational.[38]

Of course all those who affirmed the existence of the sun
from the beginning and its primitive invisibility from this
cause, believed that the heat and other effects on earth
of the luminary were less than after the fourth day; and

[34] *An Universal History, from the Earliest Account of Time to the
Present* (Dublin, 1744), vol. i, p. 42.

[35] Warren, *Geologia* (London, 1690), pp. 83-85; Warren, *Some Reflections upon the Short Consideration Of the Defence of the Exceptions
against the Theory of the Earth* (London, 1692), p. 43, where he asserted that Burnet omitted in his second edition this proposition which
he had upheld in the first. Perhaps he referred to the Latin edition,
l. 2, c. 7.

[36] Keill, *An Examination of Dr. Burnet's Theory of the Earth. Together with some remarks on Mr. Whiston's New Theory of the Earth*
(Oxford, 1698), pp. 188-192.

[37] Swinden, *op. cit.*, pp. 178-183, where he quoted Dr. Nichols, *op. cit.*,
pt. i. Hakewill, *op. cit.*, pt. ii, p. 39, also suggested that part of the work
on the fourth day was the bestowal of additional properties upon the
light, which was compacted into the body of the sun.

[38] Marsh, *op. cit.*, p. 15.

they promulgated elaborate hypotheses to show why more heat was needed to produce the higher animals. Others who, like Dickinson,[39] rejected the sun's existence at so early a date, and those who affirmed that the sun gradually developed throughout the three days and arrived at perfection on the fourth agreed that its force was less during the earlier epoch.[40] On the other hand, Comenius,[41] Riccioli [42] and Hale [43] declared that the force of the primitive light was greater than that of light during later periods and was weakened by its dispersal into various celestial spheres as a merciful adaptation to the frailty of animal frames.

Besides the philosophers, some of the scientists attempted explanations. Halley, for example, was impressed by the fact that the nebulae emitted light although they possessed no luminous bodies, and considered it an elucidation of the nature of primeval light.[44] The most influential interpretation was the contribution of Descartes, who was both scientist and philosopher. He attributed light to the pressure exerted by particles of matter in their efforts to escape as they were whirled around in their vortex. This pressure, which was exerted in a straight line, was increased by the pressure of the particles behind and was due to the centrifugal force of the whole vortex. Even if the central spot were empty, the impression of light would arise, as it did before the collection into this central sphere of the minute particles which formed the sun. These tiny particles, be-

[39] Dickinson, *op. cit.*, pp. 76, 117, 207.

[40] De Luc, *op. cit.*, letter iii, pp. 111-115. Probably this was Witty's opinion, Witty, *op. cit.*, preface, pp. 41, 42, 46, 50-67, 75, 111-113. All the followers of Descartes were naturally of the opinion that in the beginning the light was less violent than later.

[41] Comenius, *op. cit.*, pp. 13-15.

[42] Riccioli, *op. cit.*, vol. ii, p. 226.

[43] Hale, *op. cit.*, pp. 302, 303.

[44] Hastie, *Kant's Cosmogony* (Glasgow, 1900), note p. 33.

cause of their exceedingly rapid motion and their infinitesimal size, which permitted them to pass between the larger balls and to press upon them, were the chief causes of light as well as the constituents of the sun.[45]

Among those who accepted rather completely Descartes's explanation of light itself and of its presence on the first day were Joseph Glanvill [46] and Gadroys.[47] Warren qualified his apparent acceptance by the declaration " not that I believe the Sun was thus produced (any more than the Great Philosopher did)." [48] Dickinson adapted to his geocentric universe the theory of light as tiny balls in infinitely fast motion, which were separated from the chaos by its rotation, and endeavored to combine with it the other popular doctrine that the light was at first hindered in its approach to the earth by the intervention of solid particles in the atmosphere.[49] Fontenelle declared that light was composed of little balls in motion through the atmosphere; [50] and Pike spoke of them as the finest particles in the heavens, in very rapid motion. Pike [51] and Buffon,[62] as well as many others, agreed with Descartes that other elements were changed into the infinitesimal balls of light by friction. Buffon and Leibnitz [53] apparently leaned to the view that by the separation of light and darkness was meant the covering of the origi-

---

[45] Descartes, *Oeuvres* (Paris, 1824), vol. iii, *Les principes de la philosophie*, pt. iii, especially secs. 55, 64, pt. iv, sec. 28.

[46] Glanvill, *Scepsis Scientifica* (London, 1665), pt. i, pp. 142, 143.

[47] Gadroys, *Le systeme du monde* (Paris, 1675), pp. 215-219.

[48] Warren, *Geologia* (London, 1690), pp. 51-54, especially p. 53.

[49] Dickinson, *op. cit.*, pp. 67-76, 81, 82, 114, 117, 205-209, 211-214, 247, 248.

[50] Fontenelle, *Entretiens sur la pluralité des mondes* (Paris, 1821), (1st ed., 1686), pp. 35, 36.

[51] Pike, *op. cit.*, pp. 40-42, 61, 65, 73-76.

[52] Buffon, *op. cit.*, vol. iii, pp. 78, 83-90, vol. v, pp. 75-78, 82.

[53] Leibnitz, *op. cit.*, vol. ii, *Protogaea*, pp. 202, 203, 205.

nally luminous earth with scoriae as it cooled, though Buffon also called it the separation of the opaque matter that composed the planets from the luminous matter of the sun.[54] Descartes had asserted in another connection that the earth was formed by the veiling of a luminous core. Witty, who presented many theories concerning the nature of light, explained a possible cause of the primeval light in accordance with each theory. Among these theories was Descartes's hypothesis, to which he gave considerable space although he denied its validity.[55] The doctrine that air or material particles in motion produced or were fire or light was upheld by Derham,[56] Swinden [57] and Catcott.[58] Another hypothesis, based on the theory that light was in the observer's eye, was propounded by Witty. He suggested that the medium through which light came to us might have been adapted to that purpose on the first day.[59] It was the opinion of Dr. Nichols.[60] Among the oddest hypotheses as to the cause of light was the doctrine of Peter Horrebow, who in a work, on astronomy stated that it resulted from the intermixture of floods of hermetic and magnetic matter with a humid matter.[61] The recondite vagueness of that proposition resembles in futility the esoteric attempt by Comenius to correlate with the Trinity the three elements whose interaction produced the universe. He said that the production of light,

---

[54] Buffon, *op. cit.*, vol. i, pp. 174, 175, vol. v, pp. 37, 38, 83, 86, 87, 92.

[55] Witty, *op. cit.*, pp. 52-67.

[56] Derham, *Physico-Theology* (London, 1742), p. 26 note.

[57] Swinden, *op. cit.*, p. 76.

[58] Catcott, *op. cit.*, p. 58, note p. 201.

[59] Witty, *op. cit.*, pp. 61, 62, 66.

[60] Dr. Nichols, *op. cit.*, quoted by Foxton, *Remarks*, pp. 76, 77, in Burnet, *op. cit.*, after *Archaeologiae Philosophicae*, pt. i, critique.

[61] Horrebow, *op. cit.*, quoted by Delambre, *op. cit.*, p. 145. *Cf.* also *supra*, note pp. 186, 187.

which gave splendor and order, was a work of wisdom by Christ; the production of matter from nothing a work of omnipotence by the Father; and the production of the virtue infused into the creatures or the diffused soul of the world a work of goodness by the Holy Ghost.[62]   All things were made " *of* the matter, *in* the spirit, *but by* the fire or light." [63]

[62] Comenius, *op. cit.*, p. 24.

[63] *Ibid.*, p. 37.

CHAPTER IV

THE CLASSIFICATION OF MATTER

As late as 1800 the matter of which the universe consisted was still grouped under the four elements of water, earth, air and fire. They were generally believed to be mutually transmutable. Ray added that some metals, minerals, oil and salt were equally simple; and he [1] and De Luc probably denied that they could be altered from one to another. In one place De Luc mentioned water as a simple substance, apparently synonymous with element, and not a compound, and called it and light the only simple substances at present perceptible. Elsewhere he called his primeval atoms elements. [2] A few authorities, like Burton, rejected the elementary character of fire, or perhaps merely a distinct fiery sphere, which Burton considered disproved by the course of comets. Nevertheless, he still retained the attributes corresponding to all four elements, and characterized medicinal herbs as hot, cold, dry or wet. [3] Bacon declared that fire was no element, but had been feigned merely to match the others, which he believed in, and whose transmutability he accepted. [4] Van Helmont also explicitly denied that

[1] Ray, *The Wisdom of God Manifested in the Works of the Creation* (London, 1759), pp. 69-88; Ray, *Three Physico-Theological Discourses* (London, 1693), pp. 70, 71, 328-330.

[2] De Luc, *Letters on the Physical History of the Earth* (London, 1831), letter iii, pp. 99, 100; De Luc, *Lettres physiques et morales sur l'histoire de la terre et de l'homme* (The Hague and Paris, 1779, 1780), vol. i, p. 188.

[3] Burton, *The Anatomy of Melancholy* (London, 1920), vol. ii, pp. 57, 58, 248-251, 257, 260, 264, 270, 274, 275, 285, 295-298.

[4] Bacon, *Works* (Boston, ?), vol. iv, *Sylva Sylvarum*, cent. i, nos. 27, 76, 77, 80-82, 91, pp. 172, 173, 206-210, 214, 215, vol. vi, *Advancement of Learning*, p. 277.

fire was an element and said that all bodies were made from water and could be reduced to it.[5]   Wilkins[6] and Catcott[7] accepted only three elements.   Bossuet about 1670 mentioned only three but did not specify that fire was not elemental.[8]   Blancanus refused to decide whether there were three or four, but declared that their volumes were in the following ratio: water 1, air 86, earth 2290 and ether or fire between the air and the moon 321,992,320.[9]   In contrast, Alsted thought that the four elements were equal in amount.[10]

On the other hand, Postel added a fifth essence, ether, with a nature between fire and air,[11] as did Milton;[12] and Horrebow perhaps classified ether as an additional element.[13] Descartes changed the classic interpretation of the term and talked of three elements; but he subdivided the third into air, water and earth so that the final result was five.[14] Vancouver mentioned only that fire was an element, perhaps

[5] Van Helmont, *Opera Omnia* (Frankfurt, 1682), pt. i, pp. 49-61, 112, 113.

[6] Wilkins, *The Mathematical and Philosophical Works* (London, 1707-8), bk. i, pp. 29, 30, 125, 126.

[7] Catcott, *A Treatise on the Deluge* (London, 1768), p. 10.

[8] Bossuet, *Discours sur l'histoire universelle* (Paris, 1850), p. 120.

[9] Blancanus, *Sphaera Mvndi* (Bologna, 1620), pp. 67-127, especially pp. 67, 68, 110, 114, 117.

[10] Alsted, *Physica Harmonica* (Herborn, 1642), p. 231, though earlier he had said that there was less water than earth, *ibid.*, pp. 122-124.

[11] Postel, *De Universitate* (Leyden, 1635), pp. 11, 13, 23-27, especially pp. 26, 27.

[12] Milton, *The Poetical Works* (London, 1862), *Paradise Lost*, bk. iii, ll. 713-720, bk. v, ll. 180-183, 415-420.

[13] Horrebow, *Clavis Astronomiae*, in *Operum mathematico-physicorum, etc.* (1740), quoted by Delambre, *Histoire de l'astronomie au dix-huitième siècle* (Paris, 1827), p. 140.

[14] Descartes, *Oeuvres* (Paris, 1824), vol. iii, *Les principes de la philosophie*, pts. iii and iv, especially pt. iii, sec. 52 and pt. iv, secs. 32-48, 80.

because that had been challenged.[15]   Jacobus Grandius, as well as Warren,[16] in connection with their treatment of the flood, discussed the transmutation of air into water as if the two were elements.   Grandius asserted that air came originally from water and could be transformed into it again;[17] Warren said that the possibility of such a mutation was unproved, though it was believed by Bacon and Descartes as well as by Aristotle, Plato and the Egyptians.[18]

Many authors mentioned the four elements and their transmutability more or less casually as if no one doubted such a classification,[19] even so late as 1770 or 1771 when Holbach

[15] Vancouver, *A General Compendium; or, Abstract of Chemical, Experimental, & Natural Philosophy* (Philadelphia, 1785), pp. 10, 11, 31.

[16] Warren, *Geologia* (London, 1690), pp. 24, 314-316.

[17] Grandius, *De Veritate Diluvii Universalis, & Testaceorum quae procul à mari repertuntur Generatione* (Venice, 1676), letter to Johannis Quirinus, p. 29, quoted by Harris (John), *Remarks On some Late Papers, Relating to the Universal Deluge* (London, 1697), pp. 244, 245.

[18] Warren, *op. cit.*, pp. 314-316.

[19] For example, Raleigh, *The History of the World* (Edinburgh, 1820), vol. i, pp. 18, 66, 223; Mersenne, *Qvaestiones Celeberrimae in Genesim* (Paris, 1623), cols. 867, 919 and elsewhere; probably Heylyn, *Cosmography in Four Books* (London, 1674), introduction, p. 23; Riccioli, *Almagestvm Novvm Astronomiam Veterem Novamqve Complectens* (Bologna, 1651), vol. ii, pp. 235, 236; Browne, *Works* (London, 1888-1890), vol. i, pp. 326-330, vol. ii, p. 400; Spencer, *A Discourse concerning Prodigies* (London, 1665), pp. 101, 126; Milius, *De Origine Animalium et Migratione Populorum* (Geneva, 1667), p. 13; Colbert, *Regi Armis Omnia Expugnanti Architecturam Militarem Sapientia Omnia Constituenti Totius Mundi Constitutionem Belli Pacisque Arbitro Bellatricem Pacificamque Mathesin* (?, 1668), p. 11; Hale, *The Primitive Origination of Mankind* (London, 1677), pp. 102, 297-299, 302; Mallet, *Description de l'univers* (Paris, 1683), vol. i, pp. 164, 236, 237; Glaser, *Dissertationem de Variis Philosophorum Circa Principia Corporum Naturalium* (Leipzig, 1688?); Beaumont, *Considerations On a Book, Entituled The Theory of the Earth* (London, 1692-3), pp. 28, 68, 69, 87; Burnet, *Doctrina Antiqua de Rerum Originibus* (London, 1729, 1736), *Archaeologiae Philosophicae*, pt. i, p. 178; Burnet, *The Sacred Theory of the Earth* (London, 1722), vol. ii, bk. iii, pp. 100, 133, bk. iv, pp. 316-320; Warren, *op. cit.*, pp. 24, 90, 91, 314-316; Swinden, *An Enquiry*

said that they were constantly interacting;[20] but some added remarks of greater or less importance. Raleigh said that water was the source of air, not of the universe, other parts of which came from earth and light,[21] while Moncharville declared that air was the source of all,[22] and Adams derived the whole from fire.[23] Burnet affirmed that in the beginning all matter was alike minute mobile particles, and that it developed into all four elements from whichever one it began.[24] Postel,[25] Browne,[26] Kircher[27] and others repeated the ancient dictum that the elements did not appear in a pure form on earth. The location of the elements in concentric spheres with the earth at the center and the fire near the orbit of the moon was asserted by Suarez,[28] Fludd,[29] Blancanus,[30]

into the Nature and Place of Hell (London, 1727), pp. 170, 263, 267-272, 356, 359; Wolf, *Cosmologia Generalis* (Frankfurt and Leipzig, 1737), pp. 141-171, 185-188, 191, 442-447.

[20] Holbach, *The System of Nature* (New York, 1835), p. 23.

[21] Raleigh, *op. cit.*, vol. i, p. 18.

[22] Moncharville, *Preuves des existences, et nouveau systême de l'univers* (Paris, 1702), pp. 4, 14, who discussed at some length the transmutation of elements.

[23] Adams, *Lectures on Natural and Experimental Philosophy* (London, 1794), vol. iv, pp. 432, 433.

[24] Burnet, *Doctrina Antiqua de Rerum Originibus* (London, 1729, 1736), *Archaeologiae Philosophicae*, pt. i, pp. 178, 179.

[25] Postel, *op. cit.*, p. 11.

[26] Browne, *op. cit.*, vol. i, pp. 328, 330, vol. ii, p. 400.

[27] Kircher, *Mundus Subterraneus* (Amsterdam, 1664-5), t. i, pp. 162, 169, 172, 243, 244, 297, though he apparently made an exception in the case of pure earth, salt or glass.

[28] Suarez, *Works* (1630), *De Renovatione Mundi in 3 partem Thomae.* tom. 2. 9. 59. art. 6. dif. 58. sect. 4?-6? (written before 1617), quoted by Hakewill, *An Apologie or Declaration of the Power and Providence of God in the Gouernment of the World* (Oxford, 1635), pt. ii, pp. 335-337.

[29] Fludd, *Utriusque Cosmi Maioris scilicet et Minoris Metaphysica, Physica atque Technica Historia* (Oppenheim, 1617), frontispiece, pp. 9, 44, 62-68, 72-76, 133, 137.

[30] Blancanus, *op. cit.*, pp. 67-127, especially pp. 72, 79-81, 98, 99, 104, 110-112, 115.

Hakewill,[31] Postel,[32] Alsted,[33] Comenius,[34] by Schott,[35] though Kircher apparently denied it,[36] by Gale,[37] Milton,[38] Mallet,[39] Dickinson [40] and in a measure even by Descartes.[41] The creation of air was generally assigned to the second day and of fire to the first, when an attempt was made to synchronize the events with the Biblical narrative; but there was a difference of opinion about the other elements. Alsted affirmed that they were produced on the first day;[42] Comenius [43] and probably Hale [44] and Adams [45] that their formation was postponed to the third. Hakewill, however, assigned the creation of fire and of the celestial globes, as well as of air, to the second day, and said that they were comprehended under the term firmament. Though the Bible did not mention the element of fire and many philosophers repudiated it, Hakewill accepted its reality.[46] Unfortunately he gave as the strongest reason for the belief a

[31] Hakewill, *op. cit.*, pt. i, pp. 117-119, 123, 135.

[32] Postel, *op. cit.*, pp. 13, 24-27.

[33] Alsted, *op. cit.*, pp. 29-32, 117, 119, 122, 126, 127.

[34] Comenius, *Naturall Philosophie Reformed by Divine Light* (London, 1651), pp. 12, 79-81, 85, 86, 88-91.

[35] Schott, in Kircher, *Iter Extaticum Coeleste* (Würzburg, 1660), p. 21.

[36] Kircher, *Mundus Subterraneus* (Amsterdam, 1664-5), t. i, pp. 170-173.

[37] Gale, *The Covrt of the Gentiles* (Oxford and London, 1670-77), vol. i, pt. i, bk. iii, p. 47, pt. ii, bk. iii, pp. 342, 343.

[38] Milton, *op. cit., Paradise Lost*, bk. iii, ll. 713-720.

[39] Mallet, *op. cit.*, vol. i, pp. 164, 236, 237.

[40] Dickinson, *Physica Vetus et Vera* (Rotterdam, 1703).

[41] Descartes, *op. cit.*, vol. iii, *Les principes de la philosophie*, especially pt. iv.

[42] Alsted, *op. cit.*, pp. 25, 26.

[43] Comenius, *op. cit.*, p. 12.

[44] Hale, *op. cit.*, pp. 298, 299.

[45] Adams, *op. cit.*, vol. iv, pp. 432, 433.

[46] Hakewill, *op. cit.*, pt. ii, pp. 21, 32-34.

thesis soon to be discarded, "the swift motion of the heavens."[47] He thought that the heavens were created of the elements or more probably of the matter from which the elements were made.[48] Postel also affirmed that the heavenly orbs or spheres were made from the elements,[49] and Kircher reiterated it again and again. Kircher felt that the elements differed from sphere to sphere in qualities or *accidentia* because of their locations, but that they must be intrinsically like those of the earth and of man in order to act upon them by sympathy and antipathy and in order to preserve the harmony and unity of the universe.[50] Knowledge concerning the nature of the elements as well as all knowledge of natural things was infused by God into Adam, who taught his descendants.[51] Hakewill added three other statements. The first was that the sphere of fire was a partial cause for the inflammation of comets.[52] The second was the ancient dogma that in their own places the elements had neither weight nor lightness, " as appeares by this, that a man lying in the bottome of the deepest *Ocean,* hee feeles no burden from the weight thereof."[53] The third was the suggestion that the four elements were symbolized by the veil of the tabernacle and temple, blue for air, scarlet for fire, purple for sea and fine twisted linen for earth. The last two were

---

[47] Hakewill, *op. cit.*, pt. ii, p. 21.

[48] *Ibid.*, pt. i, p. 79, pt. ii, pp. 28-34. Elsewhere he declared their substance free from any admixture of the elements and made of a quintessence. *Ibid.*, pt. i, p. 81.

[49] Postel, *op. cit.*, p. 11.

[50] Kircher, *op. cit.*, t. i, p. 183; Kircher, *Itinerarivm Exstaticvm* (Rome, 1656), pp. 9, 24, 25, 51, 52, 90, 91, 190-192, 278, 305-307, 393, 398, 399 and elsewhere.

[51] Kircher, *Arca Noë* (Amsterdam, 1675), p. 5.

[52] Hakewill, *op. cit.*, pt. i, p. 135.

[53] *Ibid.*, pt. i, p. 119. Bishop Wilkins made a similar assertion. Wilkins, *op. cit.*, bk. i, pp. 121-123.

chosen as products of these elements.[54]   If the first two were supposed to be the colors of air and of fire, Hakewill differed from Postel, who declared that the true color of air was cerulean, but of fire white, of water blood-red and of earth black.   Postel,[55] Comenius [56] and Fludd still discussed the qualities of heat, cold, humidity and dryness as pertaining to the elements.   Aridity Fludd thought accidental and due to a total lack of heat.   According to him, the mixture of equal parts of cold and heat gave humidity.   He found analogies such that he grouped with each of the elements different angels, planets, signs of the Zodiac, plants and minerals.   In the formation of plants, animals and man all four shared, although air was predominant.[57]

Descartes seemed to feel the necessity for explanation as to the way in which his system produced the four elements and wherein they differed from one another since they were made from the same original matter and might be changed into one another by friction or by adhesion.   They differed in shape, and therefore in other qualities, especially in speed and in ease of motion.   Fire consisted of small balls, intensely mobile, while the ether of the vortices was composed of less swift balls, larger in size.   The earth consisted of irregular, branching shapes, tightly entwined, and the air of

[54] Hakewill, *op. cit.*, pt. i, p. 118.

[55] Postel, *op. cit.*, pp. 24-27.

[56] Comenius, *op. cit.*, pp. 56, 81, 91, 92.   He explained the creation of elements and their transmutation and discussed them, *ibid.*, pp. 13, 36, 46, 78-98, 101, 102.

[57] Fludd, *op. cit.*, pp. 16, 34, 38, 39, 44, 64-68, 72, 133, 134, 175-178. Other parts of his discussion concerning the elements appeared pp. 14, 35, 36, 62, 63, 70, 71, 73-76, 169.   Alsted discussed the elements, their qualities and the different things formed from each, Alsted, *op. cit.*, pp. 25-39, 114-127.   Gale was especially interested in fire and its vivifying effects.   Gale, *op. cit.*, vol. i, pt. i, bk. iii, pp. 46, 47, vol. ii, pt. iv, bk. ii, p. 452, where he referred to his *Philosoph. General.*, p. i, 1. 3 in Plato's *Physics* for a fuller account.

still more branching particles. Water was in the form of small rods, not stiff but pliable, which became wrapped around one another. He, like others, said that the portions of matter which we were able to perceive were not the pure elements but a mixture of them with particles of earth.[58] Almost sixty years later Dickinson evolved a similar explanation of the fundamental differences among the elements, which were composed of the same matter in different shapes; but his was perhaps more logical since in it the particles of air and of earth were not of the same shape. He agreed with Descartes in attribution of small size and round form to fire atoms, but grouped with them pointed scraps that had been eroded from other particles. With regard to the branching particles of earth, he and his predecessor were in accord; but he attributed spherical form and larger size to water, and believed that air consisted of straight stiff sticks that rotated on their centers. He made an excursion into the immaterial world in the assignment of a guardian angel to each element.[59] These ideas in mutilated form appeared in the works of other authors. The doctrine that all matter became fire when it was subdivided into minute particles was common. An example might be found in Buffon's work. He wrote a treatise on the four elements. In it he declared that fire or light differed from the other three in that particles of it expanded and repelled one another while those of the other elements felt mutual attraction. When those of air, water and earth approached one another so closely as to rub against one another, they were changed to fire, presumably by pulverization. Buffon propounded also the dictum, which he perhaps adopted from Leibnitz, that

[58] Descartes, *op. cit.*, vol. iii, *Les principes de la philosophie*, especially pt. iii, secs. 48-52, pt. iv, secs. 32-48, 80-132.

[59] Dickinson, *op. cit.*, pp. 33, 65-67, 69-102, 203-262.

the element of earth was much like glass.[60]   Leibnitz had
stated that there were no immutable or ultimate elements.
Glass was the basis of all earthly things, and all except those
which flew away into air were changed by heat to glass.[61]
Horrebow presented a somewhat similar idea in his belief
that by the constant strife of the active element, light, and
the passive element, which resembled glass, came ether, air
and water, all composed of little elastic glass balls, which
differed in radius and density, and that the earth's crust covered a kernel of glass.[62]   On the other hand, Adams affirmed
that the differences among the elements were merely differences in rate of motion.   Particles of fire, if they were slowed
down, became air, then water and finally earth.   In this
hypothesis he may have had in mind Descartes's account of
fire or light and the emphasis he had laid on the differences
in speed among the elements.[63]

An interesting suggestion was offered by Suarez.   After
the final conflagration all mixed bodies and extraneous substances, such as the saltiness of the sea, would be removed
from earth and sea.   A positive addition of light and clarity
to the elements would make the earth like glass, the water
like crystal, the air like our sky and the fire like the
heavenly lights.   But to prevent the damned from enjoying
the light, the earth would be transparent only to the confines
of hell, perhaps to the limbus of children.   Then the blessed
could see through the earth except for the central hell.   Perhaps some land would still emerge from the sea, despite its
normal position under the water, especially if the surface of
the earth instead of some subterranean section was to be

[60] Buffon, *Oeuvres complètes* (Paris, 1831-2), vol. iii, pp. 75-187.

[61] Leibnitz, *Opera Omnia* (Geneva, 1768), vol. ii, *Protogaea*, pp. 202, 203.

[62] Horrebow, *op. cit.*, quoted by Delambre, *op. cit.*, pp. 140, 141.

[63] Adams, *op. cit.*, vol. iv, pp. 431-433.

inhabited by children who had died before they had committed individual sins and when they were guilty only of
their share in original sin.[64] Burnet also prophesied the
purification of the earth by the final conflagration, but he
declared that it would probably all be transformed into a
mass of ethereal matter like a sun or a star. Ether he called
the purest and subtlest sort of fire.[65]

Not only the Aristotelian four elements lived on into the
eighteenth century, but also the principles of Paracelsus.[66]
Fludd omitted salt but stated that nothing in nature could be
generated or could grow without the union of sulphur and
mercury.[67] On the same page Alsted classified primitive
matter as a chaos of three principles equal in amount or of
four equal elements,[68] and he called the Physica Chemica,
which developed the universe from the principles of salt,
sulphur and mercury, the oldest philosophy except the
Mosaic.[69] Comenius called the three principles substantial
and intrinsic qualities of things as distinguished from the
extrinsic and accidental.[70] Descartes accepted them, and,
as with the four elements, explained the method of their
formation and their effects.[71] Kircher, in discussion of the
element earth, said that in its purest form it was salt. Glass
had lost its salt and was pure earth but dead. He declared

---

[64] Suarez, op. cit., quoted by Hakewill, op. cit., pt. ii, pp. 335-337.

[65] Burnet, The Sacred Theory of the Earth (London, 1722), vol. ii,
especially bk. iv, pp. 316-320.

[66] Wolf, op. cit., p. 183.

[67] Fludd, op. cit., p. 8.

[68] Alsted, op. cit., p. 231.

[69] Ibid., pp. 223, 231.

[70] Comenius, op. cit., pp. 50-54. He discussed the three also on pp. 62,
64, 68, 69, 127.

[71] Descartes, op. cit., vol. iii, Les principes de la philosophie, pt. iv, secs.
58-63.

that from the four elements nature generated the three principles of salt, sulphur and mercury, and on the other hand that the elements were formed from the three principles. From the three, mingled in due proportion, were produced metals, trees and animals. Salt gave mixed bodies consistency, and sulphur fiery activity. Mercury was a watery substance, which also furnished consistency to objects. Salt joined to different kinds of earth produced the other two principles as well as other minerals. All things were a mixture of the three, which was endowed with plastic and magnetic force, and among other activities caused the spontaneous generation of animals and plants from decaying matter.[72] The mercury, sulphur and salt or their exhalations were popularly supposed to be the causes of earthquakes, volcanic eruptions, hurricanes, lightning, thunder and such permanent results as metals and minerals.[73] Dickinson thought that acid or sulphurous effects resulted from the irregular or pointed bits eroded from the other matter of the universe. He attributed to the interaction of sulphurous and saline ferments, which were furnished by the blood and the heart respectively, the movement of the heart which moved the blood. Similar combinations in the earth produced eruptions and hot springs. He declared that the differing effects of the heavenly bodies, including the radiance emitted by them, were

[72] Kircher, *Mundus Subterraneus* (Amsterdam, 1664-5), t. i, pp. 162-164, 184, 185, 307, 308, t. ii, pp. 124, 134-137, 145-158, 162, 163, 169, 170, 237, 238, 251, 327-334, 336-374, 379, 380, 385, 386. He mentioned the three principles also in the following places: *ibid.*, t. i, pp. 190, 297-302, 304, 306, 324, 326, 330, 345, t. ii, pp. 6, 7 and elsewhere.

[73] For example by Fludd, *op. cit.*, pp. 174, 191; Comenius, *op. cit.*, p. 133, who considered it the cause of lightning but assigned another reason for earthquakes, *ibid.*, p. 93; Gadroys, *Le systeme du monde* (Paris, 1675), pp. 427, 428; Ray, *op. cit.*, pp. 194-197; (Le Brun), *Histoire critique des practiques superstitieuses* (Paris, 1702), p. 105; Buffon, *op. cit.*, vol. i, p. 272, vol. ii, pp. 294-394, vol. v, p. 193, though he added other causes.

due to the different proportions of the three principles. The phosphorescence of the ocean and similar lights were produced by a combination of salt and sulphur. Since he believed with others that fires required sulphurous aliment, he elaborated a system whereby it was furnished to the central fire by ducts, which led down from the bed of the sea. The sulphurous matter fell on the surface of the ocean with the rain or was carried thither by rivers, and sank to the bottom because of its excessive weight.[74] Ray also insisted that fire must have a sulphurous or unctuous *pabulum*.[75] Perhaps for this reason Thomas White affirmed that at least the outer part of the sun must consist of sulphur or bitumen. He attributed hot springs to effervescence of salt-saturated water mixed with the sulphur.[76] Among the more interesting developments was Bacon's division of matter into two families, sulphurous and mercurial, inflammable and uninflammable, oily and watery, brimstone and mercury, oil and water in plants and in animals, flame and air, the body of the star and the pure sky.[77] He called it "one of the greatest *magnalia naturae*, to turn water or watery juice into oil or oily juice," greater than the mutation of silver or quicksilver into gold.[78] Then he gave several methods to produce this result, including the assimilation of nourishment by living beings.[79] Schroeder, in his disproof of a crystalline heaven supposed to consist of waters congealed by cold, named salt as the principle of coagulation which gave solidity to

[74] Dickinson, *op. cit.*, pp. 126-132, 134, 135, 178, 179, 205, 260, 262.

[75] Ray, *op. cit.*, p. 325.

[76] White (Thomas), *Institutionum Peripateticarum Libri Quinque* (Frankfurt, 1664), pp. 65, 68.

[77] Bacon, *op. cit.*, vol. iv, *Sylva Sylvarum*, cent. iv, preliminary remarks, pp. 331, 332.

[78] *Ibid.*, pp. 331, 332.

[79] *Ibid.*, nos. 355-359, pp. 332, 333.

bodies;[80] and Calmet, in his explanation of the blood found in the corpses of so-called vampires, had recourse to the effects of the solar warmth on " nitrous & sulphurous " particles of the earth, which then decoagulated the blood in the bodies and produced by fermentation a red liquid, a kind of blood.[81]

[80] Schroeder, *Aqvas Supracoelestes à multis hactenus Doctoribus Supra Coelum Sidereum locatas* (Kiel, 1671), cap. ii, arts. x, xi.

[81] Calmet, *Dissertations sur les apparitions des anges, des démons & des esprits* (Paris, 1746), pt. ii, *sur les revenans et les vampires*, pp. 295, 296.

CHAPTER V

Misplaced Elements

ANOTHER topic in the Mosaic account of creation caused as much dispute as the primeval light, though it did not permit such variety of opinion. It was stated that on the second day God separated the waters by the firmament or expanse. The natural explanation of the inferior waters as those upon the earth's surface was generally accepted; but difficulty arose when commentators attempted to discover another approximately equal body of water beyond the firmament, a term that was used vaguely in the Bible. A chief reason for the difficulty was the belief that these superior waters were a cause of the flood, if not the most important cause. If they were beyond the stars, it was difficult to bring them to the earth without deluging the celestial spheres en route. Besides, their removal from their original location would produce a vacuum; and Descartes [1] was not unique in his rejection of any vacuum. Their restoration to their former site was attended with equal obstacles. On the other hand, the clouds were ridiculously insignificant in comparison with the oceans on the earth and with the immense quantities of water necessary for a universal deluge. Dickinson included in his book a chapter and an appendix almost wholly about the superior waters,[2] and more than one university disserta-

[1] Descartes, *Oeuvres* (Paris, 1824), vol. iii, *Les principes de la philosophie*, pt. ii, secs. 16-19, pt. iii and pt. iv.

[2] Dickinson, *Physica Vetus et Vera* (Rotterdam, 1703), pp. 231-245, 325-328.

tion was presented on that topic. Examples of the treatment customarily accorded to the subject in scholastic circles may be found in the treatises by Pfleumer [3] and by Schroeder.[4] Both analysed the topic and gave all possible interpretations with the authorities for each. Both mentioned even the allegorical explanation that had been propounded by some of the Fathers but that had apparently fallen into disrepute, which declared that the superior waters were good angels.[5] Then by *a priori* reasoning from such doctrines as that everything created must have a use and that all was for the benefit of man, they disproved the interpretations they rejected and proved the ones they chose.

Jéhan asserted that according to the general belief during the first half of the seventeenth century the waters were above all the moving heavens but below the empyreum; [6] and Kunstmann, a pupil of Heyn, in 1742 called it the common belief though it was not his.[7] Nevertheless by 1744 the *Universal History* somewhat rashly affirmed that the doctrine of super-celestial waters was denied by all.[8] Pfleumer, after his list of various interpretations, accepted this belief,[9]

---

[3] Pfleumer, *Dissertatio Theologico-Critica, de Aqvis Svpracoelestibvs* (Jena, 1733) (1st delivered, 1663).

[4] Schroeder, *Aqvas Supracoelestes à multis hactenus Doctoribus Supra Coelum Sidereum locatas* (Kiel, 1671).

[5] Riccioli also denied Origen's thesis that the superior waters were good angels. Riccioli, *Almagestvm Novvm Astronomiam Veterem Novamqve Complectens* (Bologna, 1651), vol. ii, p. 223.

[6] Jéhan, *Dictionnaire de cosmogonie et de paléontologie* (Paris, 1854), art. " Cosmogonie aux XVIe et XVIIe siècles," cols. 305, 306.

[7] Heyn, *Specimen Cometologiae Sacrae* (Leipzig, 1742), pp. 4, 5.

[8] *An Universal History, from the Earliest Account of Time to the Present* (Dublin, 1744), vol. i, p. 98 note, *cf.* also p. 42.

[9] Pfleumer, *op. cit.*, who perhaps identified them with the crystalline heaven and modestly confessed ignorance of their use although he repeated the stock uses suggested for such waters, the production by their mass of motion in the *primum mobile*, the counteraction of the heat

as did Duguet and d'Asfeld.[10]   Planer thought that the superior waters were above the air and the ether.   Since he considered the ether to be the location of the stars, his opinion may be classified here.[11]   Kirchmaier, on the other hand, definitely denied the idea,[12] as did Burnet, who rejected also their identification with the clouds and apparently all other hypotheses, considering the account another adaptation of the Mosaic narrative to popular stupidity for politic reasons.[13] In the *Theory* he had rejected the belief that the waters beyond the firmament were above the stars and that they were the clouds, but had said rather vaguely that in the antediluvian epoch they had formed the entire middle region of the air.[14]   Fludd [15] and Riccioli [16] retained the old doctrine of the superior waters in the form of a solid, frozen, crystalline heaven between the empyreum and the starry heaven, although Riccioli thought that instead it might be the frozen stellar heaven itself, and that part of the water might be liquid or vaporous.   Kircher, who denied that they were a cause of the flood,[17] thought that they were mixed with part of the primitive light.   The combination of the warm and

caused by the motion of the heavens, the production of the deluge at a suitable epoch, the stabilization of the heavens against the blows of the winds.

[10] Duguet and d'Asfeld, *Explication de l'ouvrage des six jours* (Paris, 1740), pp. 59-63.

[11] Planer, *Cometa. Coeli Pars et Partus* (Tübingen, 1682), p. 13.

[12] Kirchmaier, *De Dilvvii Universalitate* (Geneva, 1667), pp. 22-24.

[13] Burnet, *Doctrina Antiqua de Rerum Originibus* (London, 1729, 1736), *Archaeologiae Philosophicae*, pt. i, critique, pp. 38-41.

[14] Burnet, *The Sacred Theory of the Earth* (London, 1722), vol. i, bk. i, pp. 22, 23, bk. ii, pp. 320, 321.

[15] Fludd, *Utriusque Cosmi Maioris scilicet et Minoris Metaphysica, Physica atque Technica Historia* (Oppenheim, 1617), pp. 53, 54.

[16] Riccioli, *op. cit.*, vol. ii, pp. 216-218, 220-225, 271-276.

[17] Kircher, *Arca Noë* (Amsterdam, 1675), p. 131.

the humid radicals, which nourished the ethereal expanse and the celestial globes, was perhaps placed between the stars and the empyreum to veil the highest heaven from our eyes.[18] Comenius also located the superior waters at the limit of the visible cosmos, and repeated the ancient theory that a reason for such a position was to cool the ever-rolling frame of the visible world.[19] Milton's location of them as a crystalline ocean at the boundary of the universe from chaos amounted to the same doctrine, since he placed the seat of God and the angels beyond chaos. The boundary itself, according to him, was made of ether.[20]

With the passage of time the opinion grew that the superior waters were the clouds.[21] Probably Postel identified

[18] Kircher, *Itinerarivm Exstaticvm* (Rome, 1656), pp. 369-372, 376.

[19] Comenius, *Naturall Philosophie Reformed by Divine Light* (London, 1651), pp. 12, 86-89.

[20] Milton, *The Poetical Works* (London, 1862), *Paradise Lost*, bk. vii, ll. 264-273. Also bk. iii, l. 720.

[21] Raleigh, *The History of the World* (Edinburgh, 1820) (1st ed., 1614), vol. i, pp. 25-27; Hakewill, *An Apologie or Declaration of the Power and Providence of God in the Gouernment of the World* (Oxford, 1635), pt. i, pp. 80, 81; probably Wilkins, *The Mathematical and Philosophical Works* (London, 1707-8), bk. i, p. 131; Alsted, *Physica Harmonica* (Herborn, 1642), pp. 32, 33, 39, who declared that they were sustained in the air less by the force of fire than by that of the celestial bodies and their own motions; apparently Ozorio, *Theologie cvrievse* (Dijon, 1666), pp. 163-166; Schroeder, *op. cit.*, who wrote to disprove all other suppositions in favor of this belief, and who, in cap. iv, art. ii, gave a list of authorities for it; Warren, *A Defence of the Discourse Concerning the Earth Before the Flood* (London, 1691), pp. 118-120; Warren, *Geologia* (London, 1690), pp. 229-243; Ray, *Three Physico-Theological Discourses* (London, 1693), pp. 73-75; Le Clerc, *Mosis Prophetae Libri Quinque* (Amsterdam, 1735), pp. 7, 8, 65; Whiston, *A New Theory of the Earth* (Cambridge, 1708), p. 309, though he called them vapors sustained by the air as now the clouds are; Witty, *An Essay towards a Vindication of the Vulgar Exposition of the Mosaic History of the Creation of the World* (London, 1705), p. 72, who called this, his second suggestion, " the most common Hypothesis "; Shuckford, *The Sacred and Profane History of the World Connected* (Philadelphia,

them with the clouds when he said that the waters were above the middle region of the air,[22] and Thomas Foxton when he declared that they were in the air and compared modern cloudbursts with the rain from that source at the deluge.[23] Riccioli was one of the most important dissenters from this view.[24]

A few scattered voices suggested other localities for the superior waters. Some writers evolved an ingenious theory. If the whole universe was composed of the four elements, then the celestial spheres must consist of water, earth, air and fire. The waters below the firmament were, therefore, those on our earth, while the superior ones were the waters on all the heavenly bodies, both stars and planets. Obviously they were above our firmament or the air and ether between us and them. Of this opinion were Dr. Nichols, perhaps Foxton [25] and apparently Witty.[26] Hutchinson,[27] and later Pike,[28] Catcott and probably his father,[29]

1824) (1st ed., c. 1728), vol. i, p. 21; *An Universal History from the Earliest Account of Time to the Present* (Dublin, 1744), vol. i, p. 42, where Hugo Grotius was quoted to the same effect; Cockburn, *An Enquiry into the Truth and Certainty of the Mosaic Deluge* (London, 1750), pp. 260, 262, where Vossius was quoted for the same conclusion; Marsh, *An Oration, on the Truth of the Mosaic History of the Creation* (Hartford, 1798), p. 15.

[22] Postel, *De Universitate* (Leyden, 1635), p. 28.

[23] Burnet, *Doctrina Antiqua de Rerum Originibus* (London, 1729, 1736), remarks (by Thomas Foxton?) on *Archaeologiae Philosophicae*, pt. i, pp. 255-257, though later he seemed to accept another interpretation, *cf. infra*, note 25.

[24] Riccioli, *op. cit.*, vol. ii, pp. 223, 224.

[25] Dr. Nichols, *Conferences with a Theist*, pt. i, quoted by Foxton in Burnet, *op. cit.*, *Archaeologiae Philosophicae*, remarks after pt. i, critique, pp. 74, 75.

[26] Witty, *op. cit.*, pp. 70, 71.

[27] Hutchinson, *Moses's Principia* (London, 1724), pp. 22, 27-30, 44.

[28] Pike, *Philosophia Sacra* (London, 1753), pp. 109-111, and *The Explanation of the Copper Plate*, pp. 5, 6, together with the plate itself.

[29] Catcott, *A Treatise on the Deluge* (London, 1768), pp. 56-61, 418.

who promulgated a theory of creation according to which the earth by the pressure of the air or firmament both within and without the crust was solidified into a hollow sphere lined and covered with water, interpreted the superior waters as those immediately within the crust of the earth, which were manifestly above the firmament at the center. Apparently Burnet thought at first that they were the waters on the surface of the earth while those below the firmament were those beneath the surface, generally named the abyss. However, he found this position untenable and discarded it.[30] Hale thought that they had been transformed into the ether and upper air. The ether was only a purer air and both were easily transmutable into water, so that they were a cause of the deluge if not the principal cause. Air extended about seven miles above the earth.[31] Dickinson asserted that the waters were those which in minute particles were mixed with fire atoms in the empyreum, and that both types of particles constantly circulated up and down through the air. Their use was to supply the world with secret virtues and also to punish sin.[32] Kant suggested the possibility that they resembled the ring of Saturn and definitely collapsed upon the earth at the deluge.[33]

Besides the supernal waters just discussed there was believed to be beneath the thin crust of the earth a great subterranean abyss of waters. Its shape was approximately spherical, and it communicated with the ocean by means of

[30] Burnet, quoted by Warren, op. cit., pp. 226-228; Warren, Some Reflections upon the Short Consideration Of the Defence of the Exceptions Against the Theory of the Earth (London, 1692), p. 43.

[31] Hale, The Primitive Origination of Mankind (London, 1677), pp. 187, 188, 296-298.

[32] Dickinson, op. cit., pp. 81, 213-220, 237-242, 244, 245, 326, 327.

[33] Kant, Allgemeine Naturgeschichte und Theorie des Himmels (Leipzig, 1890), pt. ii, end of ch. v, pp. 52, 53. Cf. also supra, pp. 247, 248.

openings in the sea bed. Comenius gave the existence of such openings as the reason why the ocean in some places could not be plumbed.[34] Most authorities considered that the abyss contained water, but Whiston and Benjamin Franklin[35] thought that the fluid was of greater specific gravity than water. As Whiston said, it was heavier than the solids of the earth and could not be rarefied by any heat.[36] Urban Hjärne in 1712 thought the liquid " dense, turbid, and boiling hot." [37] Woodward, though he called it water, also affirmed that it contained a good deal of heat.[38] Steno[39] and Swinden[40] declared for the probability of such a subter-

[34] Comenius, *op. cit.*, pp. 140, 141.

[35] Franklin, quoted by Libby, *An Introduction to the History of Science* (Boston, New York, Chicago, 1917), p. 127.

[36] Whiston, *op. cit.*, pp. 63-66, 300, 326, 446; Whiston, *A Vindication of the New Theory of the Earth from the Exceptions of Mr. John Keill and Others* (London, 1698), pp. 3, 13-18; Whiston, *A Second Defence of the New Theory of the Earth from the Exceptions of Mr. John Keill* (London, 1700), p. 16.

[37] Hjärne, quoted by Arrhenius, *The Life of the Universe as conceived by man from the earliest ages to the present time* (London and New York, 1909), vol. i, p. 110, who also called the doctrine of a subterranean abyss communicating with the ocean the general opinion.

[38] Woodward, *An Essay toward a Natural History of the Earth* (London, 1695), pp. 117-128, 133-139 *etc.*; Woodward, *A Supplement & Continuation of The Essay towards a Natural History of the Earth* (London, 1726), introduction, pp. 7, 8, 31, 32, 122, 123, 144, 145, pt. ii, pp. 57-59, 96, 97, 101, 102, 104-114.

[39] Steno, *The Prodromus of Nicolaus Steno's Dissertation concerning a Solid Body Enclosed by Process of Nature within a Solid* (New York and London, 1916), p. 266. Woodward and Steno were quoted by Harris (John), *Remarks On some Late Papers, Relating to the Universal Deluge* (London, 1697), pp. 197, 199, 200, though he tried to deny Steno's belief in a watery abyss.

[40] Swinden, *An Enquiry into the Nature and Place of Hell* (London, 1727), pp. 83-86, who also quoted to the same effect, Dr. Hammond, *Annotations on Gen.* 1 : 2; 2 *Pet.* 3 : 5.

ranean abyss or at least of huge reservoirs, while Descartes [41] and Kirchmaier [42] agreed. Of course the reason for such persistent interest was the dogma that much of the water for the deluge was expelled from the subterranean abyss.[13] Leibnitz was not satisfied with one abyss, but thought that originally there were two, both filled with air. On the third day the surplus water from the surface drained into the upper abyss. Then at the deluge, the earth fell into the upper abyss; and later the water was drained into the lower.[44] Kircher was not contented to have merely reservoirs of water

[41] Descartes, *op. cit.*, vol. iii, *Les principes de la philosophie*, pt. iv, secs. 64-66.

[42] Kirchmaier, *op. cit.*, pp. 9-11, 32-44, though he considered such a source for the diluvial waters impossible.

[43] Kunstmann also called the thesis of a watery subterranean abyss the common opinion, with which he concurred, Heyn, *op. cit.*, pp. 5, 17, 19. Others who accepted it were: Mersenne, *Observationes et Emendationes ad Francisci Georgii Problemata* (Paris, 1623), col. 111; Hale, *op. cit.*, p. 187; Burnet, *op. cit.*, *Archaeologiae Philosophicae*, pt. ii, pp. 37-63; Thomas Foxton, *ibid.*, remarks on pt. i, pp. 255, 258-260 where he quoted Dr. Nichols, *op. cit.*, pt. ii, for the same belief; Burnet, *The Sacred Theory of the Earth* (London, 1722), especially vol. i, bk. i; Warren, *A Defence of the Discourse Concerning the Earth Before the Flood* (London, 1691), pp. 191-197; Ray, *op. cit.*, pp. 9, 10, 73, 76, 84, 121-124 *etc.*, who spoke of the water in it as a cause of the flood; Catoir, *Disputatio Theologica de Arca Noachi et Diluvio* (Gröningen, 1704), secs. xix-xxii; probably Stillingfleet, *Origines Sacrae* (London, 1709), pt. i, p. 341; Scheuchzer, a Swiss who wrote about the Alps, *Hist. de l'Ac. des Sc. de Paris*, année 1708, and l'Abbé Pluche, *Spectacle de la Nature*, tome iii, 2de partie, both quoted by De Luc, *Lettres physiques et morales sur l'histoire de la terre et de l'homme* (The Hague and Paris, 1779, 1780), vol. i, pp. 334, 336, 338-340; *An Universal History, from the Earliest Account of Time to the Present* (Dublin, 1744), vol. i, pp. 42, 102; Scheidt, in preface (1749) to Leibnitz's *Protogaea*, Leibnitz, *Opera Omnia* (Geneva, 1768), vol. ii, p. 192; Cockburn, *op. cit.*, pp. 257, 271-277, 308-311; Pike, *op. cit.*, pp. 111-115; Catcott, *op. cit.*, pp. 43-51, 65, 66, 97, 168-246, 384-387, who on p. 245 quoted Stackhouse, *History of the Bible*, p. 125, for a similar statement.

[44] Leibnitz, *op. cit.*, vol. ii, *Protogaea*, pp. 206, 220.

within the earth, but declared that there were also reservoirs of fire, of air and of earth.   His conception of the last type of receptacles, which were perhaps added for symmetry, was not very clear; but he suggested it consisted of earth largely filled with seminal principles.   His reservoirs were connected by subterranean channels of water and of fire.   They did not form one great abyss but rather an intricate system of inter-communicating cavities.   Though he believed in a constant circulation through the earth from the north pole to the south by an enormous quantity of water, he located a pyrophy-lacium at the center for hell, and therefore believed that the water did not take the most direct path.[45]

Throughout the two centuries almost the only authors who definitely denied the existence of a subterranean abyss of waters were Buffon [46] and Halley,[47] though others simply ignored it.   Halley thought that between the crust and the central loadstone, which he postulated as the cause for the variations of the magnetic needle, was a subtle luminous vapor.   His thesis of a solid central core to the earth was adopted by Whiston,[48] by Catcott [49] and probably by Hutch-inson,[50] all three of whom, however, believed that it was sus-pended in water.

[45] Kircher, *Arca Noë* (Amsterdam, 1675), pp. 128, 129; Kircher, *Mundus Subterraneus* (Amsterdam, 1664-5), t. i, pp. 56, 70-72, 74, 75, 99-103, 112-118, 145-151, 158-163, 168-177, 180-185, 189, 219, 221-223, 226-240, 256-260, 270, t. ii, pp. 390, 391.

[46] Buffon, *Oeuvres complètes* (Paris, 1831-2), vol. i, pp. 165, 166.

[47] Royal Society of London, *Philosophical Transactions* (London, 1665-1933), Halley, "On the cause of the Change in the Variation of the Magnetic Needle," no. 195, art. 3, 1692, pp. 563 *et seq.*, also no. 148; Halley, quoted by Catcott, *op. cit.*, p. 280, by Cockburn, *op. cit.*, p. 311, and by Whiston, *A New Theory of the Earth* (Cambridge, 1708), pp. 109, 110.

[48] *Ibid.*

[49] Catcott, *op. cit.*, pp. 280, 281, 357 and elsewhere.

[50] Hutchinson, *op. cit.*, pp. 41, 88.

In addition to a desire to discover sufficient water for the flood, leading reasons for the belief in a subterranean treasury of water were the existence of seas with no overt exit to the ocean, such as the Caspian, into which flowed many large rivers, and also probably the evident subsidence of various streams into subterranean caverns. The effectiveness of evaporation was generally unappreciated during the seventeenth and the eighteenth centuries. Therefore, since the Caspian grew no greater in area or in depth, the doctrine was current that its waters must be drained below the surface into the ocean or into the subterranean abyss, which in turn communicated with the ocean. Sometimes whirlpools were attributed to the entrance and exit of such streams of water.[51]

Within the earth was located also subterranean fire. Descartes [52] and his followers, including Gadroys,[53] together with Whiston,[54] Leibnitz,[55] Buffon [56] and probably Bur-

[51] White (Thomas), *Institutionum Peripateticarum Libri Quinque* (Frankfurt, 1664), p. 66; Kircher, *op. cit.*, t. i, pp. 86-89, 241-243; Warren, *Geologia* (London, 1690). pp. 214, 244, 245; Ray, *op. cit.*, pp. 75, 76, 84; Thomas Foxton and Dr. Nichols in Burnet, *Doctrina Antiqua de Rerum Originibus* (London, 1729, 1736), *Archaeologiae Philosophicae*, pt. i, remarks, p. 259; Duguet and d'Asfeld, *op. cit.*, p. 70, who did not mention a watery abyss; Cockburn, *op. cit.*, pp. 275, 276; Catcott, *op. cit.*, pp. 220-234, 356, 357. Buffon both asserted and denied the existence of such a subterranean connection, Buffon, *op. cit.*, vol. i, pp. 115, 145-147.

[52] Descartes, *op. cit.*, vol. iii, *Les principes de la philosophie*, especially pt. iii, sec. 150, pt. iv, secs. 3, 59.

[53] Gadroys, *Le systeme du monde* (Paris, 1675), pp. 313, 314, 344-347, though he suggested the possibility that the matter of the crust was so great in proportion as to have smothered and extinguished the fire, *ibid.*, pp. 348, 349.

[54] Whiston, *op. cit.*, pp. 53, 78, 441 and elsewhere.

[55] Leibnitz, *op. cit.*, vol. ii, *Protogaea*, pp. 201-213, 216.

[56] Buffon, *op. cit.*, vol. i, though on pages 153, 155 he denied that there was a central fire.

net [57] had evolved hypotheses in which the earth was originally hot and merely the surface was cooled. Therefore, naturally they assumed a central heat. However, many others,
including Fludd,[58] whose theory made a central fire most
incredible, accepted the conclusion, even though with Dickinson [59] they were compelled to postulate a direct act of God
to confine the fire lest it escape to its natural sphere. Ray
adopted the thesis, although he said that it was not demon-
strable.[60] Most authorities attributed to the subterranean
fire hot springs, eruptions, the heat in mines and similar
phenomena. Comenius thought that it was the cause of
metals, of mountains and of salt in the sea as well; [61] and
Spencer,[62] Grotius [63] and Gale,[64] as well as many others, believed that it, sometimes in conjunction with celestial fires,
would cause the final conflagration.[65] Often the various

[57] Burnet, *The Sacred Theory of the Earth* (London, 1722), especially
vol. ii, bk. iii, pp. 68-72, 101.

[58] Fludd, *op. cit.*, pp. 156, 163-166, 173, 174, 180, 189, 200, where he
spoke of the fire as central, though he also, p. 203, called the center vacant,
or perhaps vacant in winter and filled with air and water in summer, and
on pp. 34, 65 called the center of the earth the natural seat of cold.

[59] Dickinson, *op. cit.*, pp. 5, 92, 93, 252, 253, 260-262 and elsewhere.

[60] Ray, *op. cit.*, pp. 117, 318-322.

[61] Comenius, *op. cit.*, pp. 88, 89, 139, 140, 231.

[62] Spencer, *A Discourse concerning Prodigies* (London, 1665), pp. 126,
127.

[63] Grotius, *Annotat. on 2 Pet.* 3:7, quoted by Gale, *The Covrt of the
Gentiles* (Oxford and London, 1670-77), vol. i, pt. ii, p. 339.

[64] *Ibid.*, vol. ii, pt. iv, bk. ii, p. 452.

[65] Others who accepted the belief in subterranean heat were White
(Thomas), *op. cit.*, especially pp. 65, 66, 81, 82; Kircher, *op. cit.*, especially t. i, pp. 113, 114, 159, 168-190, 219, 256, 257, 260, 270; Steno,
op. cit., pp. 265-267, who was also quoted by Harris (John), *op. cit.*, p.
199; Hale, *op. cit.*, pp. 299, 307; Bentley, *The Folly and Unreasonableness
of Atheism Demonstrated* (London, 1699), p. 260; Woodward, *op. cit.*,
introduction, pp. 136, 140-143; Woodward, *An Essay toward a Natural
History of the Earth: and Terrestrial Bodies* (London, 1695), pp. 121,

activities that produced metals, minerals and plants, and permitted the existence of life on the globe were considered a proof of the subterranean heat which was their necessary cause. Buffon with lengthy calculations showed that the temperature in summer surpassed that in winter by only one-seventh, though the heat of the solar rays was sixty-six times as great. Clearly the moderation of the wintry climate was due to the internal heat of the earth.[66] De Luc declared that such a heat, original with the earth or acquired, was unquestionable;[67] Mentelle, that the subterranean heat, apparently not localized at the center, was not the remains of a primitive ignited state but resulted from the sun's rays in the torrid zone;[68] Adams, that there was either a central fire or a heat which was diffused through the whole globe from the beginning. In either case it was renewed by the sun.[69] Dissenting voices were few and weak. Warren asserted that a central fire was improbable at least;[70] and Keill, that no central hot body was needed.[71]

As has been suggested, few at the time appreciated the enormous quantity of water that was evaporated daily from the surfaces of the ocean, of lakes and of smaller pools.

133, 134, 136, 139-146, who also attributed to it most of the warmth on the earth's surface; Moncharville, *Preuves des existences, et nouveau système de l'univers* (Paris, 1702), p. 14; Derham, *Physico-Theology* (London, 1742) (1st ed., c. 1712), p. 50 note, also quoted by Catcott, *op. cit.*, note pp. 196, 197, who agreed, *ibid.*, note p. 201, pp. 235-237; Cockburn, *op. cit.*, pp. 272-277.

[66] Buffon, *op. cit.*, vol. iii, pp. 103-106.

[67] De Luc, *op. cit.*, vol. v, p. 594.

[68] Mentelle, *Cosmographie élémentaire* (Paris, 1781), pp. 118-120.

[69] Adams, *Lectures on Natural and Experimental Philosophy* (London, 1794), vol. iv, p. 545.

[70] Warren, *op. cit.*, pp. 86-89, 91-96.

[71] Keill, *An Examination of Dr. Burnet's Theory of the Earth. Together with some remarks on Mr. Whiston's New Theory of the Earth* (Oxford, 1698), pp. 186-188.

Therefore the real cause of springs, a condensation of this vapor, largely in the form of rain, its percolation through the surface soil of eminences and its emergence on lower ground where some denser stratum was exposed, seemed ridiculous to commentators. Often, from their passionate desire for symmetry, philosophers declared that the surface areas of the ocean and of the land were equal as well as their bulk, and that the altitude of the highest mountains equalled the depth of the lowest portions of the sea bed.[72] The doctrines of subterranean heat and a subterranean abyss of water substantiated one of the most natural and popular hypotheses as to the sources of springs and rivers. The heat raised vapors through the earth by means of cracks. The vapors either emerged directly or were condensed in the cold caverns near the surface and ran out.[73] Warren's only vari-

[72] *Cf. infra*, pp. 400, 401.

[73] Mersenne, *op. cit.*, col. 111; Whiston, *op. cit.*, pp. 84, 220, 221, 327; Whiston, *A Vindication of the New Theory of the Earth from the Exceptions of Mr. Keill and Others* (London, 1698), pp. 6, 7; Whiston, *A Second Defence of the New Theory of the Earth from the Exceptions of Mr. John Keill* (London, 1700), pp. 7, 8, 10, 11; Descartes, *op. cit.*, vol. iii, *Les principes de la philosophie*, pt. iv, secs. 64-67; Comenius, *op. cit.*, pp. 140, 141; Gale, *op. cit.*, vol. ii, pt. iv, bk. ii, p. 452, who mentioned the elevation of vapors by subterranean heat as the cause of springs and rivers but neglected to give the source of the vapors; Swinden, *op. cit.*, p. 86; Catcott's father, the Rev. A. S. Catcott, *Paraphrase of Ps. 104*, printed in Catcott, *op. cit.*, p. 420; Catcott, *ibid.*, pp. 43, 66, 97, 174-234 *etc.*, who gave his own opinion, quoted Pliny, Seneca etc. as authorities and gave experiments to prove the thesis. He again compared such action to the motion of the blood. Both were pressed through channels and veins by the pressure of the outer air and the penetration of the finer air and light into the bodies containing them, *ibid.*, pp. 213, 214. Woodward, *op. cit.*, pp. 121-128, 136; Woodward, *A Supplement & Continuation of The Essay towards a Natural History of the Earth* (London, 1726), introduction, p. 24, pt. ii, pp. 57, 58, 107, 110, though he thought that they were caused in part by rains and by vapors condensed by the mountains; perhaps Pike, *op. cit.*, *The Explanation of the Copper Plate*, pp. 6, 7.

ation was to substitute the heat of the sun as the elevating force.[74] Fludd gave many reasons for springs, of which this was one.[75] In another he agreed with Bacon, who thought that the water of springs was transformed air, except that Bacon attributed the mutation to cold [76] and Fludd to the condensation of the air as it was forced out of the earth by the water fallen from the clouds. He thought that it was the difficulty of penetrating the earth that transformed the air,[77] while Heylyn felt that the extreme cold of the earth changed air to water as it entered through the chinks. Heylyn added water from the sea by subterranean passages as a cause.[78] Fludd gave still another reason to the effect that in summer the solar heat by rarefaction drove air and water to the vacant center of the earth and in winter they returned to the surface and overflowed.[79] Kircher gave ten reasons for springs, one of which was circulatory action analogous to that of the blood; but his favorite cause was based upon belief in subterranean reservoirs of water high in the mountains. To these the water was raised by the pressure of storms, tides or winds on the sea, which forced the water up obliquely through subterranean channels; or it was sucked up by the dry earth.[80]

A source of springs somewhat similar to the subterranean abyss was the sea, which was supposed to raise the water by

[74] Warren, *op. cit.*, pp. 303-310, especially pp. 309, 310; Warren, *A Defence of the Discourse Concerning the Earth Before the Flood* (London, 1691), pp. 191-197.

[75] Fludd, *op. cit.*, pp. 199-204.

[76] Bacon, *Works* (Boston, ?), vol. iv, *Sylva Sylvarum*, cent. i, no. 27, p. 172.

[77] Fludd, *op. cit.*, pp. 199, 200.

[78] Heylyn, *Cosmography in Four Books* (London, 1674), introduction, p. 23.

[79] Fludd, *op. cit.*, p. 204.

[80] Kircher, *op. cit.*, t. i, pp. 227-240.

hidden channels to the surface of the dry land.   This source
was attributed to springs by Van Helmont.   He said that
water, like blood, had a vitality of its own, so that while it
was in the veins of the earth it was not governed by the laws
of hydraulics, by which he apparently meant the law of gravity.[81]   Others who derived springs from the ocean were
Hakewill,[82] Steno,[83] Dr. Robert Plot,[84] Dickinson,[85] Stillingfleet [86] and Blackmore,[87] though Stillingfleet felt that the
sea water was diluted by rains and that perhaps the source of
the water was the abyss instead of the ocean.[88]   Woodward [89]
and Ray [90] both mentioned those who attributed springs to
secret channels from the sea.

    Dr. Edmund Halley was the chief supporter of another
theory; namely, that springs were due to the condensation of
vapors on the sides of mountains.   Keill declared that he
had proved this.[91]   Keill added that the vapors were raised

[81] Van Helmont, *Opera Omnia* (Frankfurt, 1682), pt. i, pp. 52, 53,
especially secs. 7, 8.

[82] Hakewill, *op. cit.*, pt. i, p. 140.

[83] Steno, *op. cit.*, p. 266, and quoted by Harris (John), *op. cit.*, p. 200.

[84] Royal Society of London, *Philosophical Transactions* (London,
1665-1933), no. 167, pp. 862 *et seq.*, Plot, " De Origine Fontium, Tentamen
Philosophicum" (Oxford, 1685) ; *ibid.*, sec. 51, quoted by Catcott, *op. cit.*,
p. 184; Plot, *The Natural History of Staffordshire* (Oxford, 1686),
p. 79, quoted with complimentary phrases by Ray, *op. cit.*, p. 85.

[85] Dickinson, *op. cit.*, pp. 96, 99.

[86] Stillingfleet, *op. cit.*, pt. i, pp. 341-344, who also adopted the analogy
of the circulation of the blood.

[87] Blackmore, *Creation*, in *The British Poets* (Chiswick, 1822), vol.
xxviii, bk. i, p. 93, bk. iii, p. 143.

[88] Stillingfleet, *op. cit.*, pt. i, pp. 341-343.

[89] Woodward, *op. cit.*, pt. ii, pp. 147-149, who rejected the belief.

[90] Ray, *op. cit.*, pp. 84-89.

[91] Royal Society of London, *op. cit.*, no. 192, art. 4, 1690-1, pp. 468
et seq., Halley, " On the Circulation of the watery Vapours of the Sea,
and the Origin of Springs "; Halley, quoted by Ray, *op. cit.*, p. 98, by
Scheidt, preface to the *Protogaea*, Leibnitz, *op. cit.*, vol. ii, p. 183, and by
Keill, *op. cit.*, pp. 55-58.

from the sea, and that no springs were found on the summits
of mountains.[92]   Dr. Tancred Robinson was another who
accepted this hypothesis.[93]   Dr. Halley [94] and Scheidt [95]
apparently believed that springs were due to rain as well as to
vapors condensed by mountains.   As early as 1664 Thomas
White had felt that rains were the cause of springs, although
he weakened his statement by a compromise which asserted
that another cause was the subterranean reservoirs of water.
This water was mixed with heat and rose out of the mountains.[96]   Besides those already mentioned as advocates of
the proposition that springs were due to rain, Ray in England,[97] Dr. Bernardino Ramazzini in Italy [98] and probably
Le Clerc in Holland [99] and Leibnitz [100] expressed the same
opinion during the years 1691-1693.   Late in the next century De Luc came to the same conclusion,[101] and Buffon
agreed although he associated with the rains the vapor condensed on mountain peaks.[102]   Derham [103] and Cockburn [104]

[92] *Ibid.*, pp. 187, 188, who agreed with Halley, though he attributed
springs to rain as well.

[93] Robinson, quoted by Ray, *op. cit.*, pp. 111, 112.

[94] Halley, Royal Society of London, *loc. cit.*, no. 192, quoted by Keill,
op. cit., pp. 55-58, and by Buffon, together with his own opinion, Buffon,
op. cit., vol. ii, pp. 115, 116.

[95] Scheidt, in Leibnitz, *op. cit.*, vol. ii, *Protogaea*, p. 183.

[96] White (Thomas), *op. cit.*, pp. 67, 68.

[97] Ray, *op. cit.*, especially pp. 80-116, though he also leaned to the
opinion that they might come from the sea by subterranean passages.

[98] Ramazzini, Tract of the *Springs of Modena* (Modena, 1692), translated into English by Dr. Robert St. Clair (1697), pp. 121 *et seq.*, quoted
by Harris (John), *op. cit.*, pp. 245, 252.

[99] Le Clerc, *op. cit.*, p. 65.

[100] Leibnitz, *op. cit.*, vol. ii, *Protogaea*, p. 207.

[101] De Luc, *op. cit.*, vol. i, p. 345.

[102] Buffon, *op. cit.*, vol. i, pp. 157, 159, vol. ii, p. 175.

[103] Derham, *op. cit.*, pp. 23-25, note pp. 51, 52, p. 75.

[104] Cockburn, *op. cit.*, pp. 272-277.

were so eager to cover all possibilities that they impartially accepted rain, condensed vapors on the mountain sides and water raised by subterranean channels from the sea or from the abyss as causes for springs, though Cockburn felt that the chief source was the waters of the abyss, and Derham that it was the sea.

CHAPTER VI

Earthquakes and Eruptions

Two striking terrestrial phenomena, volcanic eruptions and earthquakes, were associated in the books of the seventeenth and the eighteenth centuries. Often their cause was connected with that of winds, of thunder and lightning, of hot springs, of floods and even of pestilence.[1] Cockburn tried to prove by examples that floods from the sea were preceded or accompanied by earthquakes, though honesty forced him to mention an earthquake in Peru which was preceded by a flood. His conclusion was that most floods were caused by earthquakes.[2] Burnet thought that the two resulted from

[1] Fludd, *Utriusque Cosmi Maioris scilicet et Minoris Metaphysica, Physica atque Technica Historia* (Oppenheim, 1617), pp. 189-193; Hakewill, *An Apologie or Declaration of the Power and Providence of God in the Government of the World* (Oxford, 1635), pt. i, pp. 131, 135; Comenius, *Naturall Philosophie Reformed by Divine Light* (London, 1651), pp. 104, 114, cf. also *infra*, note p. 386; Browne, *Works* (London, 1890), vol. i, *Pseudodoxia Epidemica*, pp. 178, 179; Kircher, *Itinerarivm Exstaticvm* (Rome, 1656), p. 301; Kircher, *Mundus Subterraneus* (Amsterdam, 1664-5), t. i, pp. 168, 179, 182, 183; Gadroys, *Le systeme du monde* (Paris, 1675), pp. 422-424, 427, 428; Ray, *Three Physico-Theological Discourses* (London, 1693), pp. 194-206; Woodward, *An Essay toward a Natural History of the Earth: and Terrestrial Bodies* (London, 1695), pp. 133-146, 199-215; Woodward, *A Supplement & Continuation of The Essay towards a Natural History of the Earth* (London, 1726), introduction, pp. 132, 133, 146-150; Dickinson, *Physica Vetus et Vera* (Rotterdam, 1703), p. 260; Franklin, *Gazette* (1737), quoted by Faÿ, *Franklin the Apostle of Modern Times* (Boston, 1929), p. 228; Catcott, *A Treatise on the Deluge* (London, 1768), pp. 66-69, 234-239, though the relationships he suggested were somewhat more scientifically sound than those of the earlier commentators.

[2] Cockburn, *An Enquiry into the Truth and Certainty of the Mosaic Deluge* (London, 1750), pp. 279-286, 291, 293, 294.

the same cause,[3] although he said also that floods were due to earthquakes and to the effusion of subterraneous water as the earth crust broke and was precipitated into it.[4]   Earthquakes and eruptions were considered to be a punishment for sin, perhaps a result of Adam's fall, a portent of evil or a means of terrifying and converting sinners.[5]   Burton declared that, in the opinion of some, earthquakes were caused by spirits or angels.[6]   Fludd also felt that with God's consent they might be brought about by evil angels, and compared them to diseases in man.[7]   Processions of relics and prayer were adopted for protection against both volcanic action and earth tremors as late as the eruption of 1669 and the tremor of 1692 in Jamaica, and were apparently effectual.[8]   Bacon [9] and Hakewill [10] felt that these catastrophes could be foretold by astrology.

[3] Burnet, *Doctrina Antiqua de Rerum Originibus* (London, 1729, 1736), *Archaeologiae Philosophicae*, pt. ii, pp. 50, 51, 53, 55-63.

[4] Burnet, *The Sacred Theory of the Earth* (London, 1722), vol. i, bk. i, p. 127.

[5] Ray, *op. cit.*, pp. 187, 188, 192-194, 206-208; Danforth, *An Astronomical Description of the late Comet or Blazing Star As it appeared in New-England in the 9th, 10th, 11th, and in the beginning of the 12th Moneth, 1664* (Cambridge, 1665), pp. 19, 21 (London edition, 1666, pp. 23-26); Werder, in Heyn, *Specimen Cometologiae Sacrae* (Leipzig, 1742), p. 41; Cockburn, *op. cit.*, pp. 278, 286-290, 350-355; Wesley, quoted by White (Andrew), *A History of the Warfare of Science with Theology in Christendom* (New York and London, 1910), vol. i, pp. 220, 221.

[6] Burton, *The Anatomy of Melancholy* (London, 1920), vol. ii, p. 54.

[7] Fludd, *op. cit.*, pp. 183, 198.

[8] *The Vulcano's* (London, 1669), pt. ii, *A True and Exact Relation Of the Late Prodigious Earthquake & Eruption of Mount Aetna*, especially pp. 16, 17, 20, 21; Heylyn, *Cosmography in Four Books* (London, 1674), bk. ii, p. 219; Mallet, *Description de l'univers* (Paris, 1683), vol. iv, p. 270; Ray, *op. cit.*, pp. 192, 193.

[9] Bacon, *Works* (Boston, ?), vol. viii, *De Augmentis Scientiarum*, p. 495.

[10] Hakewill, *op. cit.*, pt. i, p. 112, though he felt their prediction uncertain because of cross accidents. The stars were both signs and concurrent causes of such disasters.

The material cause for these phenomena was frequently discussed; and all possible explanations were defended, sometimes by the same author. Beaumont gave the longest list of the many causes to which earthquakes were assigned by philosophers.[11] Some said that they were caused by the struggling of vapors raised and rarefied by the sun and disrupting the earth so that the crust fell into caverns, or some " by certain Conjunctions of the Planets, some by the Motion of Comets near the Earth, others by subterraneous Fires or Ferments; . . . others . . . by the Motion of subterraneous Waters, others again by certain Moulderings or Founderings in certain Caverns of the Earth," etc.[12] The favorite explanation postulated an accumulation in caverns or galleries of exhalations or " steams " that were sulphurous or bituminous and therefore inflammable. Then they were exploded by the force of the subterranean fire or by the entrance of water or by their mixture with nitrous exhalations or salts.[13] The

[11] Beaumont, *Considerations On a Book, Entituled The Theory of the Earth* (London, 1692-3), pp. 27b, 28b.

[12] *Ibid.*, p. 28b.

[13] Browne, *op. cit.*, vol. i, pp. 178, 179; Spencer, *A Discourse concerning Prodigies* (London, 1665), pp. 25, 123, 126, 159, who attributed eruptions to the ignition of natural tinder in the earth and earthquakes to attempted escape of subterranean winds and vapors, though he also attributed some earthquakes to the devil, *ibid.*, p. 380; Steno, *Tract. de Glossopetris et Myologiae Specimen* (Florence, 1667), quoted by Harris (John), *Remarks On some Late Papers, Relating to the Universal Deluge* (London, 1697), pp. 172, 187, 188; Gadroys, *op. cit.*, pp. 422-424, 427, 428; Hale, *The Primitive Origination of Mankind* (London, 1677), p. 95; Foxton in Burnet, *Doctrina Antiqua de Rerum Originibus* (London, 1729, 1736), *Archaeologiae Philosophicae*, remarks after pt. i, critique, p. 57. Burnet himself gave more than one cause. On the other hand, he said that the sole cause of earthquakes was the hollow structure of the earth, *ibid., Archaeologiae Philosophicae*, pt. ii, pp. 55, 56, 58. He asserted apparently that earthquakes were produced by the rarefaction of vapors within the earth as the water of the abyss was evaporated through the crust, *ibid., Archaeologiae Philosophicae*, remarks by Foxton after pt. i, critique, pp. 56, 57. Elsewhere he said that they and eruptions

Aristotelian belief that they were due to the ignition of a hot, dry exhalation, imprisoned in the earth, was upheld by Hakewill.[14] Whiston attributed these violent phenomena to the central heat and to the porous and cavernous condition of the outer crust. For eruptions he insisted on the necessity for admission of air to facilitate combustion.[15] Descartes said that the exhalations would be ignited by some spark, and then would be rarefied and would expand suddenly so that the gases would push against the sides of the cavity with great violence. Sometimes they would burst open the earth at weak spots and escape as flame. This would burn for some time, as it carried up a combination of earth with sulphur and bitumen. The tops of mountains and places once fractured were the weakest spots and therefore those most susceptible to eruptions. Generally caverns of sufficient size to contain such accumulations of inflammable matter were under the highest mountains. Since the caverns or galleries

were due to the inflammation of exhalations in the earth and that they were caused by water falling into the molten mass of the earth and becoming converted into steam. Burnet, *The Sacred Theory of the Earth* (London, 1722), vol. ii, bk. iii, pp. 96, 111, 112, 133, 137. Ray, *op. cit.*, pp. 10-18, 25, 26, 194-206; Bentley, *The Folly and Unreasonableness of Atheism Demonstrated* (London, 1699), p. 271, who thought quakes and eruptions due to fermentation by the seeds of subterranean minerals; Dickinson, *op. cit.*, p. 260; Franklin, *Gazette* (1737), quoted by Faÿ, *op. cit.*, p. 228; Leibnitz, *Opera Omnia* (Geneva, 1768), vol. ii, *Protogaea*, p. 216, who declared that earthquakes and volcanoes were a proof of the central fire. To this fire he apparently attributed all eruptions, but without expatiating upon the process.

[14] Hakewill, *op. cit.*, pt. i, p. 135.

[15] Whiston, *A Second Defence of the New Theory of the Earth from the Exceptions of Mr. John Keill* (London, 1700), pp. 7, 8; Whiston, *A New Theory of the Earth* (Cambridge, 1708), pp. 84, 85, 422; Whiston, quoted and answered by Keill, *An Examination of Dr. Burnet's Theory of the Earth. Together with some remarks on Mr. Whiston's New Theory of the Earth* (Oxford, 1698), pp. 186, 187. Chiefly on the authority of Borelli, *De incendiis Montis Aetnae*, Keill thought the source of volcanic fires near the surface of the earth.

had intricate intercommunications, the shocks and eruptions over a wide area were simultaneous or nearly so. Gradually such exhalations as did not produce an eruption were dissipated in the branching caverns or galleries or were reconverted into liquids.[16] The chief variation among the opinions of commentators concerned the problem whether the heat was due to a central fire or to beds of sulphur and other combustibles nearer the surface. Whiston declared for the central fire,[17] but most authors accepted combustible matter less remote as the source. Buffon even asserted that the beds were above the level of the plains.[18] Some authors, like Ray,[19] thought that the violence of the eruptions was increased by the entrance of water, which was transformed into steam. Swinden added the suggestion that the beds were set on fire by the heat derived from the direct rays of the sun.[20] Buffon invoked the modern *deus ex machina* and asserted that eruptions were due to electricity, the basis of which was the natural heat of the earth. These invisible emanations produced a violent flame and strong explosions when they were turned in the same direction or accumulated by friction. He thought that the interior cavities of the earth contained fire, air and water, which acted upon one another either by their own volition or upon ignition by electric sparks from the interior heat, so that they exploded into steam and other vapors.[21] Comenius [22] and Kircher

[16] Descartes, *Oeuvres* (Paris, 1824), vol. iii, *Les principes de la philosophie*, pt. iv, secs. 76-79.

[17] *Cf. supra*, note p. 384.

[18] Buffon, *Oeuvres complètes* (Paris, 1831-2), vol. i, pp. 153, 154, vol. ii, pp. 300, 358.

[19] Ray, *op. cit.*, pp. 195, 196, 206.

[20] Swinden, *An Enquiry into the Nature and Place of Hell* (London, 1727), pp. 95-99.

[21] Buffon, *op. cit.*, vol. i, p. 156, vol. ii, pp. 87, 294, 295, 300, 351-354, vol. v, pp. 193-200, 205, 206, though he added other grounds for earth-

also had believed that the cavities in the earth were filled with air, water and fire, though Kircher in the discussion of volcanoes largely limited himself to mention of reservoirs containing water and those containing fire, which he said were buried in all volcanoes and were invariable associates to temper each other and to preserve the universe.[23]   Woodward[24] and De Luc emphasized the subterranean connections of volcanoes and earthquakes, both of which they attributed normally to a combination of fire and water; and De Luc accepted the fracture of cavern vaults as a cause of earthquakes.[25]   Heylyn thought that eruptions were due to subterranean winds.   Although he mentioned water as a cause, he apparently did not mean an explosion of steam, but rather

quakes. He thought that some were the results of eruptions as well as of causes similar to those which produced volcanic outbursts, and that others resulted from subterranean winds or from the fracture of the vaults in subterranean caverns.   Since this last catastrophe was not uncommon before any eruptions took place, earthquakes were an earlier phenomenon in terrestrial history. *Ibid.*, vol. i, pp. 151-157, vol. ii, pp. 296, 302, 317-321, 326-330, vol. v, pp. 205, 206.

[22] Comenius, *op. cit.*, pp. 88, 89, 93, 94, 97, 98, 104, 114. Though he also asserted that the first earthquake on the third day was caused " by the fire sunk into the earth; which giving battle to the cold there conglobated, shook the earth, and either caused it to swell variously or rent it asunder ", *ibid.*, p. 93, he accepted the popular opinion concerning the causes of these notable catastrophes.

[23] Kircher, *op. cit.*, t. i, pp. 103, 168, 175, 176, 179, 182, 183, 220-223, 307; Kircher, *Itinerarivm Exstaticvm* (Rome, 1656), p. 301, and *cf. infra,* p. 389. Besides, explosions, he gave other causes, especially the interaction of subterranean water and fire, for the production of earthquakes and eruptions.

[24] Woodward, *op. cit.*, pt. ii, pp. 104, 105; Woodward, *An Essay toward a Natural History of the Earth: and Terrestrial Bodies* (London, 1695), pp. 133-146.

[25] De Luc, *Lettres physiques et morales sur l'histoire de la terre et de l'homme* (The Hague and Paris, 1779, 1780), vol. iv, pp. 334, 335, 430, 504-511, vol. v, pp. 477-482; De Luc, *Letters on the Physical History of the Earth* (London, 1831), letter iv, pp. 147-150.

that the water fed the fire, and, like the air, made it burn more fiercely.[26]   Catcott felt that at least the Biblical earthquakes, the earthquake mentioned in 1 Kings 19:11 and the other at the flood, were due to winds, although most of them resulted from a combination of fire and water.[27]   Fludd asserted that most earthquakes were caused by water or earth, which, in great quantities, broke into some immense cave and forcibly expelled the air.[28]

Gradually the study of earth tremors and volcanoes, both active and extinct, brought to light certain facts, notably that all volcanoes now active were located near the sea.   Naturally the belief arose that the presence of water was in some way necessary; and in general this was derived from the ocean, though some, including Woodward [29] and Catcott,[30] found it in the subterranean abyss.   De Luc went so far as to assert that most or all of the extinct volcanoes, many of which he listed and elaborately described, were submarine. Water filtered to them through the earth.   Even present volcanoes started their careers in the sea or at most on its very borders, where some were still being created.   Those which had remained active had preserved open their communications with the sea.[31]   Buffon, who in his hospitality

[26] Heylyn, *op. cit.*, bk. i, p. 73.

[27] Catcott, *op. cit.*, pp. 66-69.

[28] Fludd, *op. cit.*, pp. 190, 192.

[29] Woodward, *op. cit.*, pp. 133-142; Woodward, *A Supplement & Continuation of The Essay towards a Natural History of the Earth* (London, 1726), pt. ii, pp. 104, 105, 110.

[30] Catcott, *op. cit.*, pp. 234, 235.

[31] De Luc, *op. cit.*, letter iv, pp. 150, 151; De Luc, *Lettres physiques et morales sur l'histoire de la terre et de l'homme* (The Hague and Paris, 1779, 1780), vol. ii, pp. 448, 449, 476-483, vol. iii, pp. 505, 506, 509-511, 548-552, vol. iv, pp. 147-150, 152-223, 226-229, 232-264, 283, 290, 291, 301-319, 322-335, 380-397, 401-406, 408-415, 418-425, 427-436, 439-476, 479, 481-519, vol. v, pp. 358-369, 460, 461.

to many conflicting doctrines affirmed that eruptions were due to steam as well as to other vapors, said that volcanoes could be extinguished by the destruction of these communications, and considered this a suitable and a laudable task for kings.   Although he thought that earthquakes and volcanoes proved the former submergence of the land areas under the sea,[32] and like De Luc [33] believed that the worst era of volcanic activity was the fourth or fifth epoch, he denied that most early eruptions were submarine, and asserted that an eruption thus produced would have been speedily extinguished by the inrush of water as the volcano opened its crater.[34]   Woodward's explanation,[35] which was adopted by Catcott,[36] was that subterranean heat was obstructed in passages or caverns, generally in mountainous regions.   It was collected in quantity, and, in its attempts to escape by the easiest path, found its way into the abyss, where it rarefied and swelled the waters so that they beat upon the crust.   In such countries as yielded a store of sulphur and niter, its effects were more disastrous, since the combination caused an explosion similar to that of gunpowder.   The rarefied waters pressed on the earth and the sea, either directly or through the abyss, and produced earthquakes and great waves.   Catcott and Woodward mentioned the Lisbon earthquake with its simultaneous effects over the whole globe to prove the agitation of the whole abyss, whose waves beat upon the crust, and compared the motion of some earthquakes to the waves of the sea. Finally the fire escaped through the spiracles of volcanoes, through hot springs and through new apertures; and the

[32] Buffon, *op. cit.*, vol. ii, p. 87, vol. v, pp. 193-195, 197, 204, 221, 222.

[33] De Luc, *Letters on the Physical History of the Earth* (London, 1831), letter iv, pp. 151-153.

[34] Buffon, *op. cit.*, vol. v, pp. 199, 200.

[35] Woodward, *op. cit.*, pt. ii, pp. 133, 134, 138-146.

[36] Catcott, *op. cit.*, pp. 234-239.

earth rested until a fresh accumulation of fire had collected. The suggestion that volcanic vents served as safety valves to remove surplus fire appealed also to Kircher [37] and to Derham,[38] though Kircher thought them likewise spiracles to admit air to the fires. Derham apparently attributed eruptions to a combination of subterranean fires and waters. Kircher, in addition to his view that they and earthquakes were due to explosions of combustible matter, asserted that they resulted from the combination of matter from the pyrophylacia and the hydrophylacia under each volcano. Such reservoirs contained perpetual fire and water. If the reservoir of fire was not near the surface, the fire might follow a vein of rich combustible matter to the surface. If this became depleted or obstructed, the volcanic activity would be interrupted. Subterranean winds with their damp breath accentuated the activity. Water, especially that from the sea, filled the fissures with a new mixture of combustible matter, salt, sulphur and bitumen, or, in the case of Aetna and other perpetually burning volcanoes, mixed with the ashes and produced new aliment for the fire. The subterranean explosions of niter and sulphur, which caused earthquakes, he declared were due to the mutual hostility of the two minerals.[39] Thomas White also thought that aliment was furnished to subterranean fires by sea water. He believed that the heat turned the water to vapors, and that, if it was hindered in its escape, it beat against the walls of the caverns and produced quakes and openings of the crust, or even raised the crust into mountains.[40]

[37] Kircher, *Mundus Subterraneus* (Amsterdam, 1664-5), t. i, pp. 75, 76, 113.

[38] Derham, *Physico-Theology* (London, 1742), pp. 68, 69.

[39] Kircher, *op. cit.*, t. i, pp. 168, 175, 176, 181-190, 220-222, 307. *Cf.* also *supra*, p. 386.

[40] White (Thomas), *Institutionum Peripateticarum Libri Quinque* (Frankfurt, 1664), pp. 81, 82.

De Luc, whose information on the subject was accurate and great, asserted that the fires must be ignited in galleries and not in caverns, since, if they were produced in caverns, the pressure would be lessened by the extent. He also affirmed that the fires must follow the veins of particular matter, liquefy it and make it flow along the galleries. So long as the molten matter left room for the escape of the expansible fluids which were constantly separated from the fermenting minerals, the gases were eliminated without damage at the crater; but when the galleries became overfilled with molten matter and obstructed, the vapors accumulated and pushed the molten matter ahead of them. They raised it to the surface, where it burst out as lava. If the pressure on the side found a weak spot, the lava poured out of a new hole half-way up the cone. Finally the elastic fluids or gases burst through the lava, and part of it sank back into the crater while the rest was blown to bits and expelled as pumice and ash. Sometimes, to be sure, the force of the expansible fluids was diminished or dissipated through other channels; the lava hardened; and the volcano became quiescent. The chief elastic fluid was steam, produced when water filtered through the earth and came into contact with fermenting matter. Later De Luc decided that the chief or the sole source of lava was the layer of mud, upon which had been deposited all the strata. The lowest layers were the granite. Chemical operations between this rock and the mass of pulvicules, which formed the core of the earth, made the mud there incandescent, though without great heat, and produced various expansible fluids. De Luc, however, repeated that the agent which raised the lava was fresh steam.[41]

Besides the causes, the results of earthquakes and eruptions were debated. It was obvious that the strata were cracked

[41] De Luc, *op. cit.*, vol. iv, pp. 505-511, 519, vol. v, pp. 461, 477-482.

by earthquakes; and it was declared by Steno, [42] Shuckford,[43] Buffon [44] and De Luc [45] that they were tipped as well, even to an angle of forty-five degrees. Buffon, who grouped earthquakes and eruptions as agents except for the earliest epochs, thought that sometimes the cavern vaults were broken by the shock and that thus the layers of rock were tilted.[46] Whiston, who said that earthquakes and eruptions were rare before the flood, declared that perhaps the disruption of the strata that was a concomitant of the deluge resulted from an earthquake, though he evidently preferred a less violent cause for the same effect.[47] Some of the inclination in the strata De Luc laid to volcanoes which broke through and displaced the beds of rock.[48]

An earlier associated problem, which had a more popular appeal, was whether mountains and islands had been formed by these vigorous means, which were seldom differentiated. Postel [49] and Dr. Patrick declared that at creation mountains were elevated by earthquakes, and perhaps Marsh agreed; [50]

[42] Steno, *The Prodromus of Nicolaus Steno's Dissertation concerning a solid body enclosed by process of nature within a solid* (New York and London, 1916), p. 231.

[43] Shuckford, *The Creation and Fall of Man* (London, 1753), p. 135.

[44] Buffon, *op. cit.*, vol. ii, pp. 407-409, vol. iii, p. 29, vol. v, pp. 204-206.

[45] De Luc, *op. cit.*, vol. ii, pp. 318, 319, vol. iv, pp. 292, 295-297, 301, 333, 334; De Luc, *Letters on the Physical History of the Earth* (London, 1831), letter i, pp. 7, 8, 39, letter ii, pp. 58, 59, 61, 64-66, 69, letter iii, pp. 117-124, 128, letter iv, pp. 163, 175, letter vi, p. 246.

[46] Buffon, *op. cit.*, vol. ii, pp. 327, 407-409, vol. iii, p. 29, vol. v, pp. 204-206.

[47] Whiston, *op. cit.*, pp. 422, 423.

[48] De Luc, *Lettres physiques et morales sur l'histoire de la terre et de l'homme* (The Hague and Paris, 1779, 1780), vol. ii, pp. 411-430, 433-452, 491, 504-506, 509, vol. iv, pp. 471, 472, 511, vol. v, p. 369.

[49] Postel, *De Universitate* (Leyden, 1635), p. 27.

[50] Dr. Patrick, *Com. on Gen.* 1:9, quoted with apparent approval by Marsh, *An Oration, on the Truth of the Mosaic History of the Creation* (Hartford, 1798), p. 16.

Comenius considered the hypothesis probable.[51]   Hakewill,[52] Thomas White,[53] Fontenelle,[54] Warren,[55] Scheidt [56] and Leibnitz, who added eruptions,[57] thought that they were a cause of mountain building at a later era; Kircher [58] and Hooke [59] thought eruptions and earthquakes the chief cause even to the present.   On the other hand, Woodward [60] and Buffon [61] denied that earthquakes had formed any true mountains.   Robert Boyle, Scheidt [62] and Lazzaro Moro [63] declared that volcanic action raised mountains; Hale said that it might and

[51] Comenius, *op. cit.*, p. 93.

[52] Hakewill, *op. cit.*, pt. ii, pp. 62, 63.

[53] White (Thomas), *op. cit.*, p. 81.

[54] Fontenelle, *Entretiens sur la pluralité des mondes* (Paris, 1821), p. 150, where he added that mountains were also thus overthrown.

[55] Warren, *Geologia* (London, 1690), pp. 210, 211.

[56] Scheidt in preface to Leibnitz's *Protogaea*, Leibnitz, *op. cit.*, vol. ii, p. 184.

[57] Leibnitz, *ibid.*, vol. ii, pp. 204, 218.

[58] Kircher, *op. cit.*, t. i, pp. 77, 78, who limited such changes to sporadic mountains not a part of the great mountain chains.

[59] Hooke, *Lectures on Spring* (Conjectures occasioned by Mr. G. T's Observations made on the Pike of Tenarife, at the end of his Lecture explaining the power of Springing Bodies) (1678), pp. 48, 49, 55, 65 *et seq.*, quoted by Harris (John), *op. cit.*, pp. 169-171.

[60] Woodward, *op. cit.*, pt. ii, pp. 115-118; Woodward, *An Essay toward a Natural History of the Earth: and Terrestrial Bodies* (London, 1695), pp. 110-112; Woodward, quoted by Harris (John), *op. cit.*, p. 169.

[61] Buffon, *op. cit.*, vol. ii, pp. 313-315, 321.

[62] Boyle, *Historia Aeris*, quoted by Scheidt, preface to Leibnitz's *Protogaea*, Leibnitz, *op. cit.*, vol. ii, p. 184.

[63] Moro, *De' crostacei e degli altri marini corpi che si trovano sù Monti, Libri due* (1740), quoted by De Luc, *op. cit.*, vol. ii, pp. 398-404, 489, 504-506, 510, and by Jéhan, *Dictionnaire de cosmogonie et de paléontologie* (Paris, 1854), art. " Géologie (Histoire de la)", cols. 630, 631.

had;[64] Steno[65] and De Luc[66] affirmed that it and earth-quakes did in some cases, if volcanoes might be called mountains; and Ray thought that it or perhaps the subterranean fire, which raised all the continents, elevated mountains.[67] Hutton believed that the intense subterranean heat, together with other forces, such as gravity, twisted and folded the horizontal strata and raised them into mountains. Other eminences were elevated by the intrusion into the strata of subterranean lavas.[68] Moro explained the production of the plains in a similar manner, for he believed that the strata were deposited by lava flows, and that then the whole was raised by subterranean fires; and De Luc admitted that there was some truth, though not much, in Moro's attribution of strata to lava.[69] Woodward rejected the formation of true mountains by volcanic action,[70] an opinion in which he was joined by Catcott.[71]

The similar question as to the birth of islands was settled

[64] Hale, *op. cit.*, p. 95.

[65] Steno, *op. cit.*, pp. 231, 232; Steno, *Tract. de Glossopetris et Myologiae Specimen* (Florence, 1667), quoted by Harris (John), *op. cit.*, pp. 177, 187, 188.

[66] De Luc, *op. cit.*, vol. ii, pp. 218, 398-400, vol. iv, pp. 191, 192, 207, 208, 219, 221, 257, 302-317, 324, 329-331, 334, 335, 473, 505-520, vol. v, pp. 461, 479; De Luc, *Letters on the Physical History of the Earth* (London, 1831), letter iv, pp. 148-151.

[67] Ray, *op. cit.*, pp. 11-21, 24-26.

[68] Hutton, *Theory of the Earth* (1795), quoted by Geikie, *The Founders of Geology* (London and New York, 1897), pp. 171-176.

[69] De Luc, *op. cit.*, letter iv, p. 151; De Luc, *Lettres physiques et morales sur l'histoire de la terre et de l'homme* (The Hague and Paris, 1779, 1780), vol. ii, pp. 401-404, 406, 407, 454-482, 484-486, 488, 489, 500-504, 511.

[70] Woodward, *A Supplement & Continuation of The Essay towards a Natural History of the Earth* (London, 1726), pt. ii, pp. 116-118, 120-122. He said that such elevations were only heaps of cinders.

[71] Catcott, *op. cit.*, p. 275.

along the same lines.   Burnet [72] and Kircher [73] thought that
some, like Sicily, were broken from the mainland by earthquakes; and Fontenelle declared that to be the common opinion. [74]   Kircher added a possible eruption to account for the
separation.   The others, who discussed the subject, apparently thought of islands as resembling mountains and as
having been produced in the same manner.   Horn said that
the causes of islands were the creation, the flood, earthquakes
and sometimes human effort. [75]   Leibnitz thought that they
were produced by or with earthquakes. [76]   Kircher [77] and
Buffon [78] thought that some islands were thus raised or
broken from the mainland; but Moro, [79] who gave detailed
examples of an island and a mountain raised by subterranean
fires, considered that the sole method.   Woodward consis-
tently denied such action, and declared that all true islands,
such as Sicily, had existed since the flood. [80]   Hooke attributed most or all islands to volcanoes; [81] as did De Luc, who
asserted that many such were made at the flood. [82]   Buffon

[72] Burnet, *op. cit.*, vol. i, bk. i, pp. 162, 163, 185; Burnet, *Doctrina
Antiqua de Rerum Originibus* (London, 1729, 1736), *Archaeologiae Philosophicae*, pt. ii, pp. 56, 57.

[73] Kircher, *op. cit.*, t. i, pp. 77, 78, 80, 99.

[74] Fontenelle, *op. cit.*, p. 150.

[75] Horn, *Arca Noae* (Leyden, 1666), p. 31.

[76] Leibnitz, *op. cit.*, vol. ii, *Protogaea*, p. 233.

[77] Kircher, *op. cit.*, t. i, pp. 77, 83.

[78] Buffon, *op. cit.*, vol. ii, pp. 313, 394, 395, 397, 399, 401, 402, vol. v,
pp. 282, 283.

[79] Moro, *op. cit.*, quoted by De Luc, *op. cit.*, vol. ii, pp. 392-400, 402,
506-509.

[80] Woodward, *op. cit.*, pt. ii, pp. 118-123; Woodward, *An Essay toward
a Natural History of the Earth: and Terrestrial Bodies* (London, 1695),
pp. 52, 112; Woodward, quoted by Harris (John), *op. cit.*, pp. 170, 188.

[81] Hooke, *op. cit.*, pp. 48, 49, 55, 65 *et seq.*, quoted by Harris (John),
op. cit., pp. 169-171.

[82] De Luc, *op. cit.*, vol. ii, pp. 392-400, 411, 433-452, 482, 491, 506-509,

agreed, with a limitation of the statement to some islands.[83] Paul Boccone apparently meant eruptions as a cause of islands, although he said earthquakes.[84]   Steno, on the other hand, thought that some or all islands were raised by the ignition of subterraneous vapors.[85]

Buffon felt that caverns were made in the earth's crust by volcanic activity as well as by the erosion of water and by the primitive heat as the earth cooled, and that during most of the earth's life the surface water had been lowered at frequent intervals by being drawn off into caverns when these were fractured by earthquakes.[86]   This process appealed to Steno,[87] to Leibnitz,[88] to Bishop Patrick and to Marsh, though Patrick and Marsh limited the occurrence to the original separation of water and land on the third day,[89] and Steno and Leibnitz believed that it took place only then and at the flood.   On the other hand, Kircher thought that a common effect of earth tremors was such an undermining of the crust that parts fell into the reservoirs of water and left lakes.[90]   Steno mentioned such subsidences, though

vol. v, p. 246; De Luc, *Letters on the Physical History of the Earth* (London, 1831), letter iv, pp. 140, 152.

[83] Buffon, *op. cit.*, vol. ii, pp. 313, 394-402, vol. v, p. 204.

[84] Boccone, *Recherches & observations naturelles* (Amsterdam, 1674), p. 317, quoted by Harris (John), *op. cit.*, p. 241.

[85] Steno, *op. cit.*, quoted by Harris (John), *op. cit.*, pp. 187, 188.

[86] Buffon, *op. cit.*, vol. i, p. 157, vol. ii, pp. 316, 327, 328, 402, 404, 405, 407-409, 425-430, vol. iii, p. 68, vol. v, p. 165.

[87] Steno, *The Prodromus of Nicolaus Steno's Dissertation concerning a solid body enclosed by process of nature within a solid* (New York and London, 1916), pp. 262, 263, 267, 276, 277.

[88] Leibnitz, *op. cit.*, vol. ii, *Protogaea*, p. 206; Leibnitz, quoted by De Luc, *Lettres physiques et morales sur l'histoire de la terre et de l'homme* (The Hague and Paris, 1779, 1780), vol. i, p. 323.

[89] Patrick, *Com. on Gen.* 1 : 9, quoted with apparent approval by Marsh, *op. cit.*, p. 16.

[90] Kircher, *op. cit.*, t. i, pp. 221, 240.

without saying that they were due to earthquakes.[91] Burnet,[92] Woodward [93] and Catcott [94] agreed, except that according to their hypotheses the earth fell into the abyss. Burnet,[95] Leibnitz [96] and the Abbé Pluche [97] thought that this subsidence into subterranean waters was at least a partial cause of the deluge. Cockburn [98] felt it probable, and Burnet [99] certain, that an earthquake was associated with the beginning of the flood. Burnet mentioned the destructive power of earthquakes upon mountains.[100] Woodward [101] and Catcott [102] joined Cockburn [103] in the assertion that many earthquakes preceded floods, perhaps by raising great waves

[91] Steno, *op. cit.*, p. 235.

[92] Burnet, *The Sacred Theory of the Earth* (London, 1722), vol. i, bk. i, pp. 97, 98.

[93] Woodward, *op. cit.*, pp. 134, 135; Woodward, *A Supplement & Continuation of The Essay towards a Natural History of the Earth* (London, 1726), pt. ii, pp. 58, 59, 113.

[94] Catcott, *op. cit.*, pp. 235, 236, 275.

[95] Burnet, *op. cit.*, vol. i, bk. i; Burnet, *Doctrina Antiqua de Rerum Originibus* (London, 1729, 1736), *Archaeologiae Philosophicae*, pt. ii, pp. 47, 48, 50-63.

[96] Leibnitz, *op. cit.*, vol. ii, *Protogaea*, p. 206; Leibnitz, quoted by De Luc, *op. cit.*, vol. i, p. 324.

[97] Pluche, *Spectacle de la nature*, tome iii, 2de partie, quoted by De Luc, *op. cit.*, vol. i, pp. 339, 340.

[98] Cockburn, *op. cit.*, pp. 291, 293, 294.

[99] Burnet, *op. cit.*, *Archaeologiae Philosophicae*, pt. ii, pp. 42-46, 50-63; Burnet, *The Sacred Theory of the Earth* (London, 1722), vol. i, bk. i, p. 127.

[100] *Ibid.*, vol. i, bk. i, pp. 197-199.

[101] Woodward, *An Essay toward a Natural History of the Earth: and Terrestrial Bodies* (London, 1695), pp. 135-138.

[102] Catcott, *op. cit.*, pp. 237, 238.

[103] Cockburn, *op. cit.*, pp. 279, 282-287, 289-291.

in the sea. Bacon,[104] Kircher,[105] and Burnet [106] with absolute faith mentioned Atlantis as an example of the destructive effects produced by these tremors. Steno accepted the historicity of Atlantis and the tale of its destruction but mentioned no cause.[107] Leibnitz gave earthquakes as a reason for the production of fossils, since he said that thus some lake filled with fish might be overwhelmed and the finny inhabitants might be changed to stone.[108]

Besides the foregoing more important and more widely accepted effects, others were mentioned by various authors. Among them were several suggestions by Woodward: that both earthquakes and eruptions, as well as the heat of the sun, raised to the surface and beyond various minerals, especially niter and sulphur; that eruptions helped to exhale matter which formed meteors, such as thunder and lightning, and ejected sulphurous and other exhalations which caused fevers and various malignant distempers; and that such effusions darkened and discolored the atmosphere.[109] The alteration in color of the celestial spheres by exhalations was mentioned by Burnet as if it were connected with eruptions and earthquakes, at least so far as the period immediately precedent to the end of the world was concerned.[110] Kircher thought that earthquakes as well as floods changed the center of gravity in the earth,[111] and Fontenelle [112] and Buffon that

[104] Bacon, *op. cit.*, vol. xii, Essay *Of the Viscissitudes of Things*, p. 274.

[105] Kircher, *op. cit.*, t. i, pp. 80-83, 181, who added other islands, *ibid.*, pp. 77, 78, 83.

[106] Burnet, *op. cit.*, *Archaeologiae Philosophicae*, pt. ii, pp. 58, 59.

[107] Steno, *op. cit.*, p. 269.

[108] Leibnitz, *op. cit.*, vol. ii, *Protogaea*, p. 215.

[109] Woodward, *op. cit.*, pp. 199-203, 206-215.

[110] Burnet, *The Sacred Theory of the Earth* (London, 1722), vol. ii, bk. iii, pp. 137-139.

[111] Kircher, *op. cit.*, t. i, p. 106.

[112] Fontenelle, *op. cit.*, p. 150.

they altered the course of rivers.   Buffon in addition, when he classified the matter of which the strata were composed, said that the first volcanic action introduced a new type.[113]

To these effects were added supernatural relations.   Even in the eighteenth century eruptions were still associated with the activities of evil spirits, at least by the peasants.   De Luc related a quarrel between two guides concerning a volcanic mountain near Coblentz.   The first guide affirmed that it was the site where the sorcerers held their sabbat; the other on patriotic grounds denied this current legend as a calumny. De Luc himself naturally rejected it.[114]   At almost the same era, Buffon cited as a superstition a belief held by the inhabitants of Iceland that the rumblings of the volcano were the cries of the damned and that eruptions were caused by their fury and despair.[115]

[113] Buffon, *op. cit.*, vol. v, pp. 200, 206.

[114] De Luc, *op. cit.*, vol. iv, pp. 238-240, 249-251.

[115] Buffon, *op. cit.*, vol. ii, p. 295.

CHAPTER VII

MOUNTAINS, METALS AND MINERALS

A COMMON thesis was that, as the earth consolidated out of chaos, matter settled into a smooth sphere in accordance with the specific gravity of the individual particles. Therefore the heaviest metals and minerals would be at the base and the lightest matter on top, with the water superimposed upon all. Those who believed that the earth was dissolved at the flood, or perhaps gathered from some cometary atmosphere at that epoch an accession of chaotic matter felt that so similar a state produced similar results. Woodward even asserted that shells were embedded in strata of specific gravity like their own.[1] Derham made borings into the earth and weighed samples to prove the doctrine,[2] and a famous well of unusual depth near Amsterdam was frequently mentioned in corroboration. Any discrepancies were attributed to the action of water, which eroded portions of the upper strata, and which, under the impulsion of subterranean fire, raised heavy metals from the depths to deposit them in surface veins. Gradually, however, during the last half of

[1] Woodward was a leading exponent of the proposition. Woodward, *An Essay toward a Natural History of the Earth: and Terrestrial Bodies* (London, 1695) ; Woodward, *A Supplement & Continuation of The Essay towards a Natural History of the Earth* (London, 1726) ; Woodward, quoted with approval by Harris (John), *Remarks On some Late Papers, Relating to the Universal Deluge* (London, 1697), pp. 207-210; Woodward, quoted with his denial by De Luc, *Lettres physiques et morales sur l'histoire de la terre et de l'homme* (The Hague and Paris, 1779, 1780), vol. i, p. 304.

[2] Derham, *Physico-Theology* (London, 1742), p. 66, note pp. 66, 67, p. 78.

the eighteenth century, the more important and more accurate observers denied that there had ever been such an assortment of matter.[3]

If the surface of the earth was at first perfectly spherical, an explanation of its present rugosities was needed. Even from those theorists who denied its primeval sphericity an interpretation of the phenomena presented by the present state of land and sea was urgent. The thesis that the areas of land and sea were equal was held by some commentators but gradually discarded.[4] Many felt that the need for symmetry

---

[3] A few of those who affirmed it were Isaac Vossius, *Against Hornius* (or perhaps *De Vera Aetate Mundi contra Hornium*, The Hague, 1661, 2d edition), quoted by Cockburn, *An Enquiry into the Truth and Certainty of the Mosaic Deluge* (London, 1750), pp. 267-269, with his denial of the thesis as not always true; Descartes, *Oeuvres* (Paris, 1824), vol. iii, *Les principes de la philosophie*, pt. iv, secs. 32-44, 59-63, 72-75; Ray, *Three Physico-Theological Discourses* (London, 1693), p. 9; probably Burnet, *Doctrina Antiqua de Rerum Originibus* (London, 1729, 1736), *Archaeologiae Philosophicae*, pt. i, p. 175; Burnet, *The Sacred Theory of the Earth* (London, 1722), vol. i, bk. i; Leibnitz, *Opera Omnia* (Geneva, 1768), vol. ii, *Protogaea*, pp. 207, 208; Steno, quoted with approval by Harris (John), *op. cit.*, pp. 207-210, though Harris attempted to show that Steno's account was neither clear nor sufficiently inclusive; Whiston, *A New Theory of the Earth* (Cambridge, 1708), pp. 267-270, 300, 303-305, 399, 412-418, 426-428, though he said that the full effect was prevented by various accidental causes, such as currents; Whiston, *A Vindication of the New Theory of the Earth from the Exceptions of Mr. Keill and Others* (London, 1698), p. 25; Le Catt, quoted and answered by De Luc, *op. cit.*, vol. ii, pp. 179, 180, 183, 184. Others who denied the thesis were Beaumont, *Considerations On a Book, Entituled The Theory of the Earth* (London, 1692-3), pp. 26a-28a, who thought that the original chaotic mass was full of "ferments"; Hutchinson, *Moses's Principia* (London, 1724), pp. 75-78, 96, 98, 99, who used as an argument against it the common experience of miners; Catcott, *A Treatise on the Deluge* (London, 1768), note pp. 249, 250, who rejected it on the ground of experiments and of observations to great depths.

[4] Blancanus, *Sphaera Mvndi* (Bologna, 1620), p. 109; probably, according to Mallet, *Description de l'univers* (Paris, 1683), vol. i, p. 200, and to Ray, *op. cit.*, p. 25; Burnet, *op. cit.*, vol. i, bk. i, chap. ii; Burnet, quoted with apparent approval by Keill, *An Examination of Dr. Burnet's*

would be met by the fact which they asserted that the height of the loftiest mountains was equal to the depth of the sea.[5] Kircher, who denied that the height of the mountains equalled the depth of the seas, seemed to believe in a compromise to the effect that the total volume of the raised land equalled that of the sea. The sea bed with its inequalities of contour resembled the land with its hills, valleys, rivers, plants and springs.[6]

The altitude assigned to mountains diminished with later writers. Wilkins asserted that according to Aristotle the Caucasus, which were the highest mountains, were seventy-eight miles high. He attributed to Raleigh the statement that the loftiest peaks rose nearly thirty miles into the air; but he himself named Teneriff as if it was the highest eminence, and said that it was generally considered to be above eight miles high while the mountains on the moon were at least four miles in altitude.[7] This was a misquotation of

Theory of the Earth. Together with some remarks on Mr. Whiston's New Theory of the Earth (Oxford, 1698), pp. 159, 160. Riccioli, who was doubtful about the relative proportions of sea and land in the *Almagestum*, ten years later decided that there were forty parts of land surface to twenty-five of water. Riccioli, *Geographia et Hydrographia Reformata* (1661), quoted by Roberto Almagià, " Il primo tentativo di misura del rapporto quantitativo fra le terre emerse e i mari," *Archivio di Storia della Scienza*, vol. ii (1921), pp. 51-64.

[5] Blancanus, *op. cit.*, pp. 108; Mallet, *op. cit.*, vol. i, p. 200; Hakewill, *An Apologie or Declaration of the Power and Providence of God in the Gouernment of the World* (Oxford, 1635), pt. ii, p. 76; Brerewood, quoted by Ray, *op. cit.*, pp. 32, 33, who on p. 24 asserted the doctrine as certain; Catcott, *op. cit.*, p. 167, who, however, on the same page declared that in many places the sea was unfathomable. On the other hand, Cockburn thought the depth of the ocean greater and its total mass larger than that of the raised land. Its area he thought twice as great. Cockburn, *op. cit.*, pp. 245-251, 255-258.

[6] Kircher, *Mundus Subterraneus* (Amsterdam, 1664-5), t. i, pp. 96-98.

[7] Wilkins, *The Mathematical and Philosophical Works* (London, 1707-8), pp. 72-76.

Sir Walter, who in 1614 had declared that no mountains were more than thirty miles high, not even Teneriff, the loftiest.[8] Wilkins at the same time cited Kepler and Galileo for the opposite belief that the lunar mountains surpassed in altitude the terrestrial, which were no more than a mile high.[9] Stillingfleet about the same period quoted Riccioli as saying that the Caucasus was fifty-one miles in altitude. Stillingfleet felt that no mountain attained a height greater than approximately three miles.[10] Leibnitz increased the maximum to more than four German miles, which was equivalent to sixteen English miles;[11] and Catcott to not more than four miles " by the best accounts." [12] Buffon thought that the highest mountains were those of Peru, which rose more than three thousand fathoms into the air. The height of the mountains on the earth decreased as their distance from the equator increased.[13] During the middle of the eighteenth century more accurate measurements of height were made by means of barometers, with which many amateurs were experimenting.[14]

[8] Raleigh, *The History of the World* (Edinburgh, 1820), vol. i, p. 222. The belief that Teneriff was the highest mountain was widely held. For example, Boyle thought it about seven miles high instead of less than three. Boyle, *Works* (1772), vol. iii, pp. 225-228, vol. v, pp. 703, 706, 707, quoted by Thorndike, "Measurement of mountain altitudes", *Isis* (Bruges, 1927), vol. ix, pp. 425, 426.

[9] Wilkins, *op. cit.*, p. 73.

[10] Stillingfleet, *Origines Sacrae* (London, 1709), pp. 340, 341. Apparently Riccioli was dubiously quoting Aristotle.

[11] Leibnitz, *op. cit.*, vol. ii, *Protogaea*, p. 205.

[12] Catcott, *op. cit.*, p. 246.

[13] Buffon, *Oeuvres complètes* (Paris, 1831-2), vol. ii, pp. 60, 71, 86, 87.

[14] De Luc, *op. cit.*, vol. i, pp. 349-352, vol. ii, p. 19, vol. iii, p. 274; De Luc, *Letters on the Physical History of the Earth* (London, 1831), introduction, p. 124. Robert Boyle as early as 1667 had tried to persuade careful observers to undertake the determination of the height to which Teneriff rose by the level of the mercury in barometers. Boyle,

Varied theories to explain the present existence of mountains and oceans were propounded in addition to those mentioned in the preceding chapter, which attributed the production of mountains to earthquakes, eruptions or subterranean fires in general. Perhaps the earliest and simplest suggestion was that, in order to form hollows, earth was removed directly by God from the surface in some places and piled up elsewhere on the land that emerged when the waters were drained into the hollows.[15] Blancanus, who adopted this naive thesis, thought that the ridges originally produced were altered to peaks by rivers which dug valleys through them.[16] Kircher accepted the hypothesis about the

---

A Continuation of New Experiments Physico-Mechanical, touching the Spring and Weight of the Air, experiment xxiii, in *Works* (1772), vol. iii, pp. 225-228, quoted by Thorndike, *loc. cit.* This Torricellian method had been first used in 1643, but did not give results fully satisfactory because of difficulties with the construction of the instruments, with the variations of weather between neighboring spots and at first with the mathematical interpretation and use of the data obtained. However, chiefly by this method, though also by the measurement of triangles and of the distance to which a mountain could be seen at sea, as well as by direct measurement in some cases, for the first time the heights of several mountains became known with approximate accuracy during the last half of the eighteenth century. Until that date all such estimates were wholly unreliable, and generally mere wild guesses. Cajori, "History of determinations of the heights of mountains," *Isis* (Bruges, 1929), vol. xii, pp. 494-497, 499-510, 512, 513.

[15] Blancanus, *op. cit.*, pp. 82-99; Blancanus, *De Mundi Fabrica*, translated by Ray, *op. cit.*, pp. 296-298; Brerewood, quoted by Ray, *op. cit.*, pp. 32, 33; Hakewill, *op. cit.*, pt. ii, pp. 62, 63, 73-77, who added that mountains were formed also by floods, by winds, such as those which piled up sand dunes in deserts, and by earthquakes; the Bishop of Clogher, Dr. Robert Clayton, *Explanation of the Mosaic History of the Creation and Formation of the World*, pp. 88, 108, 115, 118, quoted and refuted by Catcott, *op. cit.*, pp. 268-271. Clayton's work was really named *A Vindication of the Histories of the Old and New Testament in answer to the objections of the late Lord Bolingbroke* (Dublin, 1752, 1754), and it was part ii to which Catcott replied.

[16] Blancanus, *op. cit.*, translated by Ray, *op. cit.*, pp. 299, 300.

digging of furrows by God to receive the waters, and enlarged it to apply to all the planets; but he thought that mountains of earth or of clay were raised by earthquakes or eruptions, while the great mountain chains were formed in the beginning like a skeleton to strengthen the earth and to protect it from storms and tides. The land was hardened into rock by internal fire after the water was drawn off. The cause was a " vis lapidifica " which had acted persistently. Apparently this petrifying force was what he later called the salt of nature. It lay dormant until the land was dried and then combined with the mud to make fertile fields, or rocks and therefore mountains, depending upon the amount of moisture. As to the cause other than a miracle for the great protuberances and cavities, which, in his opinion, produced mountains and valleys, Kircher seemed to have had no clear notion.[17] Hale varied the plan slightly by the comment that God both removed matter from the surface in some localities and raised others miraculously, by means of water, which gouged out softer parts as it still did, or by means of fire " either subterraneous or ambient ". He accepted as well the doctrine of mountain formation by eruptions and thought that mountains were increased or possibly merely retained at the same height by the constant descent from the atmosphere of " more gross and terrestrial " atoms, which had been raised as vapors from the sea.[18] Wilkins satisfied himself by the assertion that mountains were useful, natural and mentioned in Scripture as primeval; hence they had existed since the beginning. They were present upon the moon in addition, although the lunar eminences were only

---

[17] Kircher, op. cit., t. i, pp. 67-70, 77, 78, 333, t. ii, pp. 5-7; Kircher, Itinerarivm Exstaticvm (Rome, 1656), pp. 297, 298, 300, 398.

[18] Hale, The Primitive Origination of Mankind (London, 1677), pp. 95, 96, 298, 299.

half so high.[19]   Derham declared that terrestrial mountains were raised by an especial providence of God from a level surface at creation and perhaps also after the flood.[20] Cockburn thought that as the earth consolidated from chaos mountains were made under the water.   Though some of the fertile top soil had been washed off by the flood, and, on the other hand, the height of some mountains had been increased by volcanic action and by accumulations of ice, the present mountains were as a whole the same as the primitive.[21]   Scheuchzer was another who attributed mountains to a direct act of God, though he timed it after the deluge. To drive the waters again into the subterranean reservoirs God broke, displaced and tipped on edge many horizontal strata in places originally stony, such as the Alps.   Those localities like Flanders where the earth's crust consisted of clay and sand retained their original contours, because there the consistence of the strata was not sufficient to preserve a vaulted form.[22]   Comenius, who seemed to hold that all mountains were raised on the third day, felt that the subterranean fire swelled the earth in some places.[23]   Woodward thought that both at creation and after the flood the level crust was all at once raised by a force within the earth.   In some parts the strata were solid and restrained from subsidence, though they were broken and propped up at various angles.   They remained elevated as mountains while the rest

[19] Wilkins, *op. cit.*, pp. 64-76.

[20] Derham, *op. cit.*, pp. 66, 78.

[21] Cockburn, *op. cit.*, pp. 176, 177, 243-252, 260, 267-271.

[22] Scheuchzer, *Hist. de l'Académie des Sciences de Paris, année 1708*, quoted by Buffon, *op. cit.*, vol. i, pp. 235, 236, and by De Luc, *Lettras physiques et morales sur l'histoire de la terre et de l'homme* (The Hague and Paris, 1779, 1780), vol. i, p. 336.

[23] Comenius, *Naturall Philosophie Reformed by Divine Light* (London, 1651), pp. 93, 146.

of the crust sank back.[24]   Warren, who defended his attempted explanation of this internal force by the statement
that he was propounding merely a possible method, declared
that the production of mountains was an act of God but by
natural means.   Possibly he considered that the crust was
elevated only in certain sections.   On the third day the
hollow of the sea was pressed down by God and the waters
rushed thither.   By a natural reaction the borders of the
sea were raised.   Those localities where the sea was deepest
would have near-by the mountains of the greatest altitude.
The rest of the earth was " soft, and light, and unctuous ";
and the pores were closed so that no vapors could escape.
By the solar heat the water within the crust was changed to
vapors, which raised the earth into mountains.   For a while
the production of elevations continued.   Then the eminences dried and hardened; and parts broke off so as to leave
rough, irregular contours and cliffs.   Earthquakes raised
other eminences by somewhat similar methods.   At that
time the sun was more efficient because it was free from
spots.[25]   Burnet pointed out that on the third day, when the
water was supposed to be vaporized, the sun had not yet been
created, though he added other objections.[26]   Perhaps because of this weakness in Warren's theory, Beaumont decided
that the hills were elevated by a multiplicity of ferments

[24] Woodward, *op. cit.*, pt. ii, pp. 101, 102, 108, 109, 115-123; Woodward,
An Essay toward a Natural History of the Earth: and Terrestrial Bodies
(London, 1695), pp. 80, 81, 110-112, 264, 265; Woodward, quoted and
answered by Catcott, *op. cit.*, pp. 274, 275.

[25] Warren, *Geologia* (London, 1690), pp. 209-214; Warren, *A Defence
of the Discourse Concerning the Earth Before the Flood* (London, 1691),
pp. 98-102; Warren, *Some Reflections upon the Short Consideration Of
the Defence of the Exceptions against the Theory of the Earth* (London,
1692), pp. 5, 6.   *Cf.* also *supra*, pp. 87, 88.

[26] Burnet, *An Answer to the Exceptions of Mr. Erasmus Warren,
Against the Sacred Theory of the Earth*, pp. 44-47, in Burnet, *op. cit.*,
vol. ii.

throughout chaos [27] " from the infinite variety of seminal
Principles . . . contained." [28] He explained the presence
of fossils in the mountains by the statement that land and sea
were constantly changing places.[29] Keill at the same epoch
presented the interesting suggestion that chaos originally
contained solid chunks of matter whose specific gravity was
so much less than that of the water or the chaotic fluid that,
like icebergs, they floated on the water in a semi-submerged
state and ultimately became mountains. Sometimes they
were made from a combination of light and heavy matter;
or the weight was decreased by cavities or caverns, such as
were still found in many mountains. In fact, all mountains
were perhaps hollow.[30]

A popular theory was that upheld by Descartes,[31] Burnet [32]
and Leibnitz. Descartes and Burnet thought that the crust
cracked and part fell through an abyss of waters to rest
upon the solid central core. Since this was smaller in area
than the outer crust, the surface strata were crumpled and
supported in various positions, sometimes covering caverns
of air and water. The higher sections formed mountains,
and the rest plains or valleys. Leibnitz agreed, except that,
according to his theory, the earth fell into caverns formed
by the globe's shrinkage as it cooled, and the great ranges, together with the ocean bed were due to hummocks produced
by the eruption of air as the earth cooled and by the erosion
of ditches in the soft foundations, while later eruptions and

[27] Beaumont, *op. cit.*, pp. 25a-30a.

[28] *Ibid.*, p. 25a.

[29] *Ibid.*, p. 30a.

[30] Keill, *op. cit.*, pp. 49-51.

[31] Descartes, *op. cit.*, vol. iii, *Les principes de la philosophie*, pt. iv, secs.
42-44.

[32] Burnet, *op. cit.*, vol. i, bk. i, especially pp. 195-201; Burnet, quoted
and answered by Catcott, *op. cit.*, pp. 274, 275.

floods also had produced mountains.[33]   Steno, who agreed in
general with the theory, said that the caverns were formed
by subterranean water and fire, and that the mountains produced by the collapse of the terrestrial crust after a smooth
surface had been renewed on the earth and then revealed by
the flood were not necessarily the same as those brought into
existence by a similar fall soon after creation.[34]

Whiston, Dickinson and Catcott approached the problem
from new angles.   Whiston thought that the crust of the
earth was perhaps four hundred miles thick.   Elsewhere he
called it two hundred miles.   It sank into the subjacent fluid
approximately one hundred miles; but, since it consisted of
columns differing in density, the distance each sank varied; and
the lightest columns formed the mountains, the medium, the
plains, and the densest, the sea bed.   Then the whole became
consolidated, though not so firmly as to prevent its disruption
by the attraction of an approaching comet.   The weight of the
particles that were annexed from the comet's atmosphere at
the commencement of the earth's diurnal rotation and again
at the deluge aided in the renewed fracture of the terrestrial
strata.[35]   This was contrary to the opinion of Postel that
mountains consisted of the densest matter.[36]   Whiston proved
them lighter because they were more porous and because the
earth of volcanoes at least was intrinsically lighter, since it

[33] Leibnitz, *op. cit.*, vol. ii, *Protogaea*, pp. 201, 203-206, 218; Leibnitz,
quoted by De Luc, *op. cit.*, vol. i, pp. 320-324.

[34] Steno, *The Prodromus of Nicolaus Steno's Dissertation concerning
a Solid Body Enclosed by Process of Nature within a Solid* (New York
and London, 1916), pp. 262-267.

[35] Whiston, *op. cit.*, pp. 13-18; Whiston, *A Second Defence of the New
Theory of the Earth from the Exceptions of Mr. John Keill* (London,
1700), pp. 15-17; Whiston, *A New Theory of the Earth* (Cambridge,
1708), pp. 64-66, 82-85, 111, 112, 312-314, 371, 372; Whiston, quoted with
disapproval by Catcott, *op. cit.*, pp. 274, 275.

[36] Postel, *op. cit.*, p. 27.

was bituminous, sulphurous or oily.[37] The *Universal History* fifty years later accepted Whiston's opinion, which it styled " more philosophical." [38] Dickinson declared that, when the earth was solidified by pressure of the air at creation so great that it forced the particles to touch at every point, the pressure was everywhere the same but the resistance of the earth differed, and hills resulted. Valleys were to be found where there had been an unusual number of watery particles, since these were expelled by the air.[39] Catcott and his father attributed the whole formation of valleys, mountains and sea beds to erosion by the water at creation and after the flood. No additional mountains had been raised since the later episode. Practically all strata retained the horizontal position in which they had been deposited at those epochs. As the pressure of the air drove the waters into the abyss, they furrowed the smooth surface. Gentle slopes and not precipices were produced because the descent of the water through the cracks in the crust was hindered and delayed by the pressure of the air from within the earth in its ascent through the same cracks. Catcott gave innumerable observations of all kinds on the present condition of the surface to prove his statements, and even contrived a successful experiment in a glass vessel, from which he let the superincumbent water escape through several holes below a mass of sand and dirt. The resultant ridges and gullies presented a marked resemblance to those of the earth.[40]

[37] Whiston, *op. cit.*, pp. 82-85.

[38] *An Universal History, from the Earliest Account of Time to the Present* (Dublin, 1744), vol. i, p. 42.

[39] Dickinson, *Physica Vetus et Vera* (Rotterdam, 1703), pp. 89, 90, 93-95.

[40] Catcott, *op. cit.*, pp. 64, 65, 90, 91, 247-359, 369, 375; Catcott's father, *ibid.*, p. 420.

Especially during the eighteenth century the opinion gained popularity in France that mountains were formed on the sea bed and later revealed.   Werner and his followers accepted it, but gave clear reasons neither for the difference in thickness of the strata, which they assumed as the cause of mountains, nor for the removal of the water.[41]   According to others, the agent was the sea, which, in its agitation by tides and currents, heaped up sand and mud.   The location of the ocean was believed to be constantly altering.   The sea travelled around the world from east to west by flooding the land on the eastern borders of the continents and islands and unveiling it on the western.[42]   De Maillet added to the doctrine of the submarine production of mountains the statement that some strata were tipped at a more acute angle because the bases of hills, upon which the matter had been plastered, were undermined.[43]   M. Baumé in his *Chemistry* thought that mountains were formed under the ocean but declared that chemical changes occurred later in the constitution and size of mountains because of their exposure to the air.[44]   Buffon at first accepted this marine cause of mountain production and this revelation by the travel of the ocean, but added several others, especially in his later works.   He even, at the demand of the Sorbonne, which objected to the doctrines just enumerated, specifically rejected all ideas about the formation of the

[41] Geikie, *The Founders of Geology* (London and New York, 1897), pp. 114-120, 127, 128.

[42] " Le mouvement de la Mer entière d'orient en occident," De Luc, *op. cit.*, vol. iv, p. 108 and elsewhere.

[43] *Ibid.*, vol. ii, pp. 271, 272, 276, 277, 317-319.

[44] Baumé was quoted and refuted by De Luc. Buffon and Le Catt were quoted for this thesis of the ocean's ceaseless peregrinations around the earth with emphatic denials by both De Luc and Catcott, both of whom emphasized the popularity of the doctrine. Catcott added De Maillet to the list of proponents. De Luc, *op. cit.*, vol. ii, pp. 179-192, vol. iv, pp. 108-118, 120-137; Catcott, *op. cit.*, pp. 271-274.

earth contrary to the narrative of Moses.[45]   Nevertheless he thought that the strata now visible were deposited on the sea bottom.   He believed in the production of occasional insignificant mountains by eruptions and by earthquakes.   Finally he came to the conclusion that the primitive mountains were raised by fire.   As the surface cooled, because of various strains, especially the centrifugal force that swelled the equator, portions of the crust were elevated into the great mountain chains.   The outer layer shrank and cracked in various directions.   Later the vaults to some caverns beneath the surface broke, and the strata were tipped.   Other cracks were produced as the strata dried and hardened in this position, and sometimes were increased by the slipping of one or both sides.   Additional mountains were raised by the sea and hardened by their own weight.   After the mountains had been carved by the ocean currents, which in turn they guided, and had been revealed by the subsidence of the sea into subterranean caverns or by its passage around the globe, they were still further carved and eroded by the frosts, winds, earthquakes, rains, torrents and the sea itself, all of which at first left only the hard, knobby rocks and finally attacked even these until perhaps half were destroyed.   The valleys were filled with matter robbed from the mountains.   This was another hypothesis rejected by the Sorbonne, and at its dictation denied by Buffon, although as late as 1778 or 1779 he included it in his *Époques de la Nature.*[46]

[45] Jéhan, *Dictionnaire de cosmogonie et de paléontologie* (Paris, 1854), art. " Géologie (Histoire de la)", cols. 635, 636; Buffon, *op. cit.*, vol. v, p. 43.

[46] Buffon, *op. cit.*, vol. i, pp. 124-133, 136-139, 141, 142, 149-151, 166, 167, 236, 289, 290, notes pp. 108-111, 122, 123, 136-138, 295, 296, vol. ii, pp. 63-70, 81-84 and note, 90-92, 123, 223-228, 231-235, 239, 313-315, 326, 327, 398-402, 407-409, 425-430, vol. iii, pp. 7-11, 19, 29-33, 39-43, 55-59, 68-70, vol. v, pp. 43, 86, 87, 99-101, 104, 110, 114-118, 140, 141, 147, 148, 151-153, 192, 205-218, 230, 258, 275, 276, 280, 301; Jéhan, *op. cit.*, art. " Géologie (Histoire de la)", cols. 635, 636.

Much earlier Blancanus had noticed the erosion of mountains and the filling of valleys.   He held that without miraculous intervention the earth, which had now an unnatural
shape, would be thus reduced to one level and reflooded by the
ocean.[47]   Kircher prophesied the same terrestrial fate, though
he later decided that the great mountain chains would not be
thus destroyed.[48]   Burnet added earthquakes and subterraneous fires to the destructive agencies of water and wind, and
considered the present elevation of the land above the sea an
infallible proof that the earth had not existed eternally in its
present shape.[49]   Ray saw the apparent truth of the statement, but wisely added that the action seemed not perceptibly
fast and there might be natural causes to prevent such a consummation.[50]   Woodward [51] and later De Luc [52] declared
that such effects were slight.   Woodward thought that some
heights were perhaps precipitated into the abyss by earthquakes; [53] De Luc, that the erosion inevitably ceased when a
state of equilibrium had been reached.[54]   Hakewill accepted
the fact that mountains were destroyed in such a manner, but
believed that they were constantly renewed, either by rotting
vegetation, which was transformed by the surrounding rock
to mineral substance, or by the earth, which, after it had been

[47] Blancanus, *op. cit.*, translated by Ray, *op. cit.*, pp. 296-305; Blancanus,
Sphaera Mvndi (Bologna, 1620), pp. 82-85, 99.

[48] Kircher, *Arca Noë* (Amsterdam, 1675), pp. 188-190; Kircher, *Mundus
Subterraneus* (Amsterdam, 1664-5), t. i, pp. 77, 78.

[49] Burnet, *op. cit.*, vol. i, bk. i, pp. 51-53.

[50] Ray, *op. cit.*, pp. 178-181, 227-230, 283-314.

[51] Woodward, *op. cit.*, pp. 231, 232, 234-241.

[52] De Luc, *op. cit.*, vol. i, pp. 397-400, vol. iii, pp. 180, 181, 262, vol. v,
p. 388.

[53] Woodward, *op. cit.*, p. 135.

[54] De Luc, *op. cit.*, vol. i, pp. 397-400, vol. ii, pp. 8-59, 88-141, vol. iii,
pp. 180, 181, 262, vol. iv, pp. 5-14, 151, 152, 286-288, vol. v, pp. 14-17,
104, 388, 503.

carried to the sea, was altered to water by agitation, raised
as vapors by the sun, then thickened again into rain and, as it
lay on the mountains, gradually condensed into earth. To
prove the possibility of a transmutation from water to stone,
he mentioned some stalactites that he had discovered in a
cave.[55]

De Luc studied the problems connected with mountain
building and realized that there was more than one variety
of mountain. He asserted that De Maillet was the first to
recognize this fact. Slightly later than De Maillet, in 1756,
Lehman,[56] a German mineralogist and director of the Prus-
sian mines, had divided mountains into three classes in accordance with their age and with their constitution; that is,
with the question whether or not they incorporated fossils and
fragments from earlier mountains. De Luc declared that, in
addition to the volcanoes, formed from lava of various types
and from ashes, there were primordial and secondary mountains. The secondary mountains consisted of strata deposited by water in horizontal layers and later tipped. At first
he thought that the cause of the primordial, which formed
the cores of all or almost all mountain chains, was unknown;
but eventually he declared that they also were stratified and
had been precipitated by chemical reactions from the sea
water, or rather from the primitive liquid, which contained
both water and the elements of the future rocks. All mountains were formed under the sea, and their contours were
there shaped by the currents. As the liquid percolated into
the pulvicules of which the earth was formed, it combined
with some of them to make solid parts. These supported

[55] Hakewill, op. cit., pt. ii, pp. 62, 63, 69.

[56] De Luc, op. cit., vol. ii, pp. 202-224, 317; Lehmann, Johann Gottlob
(d. 1767), Versuch einer Geschichte von Flötz-Gebürgen (Berlin, 1756)
(240 pp.), discussed by Geikie, op. cit., pp. 96-98; Lehman, or Lehmann,
discussed by Jéhan, op. cit., art. " Géologie (Histoire de la)", col. 637.

caverns left empty by the subsidence of other pulvicules upon the addition of liquid. Gradually the liquid undermined many supports of the caverns by removing the pulvicules beneath them, and the vaults of the caverns fell. In places the superincumbent strata of granite were still propped by the original supports. By the escape of gases from the caverns and their chemical combinations with the constituents of the liquid, different solids were precipitated; and new strata were laid down on top of the old. Again caverns were formed beneath the surface, and again the vaults collapsed. The tendency was for the first supports to form a ridge or core, upon whose sides later strata were propped. Therefore, the oldest rock was at the center. After a time, during the Mosaic third day, much of the water broke into the caverns; and the loftier mountains and plains were exposed. They became covered with vegetation and with animals, and the sea was filled with fish. The process of mountain building below the surface of the sea continued, but after this the strata contained fossils, so that these secondary mountains were fossiliferous. Finally, at the deluge, the water made its way into the enormous caverns that had been formed under the old continents; they collapsed; and the water left its original bed, which was already rough with mountains, and rushed into the hollow due to the subsidence of the primitive continents.[57]

When the varied constituents of the earth's crust were considered in detail, questions as to minerals and especially as to metals arose. The answers formulated were often those that had been current in the days of Pliny, but some-

[57] De Luc, *op. cit.*, vol. ii, pp. 193, 194, 202-244, 399, 400, 410-449, 476-483, vol. iii, pp. 162, 164, 261, 274-276, 284, 384, 385, vol. iv, pp. 256, 257, 284, 292, 294, 516-519, 543, 555-558, 566-568, 575, 595-598, 608-611, vol. v, pp. 358-369, 383, 389, 452-463, 466, 467, 485-488; De Luc, *Letters on the Physical History of the Earth* (London, 1831), introduction, pp. 54-57, letter ii, pp. 61-69, letter iii, pp. 106-111, 116-131, letter iv, pp. 151-153.

times new ideas emerged.   The supernatural was not ignored
in connection with minerals.   Dwarfs or other strange inhabitants of the mines, some of whom were friendly if well
treated and others invariably hostile, but all of whom were
easily offended and prone to mock their human co-laborers,
were often believed in, particularly by miners.   Such strange
beings were to be found as late as 1769 in the coal mines at
Whitehaven.[58]   Kircher accepted both them and other subterranean beings resembling men, some of whom were green
in color and Christian in faith.[59]

The date of creation for metals and sometimes for minerals
was discussed.   Fludd [60] and Kircher said that they were
formed on the third day, though perhaps Kircher meant
merely that the process then commenced, since he later spoke
of the regrowth of metals and minerals in deserted mines
and quarries.[61]   Even Fludd thought that they gradually
perfected themselves and became more gleaming.   The light
enclosed in the shadows or matter strove to subdue the earthy
and watery disposition of its prison and to give the whole
splendor and activity.   The metals had a secret life of their
own.[62]   Although Ray thought that metals and minerals were
included in the Mosaic narrative under the term " earth " and
therefore that they were created at the very beginning,[63]

[58] Pennant, *Tour in Scotland* (1769), p. 49, quoted by Dalyell, *The
Darker Superstitions of Scotland* (Edinburgh, 1834), p. 534.

[59] Kircher, *op. cit.*, t. ii, pp. 99-103, 184, 185, 187, 227.

[60] Fludd, *Utriusque Cosmi Maioris scilicet et Minoris Metaphysica,
Physica atque Technica Historia* (Oppenheim, 1617), pp. 173-175.

[61] Kircher, *op. cit.*, t. i, pp. 163, 190, 329, 330, t. ii, pp. 8, 39, 41.
Mersenne also finally decided that they were created during the hexaemeron
and yet that they continued to form in mines. Mersenne, *Qvaestiones
Celeberrimae in Genesim* (Paris, 1623), cols. 1145. 1147; Mersenne, *Les
qvestions theologiqves, physiqves, morales, et mathematiqves* (Paris, 1634),
pp. 24-29.

[62] Fludd, *op. cit.*, pp. 173, 174.   [63] Ray, *op. cit.*, p. 6.

most authorities felt that even the third day was too early for their complete production. Dickinson declared that they were not in existence for some years, not until the earth was properly prepared.[64]   Burnet and perhaps Descartes postponed their appearance even longer. Burnet thought that they were not to be found in the antediluvian world,[65] perhaps because with Descartes [66] he located them in the central core of the earth. While of course this did not prove their complete non-existence, it offered a longer period for their attainment of perfection. Burnet thought that they were very slowly concocted by the action of the sun upon subterranean matter. Perhaps the solar heat first raised to the outer crust the metallic principles or seeds from the central sphere.[67]   Warren [68] and Beaumont [69] entered into lively controversy with Burnet on the topic. When Warren mentioned Tubal-Cain, the ark and the prediluvial city of Enoch or Henochia as proof of iron tools, Burnet [70] ignored Tubal-Cain and denied the necessity for iron tools on the ground that the city and the ark were constructed of brick and mortar, wood and pitch or mud.[71]

[64] Dickinson, op. cit., pp. 103, 105, 253.

[65] Burnet, op. cit., vol. i, bk. ii, pp. 335, 336; Burnet, quoted and answered by Warren, cf. infra.

[66] Descartes, op. cit., vol. iii, Les principes de la philosophie, pt. iv, sec. 44.

[67] Burnet, op. cit., vol. i, bk. ii, p. 336.

[68] Warren, op. cit., pp. 26-28, 34, 52; Warren, A Defence of the Discourse Concerning the Earth Before the Flood (London, 1691), pp. 102-108, 163; Warren, Geologia (London, 1690), pp. 215-217.

[69] Beaumont, op. cit., pp. 60-63.

[70] Burnet, op. cit., vol. ii, An Answer to the Exceptions made by Mr. Erasmus Warren, Against the Sacred Theory of the Earth, pp. 47, 48.

[71] Among others who declared that metals were created after the end of the hexaemeron were Hakewill, op. cit., pt. i, pp. 163-166; Hale, op. cit., p. 307; Steno, op. cit., p. 236.

The belief that metals and minerals were constantly growing, especially in deserted mines and quarries, was very common, and was undoubtedly encouraged by the increase of limestone deposits like stalactites and by the shape of coral. Even Woodward thought that corals were stones, which had been crystallized out of the water, perhaps from dissolved rocks in the vicinity, although he rejected the interpretation of the botanist, Dr. Tournefort, who claimed to have discovered plants of stone still growing. In quoting Dr. Camerarius's belief in the reappearance of minerals and of metals in deserted mines, Woodward demanded proofs.[72] On the other hand he had earlier held that metals grew in the fissures of the strata because they were transported thither by the water.[73] Burton queried whether the recrudescence of metals and minerals in mines and quarries was true;[74] Leibnitz flatly denied it;[75] but most others, especially most miners, accepted it and found various explanations. Robert Boyle was inclined to believe it and quoted the testimony of many workers, although he asserted that the question needed more investigation, which would take a long time. He was apparently interested in the problem whether the admission of air had any effect.[76] Kircher declared that the quarry must

[72] Woodward, *Fossils Of all Kinds* (London, 1728), pp. 77-92; Camerarius, perhaps in *Dissertationes Taurinenses* (Tübingen, 1712), and Tournefort, *Memoires de l'Académie des Sciences* (1702), p. 221, both quoted by Woodward, *A Supplement & Continuation of The Essay towards a Natural History of the Earth* (London, 1726), pt. ii, pp. 49-56, with his rejection of their statements.

[73] Woodward, *An Essay toward a Natural History of the Earth: and Terrestrial Bodies* (London, 1695), pp. 195, 196.

[74] Burton, *The Anatomy of Melancholy* (London, 1920), vol. ii, pp. 46, 47.

[75] Leibnitz, *op. cit.*, vol. ii, *Protogaea*, pp. 209, 210.

[76] Boyle, *Opera Omnia* (Venice, 1697), vol. i, pp. 581-573 (by a mistake in numbering the pages begin again at 571 after 584).

be covered up in order to bear once more. He thought that the regrowth of iron and of stone was due to the entrance of sea-water, which by its sulphur became nourishment for new minerals. The matter of the earth, which had been burned to ash by subterranean fire and mixed with water, became again metallic under the influence of salt. Gold and silver drew to themselves and transformed into their own likeness suitable substances.[77] Hale thought that minerals were made of a terrestrial sap " digested by the heat of the Sun." [78] They grew like vegetables. Flint, for example, was made from water and earth hardened by the solar heat. The process took time, perhaps as much as a month. In quarries of coal and freestone, part of the earth might be found not yet perfectly digested into stone.[79] In 1657 the master of the mint in Vienna and another Italian visited the mines. A problem they investigated was whether or not metals grew like plants, by means of a circulating sap in the earth. They decided that this was the case, and that iron grew rather rapidly while gold formed more slowly. Though they came to no decision as to the cause, one of them thought that the growth was the result of accretion.[80]

The associated problem of metallic transmutation, especially the change of the baser metals into gold, was also

[77] Kircher, op. cit., t. i, pp. 190, 329, 330, t. ii, pp. 7, 8, 39, 41, 42, 237, 238.

[78] Hale, op. cit., p. 76.

[79] Ibid., pp. 76, 77, 89, 307, 310.

[80] Steno, op. cit., note pp. 232, 233, in which the editor quoted Fabronius, Vitae Italorum, p. 202. Steno himself accepted the idea, Steno, op. cit., p. 236, as did the following: Mersenne, op. cit., pp. 24-29; Hakewill, op. cit., pt. i, pp. 163-166, pt. ii, pp. 62, 63, 69; Comenius, op. cit., p. 73; Derham, op. cit., pp. 63, 64, notes; Lehman, tome iii, pp. 381 et seq., quoted with approval, at least as regards the production of iron, by Buffon, op. cit., vol. v, p. 122. It was considered probable by Shuckford, The Creation and Fall of Man (London, 1753), p. 90.

discussed. Such alteration was accepted by Bacon, who gave elaborate directions for the process,[81] and with great enthusiasm by two of Sir Thomas Browne's friends. One of them, Dr. Arthur Dee, the son of John Dee, declared that he had often beheld the change, and believed so firmly in it that he was saved from this transmutation of all his property only by the opportune death of the continental " artist." [82] Ray was originally doubtful but seemed to apologize for such scepticism as if after thirty years he had changed his mind. If the process were real, it would imply that all metals were of one species and differed only because they were mixed with different bodies.[83] Kircher was the most contradictory of all. He had studied the subject diligently.[84] He declared that he would take a middle course, and neither affirm the making of gold impossible nor accept the process suggested by the alchemists.[85] He repeatedly denied the Paracelsian belief that iron could be changed to copper,[86] and said that no man could effect such a change or the similar transmutation of metals into gold,[87] although perhaps it was not beyond the powers of angels or of demons.[88] Only nature could thus alter metals.[89] He explained the tales of such results as due to the collection of minute particles of the second metal which had been diffused through the first; [90] and, on

[81] Bacon, *Works* (Boston, ?), vol. iv, *Sylva Sylvarum*, cent. iv, no. 327 and introduction, pp. 314-318.

[82] Browne, *Works* (London, 1890), vol. i, p. lx.

[83] Ray, *The Wisdom of God Manifested in the Works of the Creation* (London, 1759), pp. 60, 61, 98.

[84] Kircher, *op. cit.*, t. ii, pp. 231, 232.

[85] *Ibid.*, t. ii, pp. 250, 256.

[86] *Ibid.*, t. i, pp. 320, 321, t. ii, pp. 223, 224, 257, 258.

[87] *Ibid.*, t. ii, pp. 231, 234, 256, 257, 326.

[88] *Ibid.*, t. ii, pp. 234, 256.

[89] *Ibid.*, t. ii, pp. 234, 236-239, 256, 257, 269, 270.

[90] *Ibid.*, t. i, pp. 319-321, t. ii, p. 289.

another occasion, he asserted that the devil deceived the eyes of alchemists.[91] Hakewill also preserved his neutrality, but declared that Solomon at least was ignorant of the process since he was compelled to seek gold in Ophir.[92] Burton rather ridiculed alchemists; [93] Spencer [94] and Woodward denied the possibility of transmutation.[95]

The causes that produced metals and other minerals, particularly those of commercial value, evoked discussion. Often, as a compromise, most of the possible agents were listed. Naturally the most frequently accepted were heat, generally from the subterranean fires though occasionally from the sun, vapors and the action of salt, sulphur and mercury or some of the trio. Dickinson accepted all these suggestions,[96] and Fludd all except the agency of salt,[97] while Leibnitz,[98] though he once refused to decide how metals originated, and Kircher [99] eliminated as a cause only the heat of the sun. De Luc, with merely the addition of the word perhaps, attributed all except gold to the mutual reactions in the mountain veins of the salt sea water and subterranean fire.[100] Kircher possibly did not wish wholly to reject the agency of solar heat, for he said that the stellar and solar influence could affect anything below the surface only through

[91] Kircher, *op. cit.*, t. ii, pp. 283, 284. The whole subject was discussed also, *ibid.*, t. i, pp. 319-321, t. ii, pp. 155, 156, 223, 224, 231-325.

[92] Hakewill, *op. cit.*, pt. i, p. 325.

[93] Burton, *op. cit.*, vol. ii, p. 204.

[94] Spencer, *A Discourse concerning Prodigies* (London, 1665), p. 402.

[95] Woodward, *op. cit.*, p. 217.

[96] Dickinson, *op. cit.*, pp. 92, 93, 103-105, 253.

[97] Fludd, *op. cit.*, pp. 172-174.

[98] Leibnitz, *op. cit.*, vol. ii, *Protogaea*, pp. 209-212, 214, 216.

[99] Kircher, *op. cit.*, t. i, pp. 159, 162, 163, 184, 190, 329, 330, t. ii, pp. 162, 163, 200, 216, 219, 237, 238, 390 and elsewhere.

[100] De Luc, *Lettres physiques et morales sur l'histoire de la terre et de l'homme* (The Hague and Paris, 1779, 1780), vol. iii, pp. 323-328.

the intermediary of air, as was true with the generation of metals.[101] Dickinson likewise affirmed the necessity for air.[102] Comenius,[103] Gale [104] and Buffon [105] proclaimed the need for subterranean heat, although Buffon was discussing both the separation of metals from one another by sublimation and their original production. Hale declared for the generation of metals by heat, and mentioned subterranean heat as an addition to solar.[106] Keill denied flatly that solar heat had any such effect.[107] Sea water in the form of either a vapor or a liquid was a commonly assigned cause, sometimes as the source of sulphur.[108] Steno introduced a variation by the derivation of the vapor from the rocks.[109] Comenius declared that all things made now, including stones and metals, were from the coagulation of vapors.[110] Kircher thought that the earth was a great distilling furnace with snow-capped mountains for alembics. In it, nature cooked the vapors for a long time after they had found suitable matrices, and produced metals, which were hardened by the evaporation of the water.[111] Leibnitz agreed in the comparison of the earth to a furnace or laboratory.[112] Dr. Jacob

---

[101] Kircher, *op. cit.*, t. ii, pp. 164-166.

[102] Dickinson, *op. cit.*, p. 261.

[103] Comenius, *op. cit.*, pp. 88, 89, 98, 142-146, 231.

[104] Gale, *The Covrt of the Gentiles* (Oxford and London, 1670-1677), vol. ii, pt. iv, bk. ii, p. 452, who mentioned only subterranean fire as a cause.

[105] Buffon, *op. cit.*, vol. v, pp. 102, 103, 105-109, 121-124, 126, 152.

[106] Hale, *op. cit.*, pp. 76, 77, 89, 307.

[107] Keill, op. cit., pp. 151, 152.

[108] Dickinson, *op. cit.*, pp. 96, 103, 104, 244; Kircher, *op. cit.*, t. i, pp. 159, 176, 190, 329, 330 and elsewhere, who appealed to Aristotle for confirmation; De Luc, *op. cit.*, vol. iii, pp. 323-328.

[109] Steno, *op. cit.*, p. 236.

[110] Comenius, *op. cit.*, pp. 28, 101, 102, 142-144.

[111] Kircher, *op. cit.*, t. ii, pp. 162, 163, 237, 238, 390, 391.

[112] Leibnitz, *op. cit.*, vol. ii, *Protogaea*, pp. 210, 211.

Grandius queried whether a juice, spirit or subtle air penetrated and petrified bodies or whether stones were generated
as in animals.[113]   Naturally crystallization from a liquid or a
vapor appealed to some as a cause for the production of gems
and even of metals,[114] while Comenius declared that precious
stones were the gums of rocks that sweated in the earth.[115]
Astrology was invoked to explain the formation of metals
and of minerals, for many asserted that the planets or stars
by occult influences produced these earthly bodies.[116] Kircher
both denied and asserted the influence of the stars in the matter.   He meant apparently that it was not direct but as a
corollary to their influence on air and on water.[117]

Two explanations of metallic production, which were propounded by Fludd and by Baumé and had little connection
with those of contemporary thought, harmonized with the
conceptions of the universe adopted by their proponents.
Fludd felt that metals were due to part of the light from the
second heaven, which was entangled in darkness or matter of
the lowest.   It was imprisoned forever because of its own
weakness and the minute size of the pores, and therefore
produced objects of weight and solidity, immobile and apparently incapable of self-propagation.   Though its heat was

[113] Grandius, *De Veritate Diluvii Universalis, & Testaceorum quae
procul à mari repertuntur Generatione* (Venice, 1676), p. 70, quoted by
Harris (John), *op. cit.*, p. 245.

[114] Woodward, *A Supplement & Continuation of The Essay towards a
Natural History of the Earth* (London, 1726), pt. ii, pp. 56, 57, who mentioned only gems and thought that the crystallization took place generally
in the fissures of the strata; Leibnitz, *op. cit.*, vol. ii, *Protogaea*, pp. 211,
213, 214, 216, who neither rejected nor clearly affirmed the theory, though
he declared it the opinion of many; De Luc, *op. cit.*, vol. iii, pp. 323-328.

[115] Comenius, *op. cit.*, p. 146.

[116] Among others, Fludd, *op. cit.*, pp. 8, 172-174; Hakewill, *op. cit.*, pt.
i, p. 111.

[117] Kircher, *op. cit.*, t. ii, pp. 162, 165-167.

too slight to repulse the cold of the mineral body and it could not be seen to grow, it strove to subdue the earthy and watery disposition of its prison and to give its mass splendor and activity, in other words, to develop into gold. It was aided and strengthened by the influence of the uncombined light, which continually penetrated to the center of the earth, and which it attracted.[118] The cause of mineral production, proclaimed by M. Baumé in his *Chemistry,* and denied by De Luc as contrary to facts observed in present mountains, was quite different. Baumé thought that the earth consisted originally of only glass and water. By marine animals the solar rays were united to these elements and formed shells. The shells produced all calcareous matter and also all metals, minerals, clay and salt. After they were raised into dry land, the rays of the sun were combined with them in other ways and formed plants and animals. Their remains passed under the sea and helped to make other varieties of minerals.[119]

To explain differences in metals, several hypotheses were offered. Gold has perhaps always seemed intrinsically superior to other metals. The alchemists generally thought that all metals strove to rid themselves of impurities and to become gold.[120] Dickinson went so far in his admiration of the metal as to assign a special cause for its production. He declared that it was nothing else than solar particles concentrated and compacted in suitable earth. The variety of the other metals he attributed to the influence of the planets.[121] Kircher denied that the planets had such an effect, and held that the difference resulted from the type of matrix or other matter with which the salt-sulphurous-mercurial vapor was

[118] Fludd, *op. cit.,* pp. 70, 133, 170, 173, 174.

[119] Baumé, quoted by De Luc, *op. cit.,* vol. iv, pp. 107-118, 120-135.

[120] Bacon, *op. cit.,* vol. iv, *Sylva Sylvarum,* cent. iv, introduction to no. 327, pp. 315, 316.

[121] Dickinson, *op. cit.,* pp. 105, 189.

combined; [122] and Ray was inclined to accept this statement.[123] Fludd believed it due to the varying proportions of sulphur and of mercury or water contained in the metal and also to the amount of light enclosed in matter. The greater the quantity of light, the purer, more gleaming, more perfect and more precious was the metal. The influences of the stars were a vital factor.[124] Descartes declared that the variations resulted from differences in size and shape of the particles broken off from the central metallic core of the earth by particles of salt moving here and there through the pores.[125] Buffon asserted that the metals were formed at different epochs and in different latitudes. The less perfect metals, like iron, were formed at a later epoch and farther from the equator than the more perfect, apparently because their production required less heat.[126]

It was generally agreed that after the metals were formed they had to be raised into the cracks or veins of the earth and there deposited by the departure of the elevating agent. Sometimes the assistance of the terrestrial cold was invoked to harden them when they had been sublimed by heat, or to liquefy the vapor that had raised them so that it passed off or perhaps could not hold in solution so great a quantity of metallic matter. Woodward gave the greatest number of ways in which metals were elevated: the heat of the sun, water in vapors from the abyss, rain-water, which perhaps

[122] Kircher, op. cit., t. ii, especially pp. 163-168, 238, though elsewhere he seemed to say that the variety resulted from the varying proportions of the three principles, ibid., t. ii, p. 163. This seems to have been Mersenne's opinion. Mersenne, op. cit., pp. 24-29; Mersenne, Qvaestiones Celeberrimae in Genesim (Paris, 1623), col. 1147.

[123] Ray, op. cit., pp. 60, 61.

[124] Fludd, op. cit., pp. 70, 133, 170, 173, 174.

[125] Descartes, op. cit., vol. iii, Les principes de la philosophie, pt. iv, sec. 63.

[126] Buffon, op. cit., vol. v, pp. 106-109.

altered merely their horizontal location, springs hot and cold and the heat generated by earthquakes and eruptions.[127] Buffon [128] and Kircher believed that they were sublimed by heat, and Kircher added that they were attracted into the fissures by a kind of magnetism.[129] Hutchinson felt that they were forced up by the pressure of the air.[130] Descartes wished apparently to make use of all three Paracelsian principles, and therefore declared that metallic particles, which were detached from the central mass by particles of salt, were enveloped by little oily branching particles, by which he meant sulphurous atoms, and were elevated to the outer crust by particles of mercury, which had been agitated and rarefied by heat. Metals were deposited in cracks on the southern or eastern slopes of mountains, since there the heat of the sun was greater and able to vaporize the mercury or any other exhalations or spirits which had raised them. Then the mercury either evaporated or redescended. In either case it left the metal.[131] Buffon [132] and Woodward [133] realized that the story was not complete and that in some cases the veins were filled with metals which had been washed out of higher veins by water and redeposited nearer the base of the mountain.

[127] Woodward, *op. cit.*, pt. ii, p. 56; Woodward, *An Essay toward a Natural History of the Earth: and Terrestrial Bodies* (London, 1695), pp. 153, 180-209.

[128] Buffon, *op. cit.*, vol. i, note pp. 108-111, vol. v, pp. 102, 103, 105-109, 121-124, 152.

[129] Kircher, *op. cit.*, t. ii, pp. 236-238, 390 and elsewhere.

[130] Hutchinson, *op. cit.*, pp. 31, 78, 79, who specifically denied that their location in fissures was due to fire and water.

[131] Descartes, *op. cit.*, vol. iii, *Les principes de la philosophie*, pt. iv, secs. 63, 72-75.

[132] Buffon, *op. cit.*, vol. v, pp. 102, 103, 105, 106, 122-124, 152, 159-162.

[133] Woodward, *Fossils Of all Kinds* (London, 1728), pt. i, p. 54.

The belief still persisted that the production of metals and minerals was possible elsewhere than in the earth.   Comenius had said that metals were made of vapor since they were concreted also in the clouds.   Both iron and brass sometimes fell from heaven, as did small fish, frogs and those stones called thunder-bolts.[134]   Woodward on the other hand denied Pliny's belief that thunder-stones fell from the clouds and insisted that they were ancient weapons.[135]   Even so late as 1734, nevertheless, Mahndel in an exposition in the Academy of Paris was ridiculed for the belief that thunder-stones were human implements rather than objects formed in the clouds.[136]   Leibnitz thought them flakes and fanciful likenesses.[137]

In addition, many had little doubt of the occult qualities of various metals, such as their sympathies and antipathies.[138] Fludd in his discussion grouped their occult with their medicinal properties.[139]   Kircher followed his example in listing

[134] Comenius, *op. cit.*, pp. 100, 130, 144.   This was Mersenne's belief also.   Mersenne, *op. cit.*, col. 1163.

[135] Woodward, *op. cit.*, pt. ii, pp. 37-43.

[136] Büchner, *Man in the Past, Present, and Future* (New York, 1894), note p. 42.   Cartailhac, *L'age de pierre dans les souvenirs et superstitions populaires* (Paris, 1877), showed how prevalent, even at a later period, was the doctrine rejected by Woodward, and gave as well many superstitious practices, which connected these implements with evil spirits and with witchcraft.   A smaller variety, much used by witches in popular opinion and called elves' arrows, was discussed in detail by Dalyell, *op. cit.*, pp. 354-358, 535, 539, 540, by White (Andrew), *A History of the Warfare of Science with Theology in Christendom* (New York and London, 1910), vol. i, pp. 266, 267, who discussed thunder-stones also, and by others.

[137] Leibnitz, *op. cit.*, vol. ii, *Protogaea*, p. 222.

[138] Le Brun, *Histoire critique des practiques superstitieuses* (Paris, 1702), preface, pp. 48-52, 105, 109-112, 122, 123, 140-144, 160, 208-211, 230-233, 251-254.

[139] Fludd, *op. cit.*, p. 174, vol. ii, tract 4.

the magic and medicinal properties of minerals and metals.[140] Some stones, like the glossopetrae, were supposed to sweat at the approach of poison, and were therefore inserted in rings or in drinking-cups. Even so early as 1644, however, Boëce de Boot in his book *The Perfect Jeweler* showed the presence of a sceptical spirit in his denial of this useful virtue.[141] Other stones were talismans for the protection or healing of men and animals, either directly or through the agency of water in which they had been immersed; or they endowed their fortunate possessors with various pleasant gifts, such as luck in their undertakings.[142]

[140] Kircher, *op. cit.*, t. ii, pp. 77-82, 201, 202, 206, 219, 220.

[141] Boëce de Boot, *Le parfait joaillier* (Lyon, 1644), quoted by Cartailhac, *op. cit.*, p. 93 note.

[142] Dalyell, *op. cit.*, especially pp. 130, 131, 139-142, 145, 150-157.

CHAPTER VIII

Spontaneous Generation, Permanence of Species and Fossils

THE creation of plants and of animals offered numerous problems. First came the question as to the manner in which they were created in the beginning, whether as embryos or adults, whether in pairs or in quantity, whether immediately by the hand of God or through secondary causes. Microscopes as well as the naked eye showed that seeds contained actual plants in diminutive form. Ray was so convinced that the work of creation was beyond any but divine power as to declare that God at the beginning created the embryos of all plants and animals to the end of the world, and that each contained a miniature copy of all its future descendants, so that merely growth was needed to produce the adult.[1] The *Universal History* quoted Ray with approval,[2] and Whiston also apparently accepted this theory,[3] which enjoyed a certain vogue. Nevertheless, the common opinion naturally asserted that at least a large proportion of the first animals and plants were formed as adults. As to the number of animals created at first, the ordinary belief was that they were produced in quantity in all sections of the earth. The chief arguments that favored the creation of animals in pairs were the analogy with the production of man, the analogy with conditions

[1] Ray, *Three Physico-Theological Discourses* (London, 1693), pp. 49-60.

[2] *An Universal History, from the Earliest Account of Time to the Present* (Dublin, 1744), vol. i, pp. 43, 44.

[3] Whiston, *A New Theory of the Earth* (Cambridge, 1708), pp. 290, 291, 335.

428

after the flood when pairs of animals sufficed to repopulate the earth, the beliefs that God would not produce more than were necessary and that mankind would have been swamped by the increase in animals had too many been created at first, together unquestionably with the unexpressed sentiment that two were easier to create than a multitude and that the production of a pair was less overwhelming to contemplate than that of many.[4]

The belief in the spontaneous generation of plants and of small animals from inanimate matter, not only at creation but also ever since, was almost universal to the end of the seventeenth century. Even after the doctrine was generally rejected, atheists in their desire to eliminate any intervention by God continued to credit it.[5] Insects were the type of animal most commonly mentioned, but the term included both worms and mice. Sometimes those creatures which might

[4] The creation of animals in pairs only was upheld by Cockburn, *An Enquiry into the Truth and Certainty of the Mosaic Deluge* (London, 1750), pp. 116-119, 127-129, 131, 134; Buffon, *Oeuvres complètes* (Paris, 1831-2), vol. v, p. 256. It was implied by Whiston, *op. cit.*, pp. 320, 332, and declared the general belief by Burnet, *Doctrina Antiqua de Rerum Originibus* (London, 1729, 1736), *Archaeologiae Philosophicae*, pt. i, critique, p. 21. De Maillet thought that they were produced in quantity, but perhaps on their emergence upon dry land no more than a pair survived, De Luc, *Lettres physiques et morales sur l'histoire de la terre et de l'homme* (The Hague and Paris, 1779, 1780), vol. ii, pp. 327, 333-335. On the other hand, the following believed that animals were created in quantity: Vossius and Stillingfleet, quoted by Cockburn, *op. cit.*, pp. 27, 36-38, 116; Stillingfleet, *Origines Sacrae* (London, 1709), pt. i, pp. 338, 339, who called it very strange that so much land and water could produce only two animals; Comenius, *Naturall Philosophie Reformed by Divine Light* (London, 1651), p. 15; Ray, *op. cit.*, pp. 7, 8, 47-49, although he spoke also in favor of the thesis that only pairs were created; *An Universal History, from the Earliest Account of Time to the Present* (Dublin, 1744), vol. i, p. 43.

[5] Holbach, *The System of Nature* (New York, 1835), p. 20; Bentley, *The Folly and Unreasonableness of Atheism Demonstrated* (London, 1699), pp. 116, 117, 120-129.

be so produced were called imperfect, and the process was limited to animals which underwent metamorphosis.[6]   On the whole, as by Hale, man and the larger animals were definitely excluded except by miraculous intervention at creation.[7] Whiston and Burnet offered an interesting compromise. Whiston declared that spontaneous generations were limited to the prediluvial earth and perhaps to the epoch of creation and the locality of Paradise, though possibly spontaneous generation is hardly an accurate term since he attributed the production of all plants and animals, both in the beginning and throughout all ages to seeds that were miraculously shaped by God Himself.[8]   Burnet thought that before the flood plants and animals were produced by the richness of the soil, the dews of heaven, the continuous warmth of the sun because of the perpetual equinox and the fructifying influence of the ether.   Even contemporaneously, insects and little creeping things were still produced.[9]   Another compromise was illustrated by the work of Comenius,[10] of Sir Thomas Browne [11] and of Hale,[12] who asserted that the same species was produced sometimes in one way and sometimes in another.   Stillingfleet spoke on both sides.[13]   As has been mentioned, the animals to which this origin was most frequently attributed were insects, worms, mice and frogs. Bees, wasps and parasitic vermin were supposed to be pro-

---

[6] Browne, *Works* (London, 1888-1890), vol. i, pp. 197, 258, vol. ii, p. 157.

[7] Hale, *The Primitive Origination of Mankind* (London, 1677), pp. 76, 77, 247, 256-266, 269, 272, 276-290, 306, 336, 337.

[8] Whiston, *op. cit.*, pp. 226, 227, 319-321, 332-336.

[9] Burnet, *The Sacred Theory of the Earth* (London, 1722), vol. i, bk. ii, pp. 247-250, 254-258, 269-272, 335.

[10] Comenius, *op. cit.*, p. 200.

[11] Browne, *op. cit.*, vol. i, p. 289.

[12] Hale, *op. cit.*, pp. 209, 263, 265-282, 306, 336, 339.

[13] Stillingfleet, *op. cit.*, pt. i, p. 43, pt. ii, pp. 16-25, 28, 30, 31.

duced from decaying animal matter, either of animals on which they preyed or of those which according to some fanciful analogy they resembled. Basilisks and "other kinds of serpents" were named by Ross as arising from putrefied matter; [14] and Kircher, in an attempt to discover a suitable source for dragons, decided that they were born from the decaying remains of all kinds of prey, which had been killed by vultures and piled up in the mountains.[15] As late as 1705 Witty could state that the belief was common but was in truth a mistaken doctrine cherished by atheists.[16] A certain L. P., derided by Harris, asserted the spontaneous generation of plants and animals as proving the formation of fossils by nature directly. Harris implied that the doctrine of spontaneous generation was atheistical.[17]

The causes of this phenomenon were variously given. The most common was putrefied matter; but mud or muddy and stagnant water, especially that of the Nile on its retreat, was a close second. Glanvill thought that life could be produced even from a drop of dew,[18] and Van Helmont said that even the purest spring water generated worms.[19] Water in some form was generally considered necessary, as was heat, either of the sun, particularly in spring and summer, or of the ether. Hale felt that the air and the interven-

[14] Ross, *Arcana*, p. 146, quoted by Browne, *op. cit.*, vol. i, p. 258 note.

[15] Kircher, *Mundus Subterraneus* (Amsterdam, 1664-5), t. ii, p. 96.

[16] Witty, *An Essay towards a Vindication of the Vulgar Exposition of the Mosaic History of the Creation of the World* (London, 1705), pp. 118-132.

[17] L. P., *Letter from Oxford to a Nobleman in London* (?), quoted and refuted by Harris (John), *Remarks On some Late Papers, Relating to the Universal Deluge* (London, 1697), pp. 46-50, 76-81, 86-88, 105.

[18] Glanvill, *Scepsis Scientifica* (London, 1665), pt. i, pp. 33, 155, pt. ii, p. 38.

[19] Van Helmont, *Opera Omnia* (Frankfurt, 1682), pt. i, p. 112, especially sec. 33.

tion of the ether were probably necessary;[20] but Van Helmont emphasized the need for the exclusion of air from the animal remains or the wheat, water and dirt in order to produce insects or mice. Van Helmont, on the other hand, asserted that the water in the earth produced plants when it was agitated by heat. His theory was that all solids came from water and ferments alone.[21] Hale likewise thought that ferments helped to bring forth animals spontaneously,[22] and Holbach may have meant the same when he said that such action was due to fermentation.[23] Van Helmont[24] and probably Hale agreed in the assertion that the influence of the stars was another cause. Hale's chief thesis concerning the production of animals was that they were made by plastic nature or the plastic power of the earth.[25] A somewhat similar statement was made by Comenius, who called it the diffused soul of the world. He added that heat was necessary and a humid or putrefied matter.[26] Naturally the hypothesis that spontaneous generation was caused by the interaction of salt-sulphur-mercury was promulgated. Kircher spent some pages on the exposition of this doctrine.[27] The most reasonable suggestion was one by Browne, who de-

[20] Hale, op. cit., p. 76. He mentioned the problem as a whole also p. 310.

[21] Van Helmont, op. cit., pt. i, pp. 108-113, secs. 9-34.

[22] Hale, op. cit., p. 274.

[23] Holbach, op. cit., p. 20, who grouped putrefaction with fermentation and advocated the exclusion of air.

[24] Van Helmont, op. cit., pt. i, p. 112, sec. 32.

[25] Hale, op. cit., pp. 193, 270, 275, 306 and especially pp. 336, 337.

[26] Comenius, op. cit., pp. 22, 23, 72, 73, 130, 154, 200, 210.

[27] Kircher, op. cit., t. ii, pp. 336-338. On the general subject of spontaneous generation see also ibid., t. i, p. 158, t. ii, pp. 86, 96, 105, 107, 108, 119, 120, 257, 338-374, 409; Kircher, Itinerarivm Exstaticvm (Rome, 1656), p. 219; Kircher, Arca Noë (Amsterdam, 1675), pp. 48, 49, 51, 53, 54.

clared that nature was everywhere filled with the seeds and principles from which animate beings could be developed by means of heat.[28]   The idea appealed to Buffon, who was one of the very few to assert that the creation of the larger animals was not completed at one time but continued over thousands of years as the earth cooled, and perhaps still occurred.   Buffon thought that all animals were formed by the union of living organic molecules, which were indestructible and always active.   They nourished and reproduced animals, and, if present species were destroyed, would develop new types.   However, all molecules appropriate for large animals at least were already in use, and therefore could not produce new species.   The molecules were more numerous in northern climes than in southern, and therefore more important animals were first formed in those localities.   The greater abundance of molecules in the north resulted from the fact that all the watery, oily and ductile particles necessary for their production fell there earlier and more abundantly.   Organic molecules were produced only by the action of heat on ductile matters.[29]   De Maillet went further and asserted firmly that in the waters disposed to fecundity large animals and men were yet produced in northern climes, though with great difficulty, and then became terrestrial.   The universe was filled with particles which brought forth all forms of life as the heavenly bodies became successively able to support them.[30]

[28] Browne, *op. cit.*, vol. ii, p. 340.

[29] Buffon, *op. cit.*, vol. i, ii, v, especially vol. v, pp. 243-245.

[30] De Maillet, *Telliamed*, tome ii, pp. 158, 169, 170, 177, 178, 181, 184, 189, 191, 196, 237, 245, 246, 249, 251, 253, 257, quoted by De Luc, *op. cit.,* vol. ii, pp. 327, 333-353, 370, 373-381. Others who affirmed spontaneous generation of animals and sometimes of plants were as follows : Bacon, *Works* (Boston, ?), vol. iv, *Sylva Sylvarum*, cent. iv, no. 329, preliminary remarks, p. 319, cent. vi, p. 400, nos. 537-572, pp. 405-415, cent. vii, nos. 605, 606, 692, 696, 697, pp. 430, 431, 468, 471-474, preliminary remarks

The rejection of spontaneous generation was half-hearted and impotent at first.   The friends of Steno, who himself denied it of oysters and like animals, were the first to combat scientifically this theory.   Perhaps the development of the microscope was a necessary antecedent.[31]   Bentley called

to 696, pp. 470, 471, vol. v, cent. ix, no. 900, pp. 115, 116; Fludd, *Utriusque Cosmi Maioris scilicet et Minoris Metaphysica, Physica atque Technica Historia* (Oppenheim, 1617), frontispiece and p. 8; Heylyn, Μικρόκοσμος (Oxford, 1633), p. 739; Heylyn, *Cosmography in Four Books* (London, 1674), bk. iv, pt. i, pp. 7, 8; Bochart, *Opera Omnia* (Leyden, 1692), vol. iii, *Hierozoicon*, cols. 502-506, 543, 577, 657, who proved its truth from the Bible, from Greek and Roman authors, such as Pliny and Galen, and from Church Fathers, including Origen; Milius, *De Origine Animalium, et Migratione Populorum* (Geneva, 1667), pp. 9, 10; Boyle, *Opera Omnia* (Venice, 1697), *Generalia Capita pro Historia Natvrali Plvrivm Regionvm*, vol. iii, pt. ii, p. 331; Plot, *The Natural History of Staffordshire* (Oxford, 1686), c. i, sec. 47, quoted by Derham, *Physico-Theology* (London, 1742) (Delivered 1711, 1712), p. 244 note; Blackmore, in *The British Poets* (Chiswick, 1822), vol. xxviii, Song of Mopas from *Prince Arthur*, quoted by Johnson in his life of Blackmore, p. 72; *ibid., Creation*, bk. ii, p. 123, bk. vi, p. 206; F. Fournier, *Hydrography*, quoted by Cockburn, *op. cit.*, p. 203.

[31] Harvey, *Exercitationes de Generatione Animalium* (London, 1651); Redi (Francisco), *De Generatione insectorum (Esperienze intorno alla Generazione degli' Insetti)* (Florence, 1668), Swammerdam, *De gen. Insect. (Historia Insectorum Generalis)* (Utrecht, 1669), all quoted by Winter in a note in Steno, *The Prodromus of Nicolaus Steno's Dissertation concerning a Solid Body Enclosed by Process of Nature within a Solid* (New York and London, 1916), note p. 251, and with the addition of Leuwenhoek, *Epistol.*, by Bentley, *op. cit.*, pp. 24, 116, 117, 120-129, with his own rejection of the doctrine; Redi, quoted and answered by Kircher, *op. cit.*, p. 53; Steno, *op. cit.*, p. 251. Others who denied it, sometimes as limited to specific animals, were as follows: Ray, *The Wisdom of God Manifested in the Works of the Creation* (London, 1759), pp. 298-326, especially p. 298, where he called the belief popular with atheists; Huygens, *Nouveau traité de la pluralité des mondes* (Amsterdam, 1718), pp. 53, 54; Dickinson, *Physica Vetus et Vera* (Rotterdam, 1703), p. 153; Leibnitz, *The Philosophical Works* (New Haven, 1890), *The Principles of Nature and of Grace* (1st ed. in French, 1714), sec. 6, p. 212; Duguet and d'Asfeld, *Explication de l'ouvrage des six jours*

new the discovery that all insects had parents, and appealed to observation and experiment for proofs, though naturally he retained belief in miraculous instances of the contrary like the Egyptian plagues.[32]   Only about twenty years later, however, Derham declared that the doctrine of spontaneous generation was so generally exploded as not to require disproof.[33]   Harris quoted against it Ray, Dr. Tancred Robinson, Redi, Swammerdam and Malpighi.[34]   By 1798 Marsh could say that it was fully disproved, so much so that, according to him, even at creation all organic beings were formed by supernatural power, and both earth and water were merely the matter used.[35]   Le Clerc's rejection of the doctrine led him to the conclusion that flies must have been taken into the ark.[36]

A peculiar belief concerning plants and animals that flourished in some quarters was named palingenesis.   Calmet described it as possibly analogous to the appearance of ghosts in cemeteries.   Chemists

take a flower, burn it, & collect all its ashes, from which they extract the salts by means of calcination.   These salts they put in a glass vial, where having mixed certain compositions capable of putting them into motion when one warms them, all this matter forms a dust, whose color tends to blue.   From this

(Paris, 1740), p. 178; *An Universal History, from the Earliest Account of Time to the Present* (Dublin, 1744), vol. i, p. 43; Cockburn, *op. cit.,* p. 203.

[32] Bentley, *op. cit.,* pp. 121-129.

[33] Derham, *op. cit.,* notes pp. 244, 245, 373, who listed many others as opposed to the hypothesis of spontaneous generation.

[34] Harris (John), *op. cit.,* pp. 78, 79, 81, who also himself disbelieved it, *ibid.,* pp. 49, 50.

[35] Marsh, *An Oration, on the Truth of the Mosaic History of the Creation* (Hartford, 1798), pp. 20, 21.

[36] Le Clerc, *Mosis Prophetae Libri Quinque* (Amsterdam, 1735), pp. 65, 68.

dust, excited by a gentle warmth, there rises a trunk, leaves, &
a flower; in one word one perceives the apparition of a plant,
which rises from the midst of its ashes.   When the heat ceases
all the spectacle vanishes.[37]

The matter settled as dust to the bottom.   The experiment,
which was likewise possible with animals, could be repeated
indefinitely.   Kircher was said to have performed it on a
sparrow.[38]   He himself mentioned plants as having been
subjected to the process in his sight, and narrated a similar
experiment on a snake.   The explanation he offered was
that the seminal virtue was concentrated in the salts of the
plant, and that this plastic force, excited by the gentle
warmth, put into motion the corpuscles so that each sought
its original situation.   He declared that any ill success in
repetition of the experiment with an animal might be due
to the fact that not always would the seminal principle be
present in the salts or liquid.[39]   Glanvill,[40] who accepted the
verity of the process, acceded also to Kircher's statement [41]
that a similar result occurred in the water under the ice when
it congealed in the form of foliage.[42]

[37] " Ils prennent une fleur, la brûlent, & en ramassent toutes les cendres,
dont ils tirent les sels par le moyen de la calcination. Ils mettent ces
sels dans une phiole de verre, où ayant mêlé certaines compositions
capables de les mettre en mouvement lorsqu'on les échauffe, toute cette
matiere (sic) forme une poussiere (sic), dont la couleur tire sur le bleu.
De cette poussiere, excitée par une chaleur douce, il s'en éleve un tronc,
des feuilles, & une fleur; en un mot on apperçoit l'apparition d'une plante,
qui sort du milieu de ses cendres. Dès que la chaleur cesse tout le spectacle s'évanoüit." Calmet, *Dissertations sur les apparitions des anges,
des démons & des esprits* (Paris, 1746), p. 489.

[38] *Ibid.*, pp. 489, 490.

[39] Kircher, *Mundus Subterraneus* (Amsterdam, 1664-5), t. ii, pp.
413-417.

[40] Glanvill, *op. cit.*, pt. i, pp. 35, 36.

[41] Kircher, *op. cit.*, t. ii, p. 414.

[42] The doctrine of palingenesis was upheld by the following also:

As has been already mentioned [43] it was generally believed that no new species had been created and none destroyed, though some evolutionary dicta were proclaimed without realization of their implications [44] by those who saw how cultivated plants and domesticated animals had varied, how closely some species resembled one another, and how many species must be postulated at an original creation and worse still as confined within the ark if they were absolutely unvarying. The discussion concerning the number of species created arose largely in connection with the size of the ark. Naturally fish and hybrid animals never disturbed the calculators, for the deluge would not prevent their reappearance in the postdiluvial world. In the attempt to decrease the number of species for which room must be found in the ark, the hypothesis which attributed to the effects of environment great changes, such as those of color and size, was widely accepted. The dimensions of the ark were fixed by the Biblical data, though its capacity might be slightly enlarged if the commentator chose as a unit of measurement one of the more unusual and longer cubits. The difficulty then was the increased vulnerability of the ark to winds and waves. Many authors evolved mathematical proofs that the ark would be large enough for all animals necessary and for their food. Dickinson solved the problem of food space by the thesis that Noah hung up in the ark an astrologically prepared oleaginous liquid, radiant as the sun, which reduced

Comenius, *op. cit.*, pp. 158, 159; Warren, *Geologia* (London, 1690), p. 15, who spoke of the belief as if it were generally accepted. It was mentioned as an acknowledged fact by Spencer and Sir Thomas Browne, Spencer, *A Discourse concerning Prodigies* (London, 1665), p. 218; Browne, *op. cit.*, vol. ii, *Religio Medici*, sec. 48, pp. 395, 396. Hale, however, said that he had heard such a process described, but never by an eye-witness, Hale, *op. cit.*, p. 288.

[43] *Cf. supra*, pp. 94, 220, 221 and note, 433.

[44] *Cf. supra*, note pp. 220, 221.

greatly the amount of nourishment requisite for the animals' health.[45]   Wilkins [46] and F. Fournier [47] gave elaborate calculations to prove that the ark was large enough, as did Sir Walter Raleigh.   Raleigh thought that there were only eighty-nine distinct species, though he allowed one hundred for good measure.   Then he considered their sizes as compared with cows, sheep and wolves, and decided that there would have been seventy-seven large animals and fifty-eight small, equivalent to ninety-one oxen, eighty sheep and sixty-four wolves.   Therefore the first story of the ark would have furnished plenty of room.[48]   Catoir thought that there were hardly above one hundred and fifty genera, not more than six of which were larger than the horse and bull while many were much smaller.[49]   Bochart gave an elaborate account of the animals and arrived at approximately the same number.[50]   Kircher even decreased it.   Though he counted separately five kinds of dog, he limited the species of quadrupeds to about twenty-five and those of birds to thirty-four or sixty-eight.[51]   Gradually, with greater knowledge, the numbers of animals increased, until Ray declared that there were 20,866 species of animals besides 4,500 of fish, and 18,000 of plants.[52]

[45] Dickinson, *op. cit.*, pp. 329-333, and note p. 328.

[46] Wilkins, *The Mathematical and Philosophical Works* (London, 1707-8), pt. iii, p. 181, *An Abstract of Dr. Wilkins's Essay Towards a Real Character, and a Philosophical Language.*   The *Essay* was quoted also by Cockburn, *op. cit.*, pp. 205-207, who referred to pp. 162 *et seq.*

[47] Fournier, *op. cit.*, quoted by Cockburn, *op. cit.*, pp. 202-204.

[48] Raleigh, *The History of the World* (Edinburgh, 1820), vol. i, pp. 231-236, and as quoted by Cockburn, *op. cit.*, p. 209.   His mathematics is peculiar.

[49] Catoir, *Disputatio Theologica de Arca Noachi et Diluvio* (Gröningen, 1704), sec. ix.

[50] Bochart, *op. cit.*, vol. ii, iii, *Hierozoicon.*

[51] Kircher, *op. cit.*, pp. 48-67, 71-94, 98-116, where he added various pictures and plans of the ark and its inhabitants.

[52] Ray, *op. cit.*, pp. 21-25.   *Cf.* also *supra*, p. 94 and note.

In contrast with the other topics mentioned in this chapter, the problems presented by fossils, whose enormous numbers and wide distribution were revealed ever more clearly by the intensive and extensive study of the earth, by the exchange of ideas and of data as well as by the cooperation of the new scientific societies and by the improvement of tools, such as the microscope, became more and more exigent during the seventeenth and the eighteenth centuries. The name of fossil was not limited to what are now distinguished by the term until the end of the period. It originally meant stone, not only with but also without organic relationship. The first problem was the nature of those objects which resembled organic remains. To the time of Steno, probably most observers denied that they were relics of real animals. They were frequently thought to be freaks of nature.[53] Catcott

[53] They were considered to be due to seeds of all things scattered in the earth at creation, to the hidden plastic virtue of the earth or to a principle falling in rain into the cracks of the earth by the following: L. P., *op. cit.* (?), with perhaps some wavering to a belief in their animal origin, Mr. Lhwyd, *Notes on Camden* in Camden's *Britannia*, pp. 692, 693, Dr. Lister, *Phil. Trans. No. 76 Conf. Lib. Cochlitarum Angliae* 40 (1671), Reiskius (John), *Comment. de Glossopetris Luneberg* (Norim. 1687), pp. 5, 20, 27, 35, 58 *et seq.*, Ray, *Synops. stirpium Britanic.* (1696), preface, where he doubted the reality of fossil plants, Ray, *Three Physico-Theological Discourses* (London, 1693), p. 127, Plot, *Natural History of Oxfordshire* (Oxford, 1677), Plot, *Natural History of Staffordshire* (Oxford, 1686), and others, all quoted and their opinion denied by Harris (John)', *op. cit.*, pp. 18, 46, 51, 55-57, 88, 105, 113-118, 253, 254, 258-270. Ray and Dr. Plot's two books were quoted to the same effect by *An Universal History, from the Earliest Account of Time to the Present* (Dublin, 1744), vol. i, p. 97, with a denial; and Plot was quoted by Jéhan, *Dictionnaire de cosmogonie et de paléontologie* (Paris, 1854), art. "Géologie (Histoire de la)", col. 618. Jéhan, *loc. cit.*, and Harris (John), *op. cit.*, p. 269, quoted also to the same effect Quirini (John), *De testaceis fossilibus Musaei Septatiani* (Venice, 1676). Catcott mentioned the popularity of the doctrine that fossils were not organic remains but due to plastic nature, Catcott, *A Treatise on the Deluge* (London, 1768), pp. 363-367. Catcott's own opinion was that they were real remains and resulted from the deluge, *ibid.*, pp. 329-331, 358-374, 381-383, 396-401, 404, 405, 407-410.

asserted that this theory was discarded a century or two before his time, perhaps because the date 1668, one hundred years before the time affixed to the title page of his book, coincided with the publication of Steno's *Prodromus*. He quoted Steno's work.[54]   Even after Steno's time, however, the compromise was still often suggested that some such objects were freaks while others were genuine animal or vegetable remains.   Kircher,[55] Hale,[56] Paul Boccone, Dr. Jacobus Grandius [57] and Scheidt adopted this stand, though Kircher also said that all stones which seemed to be bones or teeth were *lusi naturae,* which were formed when nature found in the earth holes of just that size.[58]   Grandius later denied that fossils could be formed on land.[59]   Scheidt wavered in his opinion but gave the doctrine that the stones were natural freaks as one cause for their appearance.   He seemed averse to rejecting it.[60]   Woodward, who denied that they were freaks of nature, called the hypothesis the received

[54] Catcott, *op. cit.*, pp. 362, 368.

[55] Kircher, *op. cit.*, p. 4; Kircher, *Mundus Subterraneus* (Amsterdam, 1664-5), t. ii, pp. 27-53, 58-62, 66.

[56] Hale, *op. cit.*, pp. 192, 193.

[57] Boccone, *Recherches et observationes naturelles* (Amsterdam, 1674), pp. 305, 308, 309, 318, and Grandius, *De Veritate Diluvii Universalis, & Testaceorum quae procul à mari repertuntur Generatione* (Venice, 1676), letter to Johannis Quirinus, pp. 59, 65-67, both quoted by Harris (John), *op. cit.*, pp. 240-244.

[58] Kircher, *op. cit.*, t. ii, pp. 58-62.

[59] Grandius, *loc. cit.*, in Harris (John), *loc. cit.*; Steno, *op. cit.*, pp. 249-262, and note pp. 211, 212, where the editor quoted from an earlier treatise by Steno, *Canis Carchariae Dissectum Caput* (1667) (ed. by Maar, Steno, *Opera Philosophica* (Copenhagen, 1910), vol. ii, pp. 127, 128), in which Steno refused to take sides on the ground of insufficient knowledge.

[60] Scheidt, preface to Leibnitz's *Protogaea*, in Leibnitz, *Opera Omnia* (Geneva, 1768), vol. ii, pp. 185, 188-195.

opinion as late as 1690; [61] but Bentley in 1692 said that it was generally rejected, and affirmed only by atheists. [62]   Dr. Andrias (or Jacob John?) Scheuchzer, a professor of mathematics at Zürich, had declared that fossils were of terrestrial origin, but after perusal of Woodward's *Essay* made public retraction in the dedicatory epistle to a Latin translation entitled *Geographia Physica*.   Dr. Camerarius, however, a professor of physical science at Tübingen, continued fixed in his opinion that the Glossopetrae were not fossil teeth, although he accepted some other remains as organic. [63] Hakewill, who thought that the nature of fossils was impossible to prove, nevertheless gave several possible explanations, including their reality and attribution to the deluge and their production as freaks. [64]

Gradually the doctrine gained credence that all fossils were remains of real animals.   It was held by Leibnitz, who specifically denied that they were freaks.   He was much impressed with them, discussed them at considerable length and gave many illustrations. [65]   The genuinely organic nature of these relics was accepted by Steno, by Woodward, by Harris, by Catcott and by the author of the *Universal History*, while all those who, as a compromise, assigned some to the pro-

[61] Woodward, *An Essay toward a Natural History of the Earth: and Terrestrial Bodies* (London, 1695), especially p. 38.

[62] Bentley, *op. cit.*, pp. 129, 130.

[63] Scheuchzer, *De Generatione Conchitarum* (1695), and Camerarius, probably in *Dissertationes Taurinenses* (Tübingen, 1712), especially pp. 272, 273, both quoted by Woodward, *A Supplement & Continuation of The Essay towards a Natural History of the Earth* (London, 1726), pt. ii, pp. 4, 5, 86-90.   Woodward's own opinion was expressed throughout this book and the *Essay*.

[64] Hakewill, *An Apologie or Declaration of the Power and Providence of God in the Government of the World* (Oxford, 1635), pt. i, pp. 33, 160, 228-231.

[65] Leibnitz, *op. cit.*, vol. ii, *Protogaea*, pp. 214-233, 237, 238, 240.

duction of nature as freaks felt that others were genuine.[66] The belief in their organic origin was accepted as well by Webb,[67] Agostino Scilla, a Sicilian painter who became interested in the topic, Fabius Columna, Hooke,[68] Fontenelle,[69] Beaumont,[70] Whiston,[71] Foxton,[72] Buffon,[73] Shuckford,[74] Le Catt,[75] Maupertuis,[76] De Luc,[77] Marsh [78] and probably by

[66] Cf. supra, pp. 439-441.

[67] Webb, An Historical Essay Endeavoring a Probability That the Language Of the Empire of China is the Primitive Language (London, 1669), pp. 14, 15.

[68] Scilla, Lettera circa î corpi Marini petrificati &c. (Naples, 1670), Columna, Aquatilium & Terrestrium aliquot Animalium Observationes, pp. 46, 48, 49, Columna, Dissertatio de purpurâ, c. xiii, Columna, Dissertatio de Glossopetris, p. 36, all published by Columna in one volume (Rome, 1616), Hooke, Micro., p. 111, all quoted by Harris (John), op. cit., pp. 18, 162, 166, 222-230; Scilla, and Hooke, Oeuvres posth., lecture du 15 février, 1688, quoted by Jéhan, op. cit., art. "Géologie (Histoire de la)", cols. 616, 621-623.

[69] Fontenelle, Entretiens sur la pluralité des mondes (Paris, 1821), p. 149.

[70] Beaumont, Considerations On a Book, Entituled The Theory of the Earth (London, 1692-3), p. 30a.

[71] Whiston, op. cit., pp. 266-272, 417, 423-425; Whiston, quoted with approbation by Keill, An Examination of Dr. Burnet's Theory of the Earth. Together with some remarks on Mr. Whiston's New Theory of the Earth (Oxford, 1698), p. 217; Whiston, The Accomplishment of Scripture Prophecies (Cambridge, 1708), p. 99.

[72] Foxton, in Burnet, Doctrina Antiqua de Rerum Originibus (London, 1729, 1736), Archaeologiae Philosophicae, pt. i, remarks, pp. 249, 251, where he quoted Woodward.

[73] Buffon, op. cit., especially vols. i, ii, v.

[74] Shuckford, The Creation and Fall of Man (London, 1753), pp. 130-135.

[75] Le Catt, quoted by Catcott, op. cit., pp. 369-371.

[76] Maupertuis, Essay de cosmologie (Paris? or Amsterdam?, 1750), pp. 130, 131.

[77] De Luc, op. cit.

[78] Marsh, op. cit., pp. 40-42.

Burton [79] and by Ray [80] in spite of some dubious statements on their part. Ray discussed fossils, especially those of fish, at some length, and gave arguments both for their reality and for their being *lusi naturae*.[81]

A few other sources were asserted for fossils. Camerarius [82] and Johann Beringer [83] said that they were made directly by God, for His own pleasure. Scheidt gave this as a reason sometimes mentioned.[84] Others, like Dr. Theodore Arnold in 1733, assigned a more intelligent purpose, and stated that they served as models.[85] Many, according to Jéhan, declared that they were produced from germs of animals and plants deposited by water on the land, perhaps at the time of the flood.[86] Sometimes only enough was deposited in one place to form part of an animal, perhaps one tooth. Catcott stated that in 1768 this attribution of fossils to scattered germs or seeds was " a *prevailing opinion* ", but that the seeds were believed to have been scattered through

[79] Burton, *The Anatomy of Melancholy* (London, 1920), vol. ii, p. 47.

[80] Ray, *op. cit.*, pp. 127-162. *Cf.* also *supra*, p. 439, note.

[81] In addition Scheidt quoted a long list of those who with Leibnitz agreed that fossils were real and were relics of the deluge. Among them he included Ray. He declared also that Germany was full of men who were studying the rocks and communicating with one another. Leibnitz, *op. cit.*, vol. ii, *Protogaea*, preface, pp. 185, 186, and note pp. 186, 187.

[82] Camerarius, quoted and refuted by Woodward, *op. cit.*, pt. ii, pp. 149-159.

[83] Beringer, *Lithographiae Wirceburgensis Specimen Primum*, p. 91, quoted by White (Andrew), *A History of the Warfare of Science with Theology in Christendom* (New York and London, 1910), vol. i, p. 216.

[84] Scheidt, in Leibnitz, *op. cit.*, vol. ii, *Protogaea*, preface, p. 188.

[85] White (Andrew), *op. cit.*, vol. i, p. 222.

[86] Jéhan, *op. cit.*, art. " Géologie (Histoire de la)", col. 618, where he quoted Quirini, *op. cit.*, and art. " De Luc ", col. 447, where he quoted from l'Abbé Maupied, *Dieu l'homme et le monde*, tome iii.

the earth at creation.[87]   Scheidt mentioned the suggestion of
Antonius Lazarus Moro that fossils were from volcanoes,
and added many other proposed sources, including the following: that they were due to the influence of the stars; that they
were formed by subterranean genii; that they were insects
and other animals sent by the devil to terrify hermits and
transformed by the holy men into stone by the sign of the
cross.   He conservatively concluded that there was more than
one origin for fossils.[88]   Hakewill thought that perhaps they
were due to demons, who in an attempt to persuade men to
idolatry either acted themselves or aided men, presumably
by the assimilation of fossils to real organic remains.   Those
human agents whom he accused of such activities were
princes, who were motivated by a desire for fame, or
" *cunning workmen* out of curiosity." [89]   Columna, who
thought that marine fossils were real, attributed their presence on land to various agencies, including mankind.[90]
Harris quoted some one, apparently Dr. Tancred Robinson,
for the suggestion that they might have been brought on
land by army encampments, by the inhabitants of vanished
cities or by monkeys.[91]   Columna attributed them to the
deluge or to an exchange of land and sea as well as to the
casual rubbish heaps of man.[92]

If fossils, especially marine ones, were genuine, their
burial deep in the earth in all localities, even mountain summits, demanded explanation.   The belief which replaced the
opinion that they were natural freaks was that their appearance was due to the Noachian flood.   This widely current

[87] Catcott, *op. cit.*, pp. 363, 364.
[88] Scheidt, in Leibnitz, *op. cit.*, vol. ii, *Protogaea*, preface, pp. 188-191.
[89] Hakewill, *op. cit.*, pt. i, p. 230.   *Cf.* also *supra*, p. 441.
[90] Harris (John), *op. cit.*, p. 166.
[91] *Ibid.*, p. 51.
[92] *Ibid.*, p. 166.

doctrine lasted a century and a half,[93] and fossils were held by many to be a sure proof for the historicity of a universal deluge. Burton,[94] Hakewill [95] and Hale [96] suggested the possibility of such a source for at least some fossils; and Shuckford thought it probable.[97] Others who accepted it, sometimes without any great amount of explanation, were Kircher,[98] Webb,[99] Bentley,[100] Scilla,[101] Steno,[102] Whiston,[103] the *Universal History*,[104] Catcott,[105] Leibnitz and his associates, though Leibnitz attributed some fossils to later catastrophes.[106] Marsh felt that quantities of shell-fish deserted the ocean bed for the newly submerged land. The duration of the flood sufficed for the growth of vast numbers, only a small proportion of which were able to follow the retreating waters. The rest by the enormous weight of the water were forced deep into the earth, especially since

[93] Jéhan, *op. cit.*, art. " Géologie (Histoire de la)", cols. 616, 617.

[94] Burton, *op. cit.*, vol. ii, p. 47, who, however, said that the location of fossils might be due to earthquakes or to an occasional complete disruption of the world.

[95] Hakewill, *op. cit.*, pt. i, pp. 33, 160.

[96] Hale, *op. cit.*, pp. 192, 193.

[97] Shuckford, *op. cit.*, pp. 130-135.

[98] Kircher, *Arca Noë* (Amsterdam, 1675), p. 4.

[99] Webb, *op. cit.*, pp. 14, 15.

[100] Bentley, *op. cit.*, p. 130.

[101] Jéhan, *op. cit.*, art. " Géologie (Histoire de la)", col. 616, though Jéhan suggested scepticism concerning Scilla's sincerity.

[102] Steno, *op. cit.*

[103] Whiston, *op. cit.*, p. 99; Whiston, *A New Theory of the Earth* (Cambridge, 1708), pp. 266-272, 417, 423-425; Whiston, quoted with approval by Keill, *op. cit.*, p. 217.

[104] *An Universal History, from the Earliest Account of Time to the Present* (Dublin, 1744), vol. i, p. 97.

[105] Catcott, *op. cit.*, pp. 329-331, 358-374, 381-383, 396-401, 404, 405, 407-410.

[106] Leibnitz, *op. cit.*, vol. ii, *Protogaea*.

the earth was then soft.[107]   Woodward [108] and Catcott [109] solved the difficulties due to the extraordinary numbers of marine fossils and to their location deep in the strata by a dissolution of the entire earth.   De Luc decided that the flood was due to a complete exchange of sea and land so that the sea bed became the continents after an existence under the water of sufficient duration to permit the precipitation from the water of many and varied strata and the accumulation of fossils at different levels.[110]   Ray had earlier explained the multitude of fossils by the declaration that at creation only a small part of the land was dried while the rest remained covered long enough for accumulations of shell-fish to be deposited.[111]

On the other hand, many authors in the eighteenth century, among whom was Buffon,[112] declared that for long eras the dry land formed the bed of the sea, upon which were precipitated strata and innumerable varieties of marine fossils. It was not all exposed simultaneously.   The sea and the land were constantly exchanging places.   This opinion had appealed during the preceding century to Fontenelle [113] and to Beaumont.[114]   Moreover, it was often granted, as by

[107] Marsh, *op. cit.*, pp. 41, 42.

[108] Woodward, *op. cit.*; Woodward, *Fossils Of all Kinds* (London, 1728) ; Woodward, *An Essay toward a Natural History of the Earth: and Terrestrial Bodies* (London, 1695).

[109] Catcott, *op. cit.*

[110] De Luc, *op. cit.*; De Luc, *Letters on the Physical History of the Earth* (London, 1831), especially letter iv, pp. 155, 156, 159-168, 176-178, letter v, pp. 185, 186.

[111] Ray, *op. cit.*, pp. 144-146, 149, and especially note before p. 132.

[112] Buffon, *op. cit.*, especially vol. v.

[113] Fontenelle, *op. cit.*, pp. 149-151.

[114] Beaumont, *op. cit.*, p. 30a.

Hooke,[115] by Leibnitz[116] and by Camerarius,[117] that the presence of some fossils at least was the result of partial floods later than the deluge.   Another conjecture of Camerarius and of others, which was discredited by Woodward, asserted that fossils were the remains of animals which, when they were alive, had been driven up subterranean passages to their present resting places.   However, the close of the century found the belief in the diluvial source of fossils firmly established.

[115] Hooke, *Micro.*, p. III, who attributed them to "some" flood, earthquake or similar catastrophe, quoted by Harris (John), *op. cit.*, p. 18.

[116] Leibnitz, *op. cit.*, vol. ii, *Protogaea*, pp. 215-218, 229, 238.

[117] Camerarius, *Dissertationes Taurinenses?* (Tübingen, 1712), pp. 290, 346, 347, quoted with disapproval by Woodward, *A Supplement & Continuation of The Essay towards a Natural History of the Earth* (London, 1726), pt. ii, pp. 141-149.

CHAPTER IX

The First Men

As has been already mentioned, the date of creation evoked innumerable opinions.[1] The season offered less opportunity for discussion. It was clear from the Scriptures that the season of creation was the same as that of the commencement and the conclusion of the deluge.[2] The decisions as to which was the favored time of year were based not only on the date at which the year was begun by ancient people, such as the Egyptians, Assyrians and Hebrews, and the season which *a priori* seemed most suited to a beginning, but also on such arguments as the appropriateness of autumnal decay and approaching winter immediately after the Fall, the indubitable abundance of ripe fruits, the necessity for Noah and even for Adam of a protracted warm period to prepare for the winter cold. Almost unanimous was the agreement that the earth was created at one of the equinoxes; but Kepler preferred as the date the summer solstice;[3] and Webb quoted the Chinese philosophers, whose doctrines he thought were derived from their ancestor Noah, for the winter solstice as the date.[4] Sir Thomas Browne[5] and Warren[6] cleverly

---

[1] *Cf. supra*, p. 195.

[2] Gen. 7: 11; 8: 13, 14.

[3] Kepler, quoted by Riccioli, *Almagestvm Novvm Astronomiam Veterem Novamqve Complectens* (Bologna, 1651), vol. ii, p. 232.

[4] Webb, *An Historical Essay Endeavoring a Probability That the Language Of the Empire of China is the Primitive Language* (London, 1669), pp. 90, 92.

[5] Browne, *Works* (London, 1888-1890), vol. ii, pp. 119-121, 350, 351.

[6] Warren, *Geologia* (London, 1690), p. 176; Warren, *A Defence of the*

THE FIRST MEN 449

compromised the opposing views by the statement that creation took place at all seasons since at any given date all were
simultaneous though in different latitudes. Burnet thought
that it was in the spring because the axis of the antediluvian
earth was untipped and therefore the sphere enjoyed a perpetual equinox.[7] However, most authors treated the matter
more simply; and the majority agreed with Usher in assign-
ing creation to the end of October.[8]

Discourse Concerning the Earth Before the Flood (London, 1691), pp.
67, 68.

[7] Burnet, quoted *ibid.*, pp. 67, 68; Burnet, *Doctrina Antiqua de Rerum
Originibus* (London, 1729, 1736), *Archaeologiae Philosophicae*, pt. ii,
pp. 17, 21, 28-30, 63-70, 72, 73, 76-81, 84-94, 96; Burnet, *The Sacred
Theory of the Earth* (London, 1722), vol. i, bks. i, ii, vol. ii, *An Answer
to the Exceptions made by Mr. Erasmus Warren, Against the Sacred
Theory of the Earth*, pp. 31-37.

[8] Draper, *History of the Conflict between Religion and Science* (New
York and London, 1928), p. 185. Among those who accepted an autumnal
creation were Hakewill, *An Apologie or Declaration of the Power and
Providence of God in the Government of the World* (Oxford, 1635),
pt. i, p. 7; Ozorio, *Theologic cvrievse* (Dijon, 1666), pp. 44-61, who said
that the opinion was not so popular as that which assigned a vernal date;
Horn, *Arca Noae* (Leyden, 1666), p. 5; Ray, who asserted that the
"*most learned*" Scriptural interpreters preferred the autumn, quoted by
Harris (John), *Remarks On some Late Papers, Relating to the Universal
Deluge* (London, 1697), p. 256; Duguet and d'Asfeld, *Explication de
l'ouvrage des six jours* (Paris, 1740), pp. 49-51; *An Universal History,
from the Earliest Account of Time to the Present* (Dublin, 1744), vol. i,
p. 48; Shuckford, *The Sacred and Profane History of the World Connected* (Philadelphia, 1824), vol. i, p. 41 note; Pike, *Philosophia Sacra*
(London, 1753), *The Explanation of the Copper Plate*, pp. 7, 8; Whiston,
A New Theory of the Earth (Cambridge, 1708); Whiston, quoted by
Draper, *op. cit.*, p. 185. Whiston delayed the flood to the twenty-eighth
of November so as to make it coincide with the approach of Halley's
comet. On the other hand, the following preferred the vernal equinox:
Fludd, *Utriusque Cosmi Maioris scilicet et Minoris Metaphysica, Physica
atque Technica Historia* (Oppenheim, 1617), p. 105; Riccioli, *op. cit.*,
vol. ii, p. 232, who, having committed himself to a date which combined
the vernal equinox with the full moon, was forced to accept April 19,
4056 B. C. as the first day; Kircher, *Arca Noë* (Amsterdam, 1675), pp.

As the desire to believe the universe created by God through secondary causes became more widespread, and the multifarious changes that in such a case must succeed one another were more clearly envisaged, the sentiment grew that the period of creation must have taken more than six days of twenty-four hours each, particularly since, according to the account, the first three occurred before the sun was created and therefore before there was a measure for the days.[9] Postel added that no count was possible until the end of the sixth day, since Adam was the first numberer.[10]   La Peyrère based his doctrine of Pre-Adamites partly on the idea that the time suggested from the creation of Adam through that of Eve was too brief for all the events which were supposed to have occurred.   These included the journey of animals from distant parts of the globe, such as India, to be named.   He decided that Adam and Eve were both created as babies and grew naturally until Adam reached the perfect age of thirty-three.   Among the Pre-Adamite women, who were called *feminae* while Eve was called *virago,* he could find no mate.   It would have been foolish to seek a mate

127, 128; Beaumont, *Considerations On a Book, Entituled The Theory of the Earth* (London, 1692-3), p. 141; John Gerard Vossius, *Isagoge Chronologica,* quoted by Cockburn, *An Enquiry into the Truth and Certainty of the Mosaic Deluge* (London, 1750), pp. 317-322; Cockburn, *ibid.,* pp. 312-329; Woodward, *An Essay toward a Natural History of the Earth: and Terrestrial Bodies* (London, 1695), pp. 272-275; Woodward, *A Supplement & Continuation of The Essay towards a Natural History of the Earth* (London, 1726), pt. ii, p. 18, who considered the date an important argument for his theory; Harris (John), *op. cit.,* p. 256, who asserted that he could produce twice as many learned authorities for that season as Ray could for autumn; Catoir, *Disputatio Theologica de Arca Noachi et Diluvio* (Gröningen, 1704), secs. xxxix, xlvii.

[9] Draper, *History of the Intellectual Development of Europe* (New York and London, 1900), vol. ii, pp. 295, 296.

[10] Postel, *op. cit.,* pp. 20, 21, who assumed the position later taken by De Luc.

among the lower animals.[11]   Those who asserted that solar
days were meant argued anxiously and aggressively, and could
find no good explanation for the speed of creation except a
miracle.   Hale,[12] Le Clerc,[13] Dickinson [14] and Bishop Patrick [15]
thought that the best solution lay in an indefinite period of
darkness, which stretched to myriads of years, before the
creation of light.   Much consolidation and assortment could
take place during that period.   Whiston thought that his
theory solved the problem skilfully.   He declared that the
account dealt merely with the creation of the earth, a limitation to which many agreed, and which was almost necessitated by the new belief in the central location of the sun and
the laws of gravity, that matter was created before the first
day, and that, since the earth did not at first rotate on its
axis, a day was measured by its circuit of the sun, in other
words, that it equalled a year.   In addition, processes were
naturally speeded by six months of continuous light and even
by six months of darkness, although the dark would be modified by twilight and moonlight.[16]   This theory was accepted
nearly fifty years later by Werder, a pupil of Heyn, who
declared that it had not been confuted.[17]   A more far-reaching and useful alteration was the one of which De Luc was

[11] La Peyrère, *Praeadamitae* (?, 1655), *Systema Theologicvm, ex
Praeadamitarvm Hypothesi*, pp. 121-128, 130, 131.

[12] Hale, *The Primitive Origination of Mankind* (London, 1677), pp.
307, 308.

[13] Le Clerc, *Mosis Prophetae Libri Quinque* (Amsterdam, 1735), p. 7.

[14] Dickinson, *Physica Vetus et Vera* (Rotterdam, 1703), pp. 209, 210.

[15] Patrick, *On Genesis*, quoted by Whiston, *op. cit.*, pp. 69, 70.   The
bishop added that the Mosaic account was limited to the creation of the
earth.

[16] Whiston, *op. cit.*, especially introduction, pp. 4-43, 52-54, 58-73, 87-94,
pp. 85-111, 115-117, 232, 297, 298, 312-315.

[17] Werder, in Heyn, *Specimen Cometologiae Sacrae* (Leipzig, 1742),
p. 59.

the leading exponent. It changed the days into periods. He said that almost all Christian scientists agreed to it. De la Fite, his translator, declared that the idea, which had been current among Etruscans, Persians and Hindus, was upheld also by some of the Church Fathers, notably Origen, St. Augustine and Bede.[18] Buffon, who proclaimed the same idea enthusiastically, thought that the periods did not even agree in length. He gave approximate figures for each.[19] Probably Burnet, who baldly stated that the six days of the Mosaic narrative were merely an accommodation to vulgar apprehensions,[20] and certainly M. le Bailliff Engel of Berne agreed.[21]

The narrative of man's creation caused little controversy. No commentators ventured to deny that it was the act of God Himself. A few, like Jordan,[22] Swinden[23] and Swedenborg,[24] suggested that the purpose was to refill heaven, which had been depleted by the rebellion of Lucifer and his cohorts. From a neo-Platonic desire to protect God

[18] Jéhan, *Dictionnaire de cosmogonie et de paléontologie* (Paris, 1854), art. " Jours-Périodes ", especially col. 765, art. " Deluc," col. 444; De Luc, *Letters on the Physical History of the Earth* (London, 1831), introduction (by De la Fite), pp. 5, 46, 86-117, letter iii, pp. 82, 83; De Luc, *Lettres physiques et morales sur l'histoire de la terre et de l'homme* (The Hague and Paris, 1779, 1780), vol. i, pp. 356, 357, vol. v, pp. 638, 639.

[19] Buffon, *Oeuvres complètes* (Paris, 1831-2), especially vol. v, pp. 33-39 and elsewhere.

[20] Burnet, *op. cit.*, vol. ii, pp. 387-390; Burnet, *Doctrina Antiqua de Rerum Originibus* (London, 1729, 1736), *Archaeologiae Philosophicae,* pt. i, critique, pp. 30-37, 43-50.

[21] Engel, *Quand & comment l'Amérique a-t-elle été peuplée?* quoted by De Luc, *op. cit.*, vol. i, pp. 368-370.

[22] Jordan, *The Creation of the World, with Noah's Flood* (London, 1827) (Written 1611), pp. 18-27.

[23] Swinden, *An Enquiry into the Nature and Place of Hell* (London, 1727), pp. 88-93, 275.

[24] Swedenborg, *Miscellaneous Theological Tracts* (New York, 1863), *The Earths in the Universe*, secs. 3, 20, 126.

from the pollution of contact with matter, Whiston attributed the actual formation of Adam to Christ, who perhaps
assumed human shape for the occasion.[25] Bochart[26] and
Milton[27] likewise thought that God created the universe
through Christ as agent.

A few bold adventurers asserted that there were other
men in the world at the time of Adam's creation.   Growth of
population from one pair was too slow, especially in view of
the vagabonds with whom Cain was associated and for whom
he built a city.   Even the wives of Cain and of Seth, if not
of Abel, required explanation; and some commentators did
not approve of the suggestion that they also were the children of Adam and Eve, although that was the orthodox
view.[28]   In addition, writers were perplexed by the problem
as to the settlement of America, and by the verse which
stated that the sons of God married the daughters of men.
One explanation of this had always been that men of the
holy race intermarried with women of an ungodly descent.
Bellonius was said by Bochart to have defended the doctrine
that Adam was not the first man about 1647, in a tract, *De
Prae-Adamitis.*[29] A certain C. B. expressed the same views
in an introductory letter to Burnet's *Doctrina Antiqua;*[30]

[25] Whiston, *op. cit.*, pp. 321, 322; Whiston, *A Second Defence of the
New Theory of the Earth from the Exceptions of Mr. John Keill* (London, 1700), p. 9.

[26] Bochart, *Opera Omnia* (Leyden, 1692) (3rd ed.), vol. iii, *Hierozoicon,*
col. 350.

[27] Milton, *The Poetical Works* (London, 1862), *Paradise Lost*, bk. vii,
ll. 163-175, 208, 209, 219-242.

[28] Jordan stated that Adam and Eve had thirty-four sons and thirty-
two or thirty-three daughters, and that the men married their sisters.
Jordan, *op. cit.*, pp. 94-97, 144, 145.

[29] Bochart, *op. cit.*, vol. ii, *Hierozoicon*, col. 955.

[30] C. B. (Charles Blount?), in Burnet, *op. cit., Letter to Bookseller*,
pp. viii, ix.

but the chief proponent of the "miserable system", as Sticht entitled it,[31] was Isaac de La Peyrère, who in 1655 wrote a book on the subject.[32] He published it anonymously, but its authorship was evidently well-known and evoked much bitter condemnation and even scurrilous attack. Horn talked of the "impious camps of the *Pre-Adamites*"; [33] Stillingfleet asserted that it was a frivolous suggestion; [34] Wiethof [35] and even Scheidt [36] applied opprobrious epithets to the author. La Peyrère thought that men were created everywhere in large numbers, so that the animals and the plants at the antipodes were not useless. The Pre-Adamites were the ancestors of the Gentiles. Though they both sinned and died before Adam, their sin was individual and not inherited, as original sin was by all Adam's progeny. He was more interested in a consideration of this theological point than in an exposition of their lives and characteristics. In fact his twenty years' meditation on the subject was aroused by the effort to explain a verse in Romans which stated that sin was not imputed to men before the law. The law, he declared, was the one revealed to Adam.[37] Besides the opponents of the Pre-Adamite doctrine already named, it was denied by Bochart [38] and by the *Universal History*.[39]

[31] Sticht, *Dissertatio Philologica de Urbe Hanochia* (Jena, delivered 1727), p. 4.

[32] La Peyrère, *op. cit.*

[33] Horn, *op. cit.*, p. 12, "*Praeadamitarum* impia castra".

[34] Stillingfleet, *Origines Sacrae* (London, 1709), pt. i, preface, pp. 334-336.

[35] Wiethof, *Exercitatio Theologico-Philologica, de Polytheoteti ante Diluviana Occasione* (Bremen, 1716), p. 7.

[36] Scheidt, in Leibnitz, *Opera Omnia* (Geneva, 1768), vol. ii, *Protogaea*, introduction, p. 187.

[37] La Peyrère, *op. cit.*

[38] Bochart, *op. cit.*, vol. ii, *Hierozoicon*, col. 955.

[39] *An Universal History, from the Earliest Account of Time to the Present* (Dublin, 1744), vol i, p. 47.

Denials are still current, since so lately as 1929 the Brooklyn *Eagle* printed a letter to that effect.[40]

Throughout the Christian era there had been many hypotheses concerning the location of the earthly Paradise. They continued during the seventeenth and the eighteenth centuries; but the wilder versions were becoming less popular, though Jéhan declared that reputable writers in the seventeenth century believed it above the clouds half-way to the moon.[41] So early as 1662 Samuel Butler ridiculed the philosophers who discussed the problem.[42] Burnet in his *Theory* asserted that it was probably in the southern hemisphere, while the impassable torrid zone was perhaps the flaming sword. He specifically denied its location in Mesopotamia.[43] Wilkins preferred the idea that it was in the moon, and that Enoch and perhaps others of the blessed were still there. He may have been drawn to this opinion because of his belief in lunar inhabitants who were superior to the terrestrial and whom we might some day visit by flying. After a discussion of various difficulties involved and the methods by which they might be obviated, he prophesied "seriously" the invention of a "Flying-Chariot" sufficiently commodious to accommodate several men with their food and commodities for interplanetary traffic.[44] George Bruyn said that Paradise had been removed by God

[40] Brooklyn *Daily Eagle* (June 12, 1929), letter by H. J. Latham of Richmond Hill.

[41] Jéhan, *op. cit.*, art. "Géologie (Histoire de la)", col. 626.

[42] Butler, *Hudibras* (London and New York, 1886), pt. i, canto i, p. 13.

[43] Jéhan, *loc. cit.*; Burnet, *The Sacred Theory of the Earth* (London, 1722), vol. i, bk. i, p. 125, bk. ii, pp. 345-363; Burnet, quoted and rejected by Warren, *op. cit.*, pp. 126, 149-154, and by Beaumont, *Considerations On a Book, Entituled The Theory of the Earth* (London, 1692-3), pp. 113-115, 131, 132.

[44] Wilkins, *The Mathematical and Philosophical Works* (London, 1707-8), pp. 104-135.

to the south pole in order to be inaccessible.   As a proof, he
declared that those who had sought to sail south from South
America had been driven back by extremely strong currents.[45]
Milton thought that it was located on top of a mountain in
Eden and that at the time of the flood the whole mountain
was dislodged and carried down the river.   Finally it was
transformed into a bare salt island.[46]   Kirchmaier affirmed
that several places with the name Paradise were mentioned
in the Bible.   Adam's home, which was on the Tigris-
Euphrates, had been destroyed by time or by the deluge.
That in which Enoch and Elias dwelt was perhaps on top
of a mountain above the clouds, probably Mt. Atlas.[47]   Postel placed the original garden on top of a mountain, whence
subterranean rivers could flow toward any point of the
compass.   He located it both in Molucca and in the
eastern part of Syria,[48] with no explanation of the discrepancy.[49]   According to Heylyn, Zeilan, an island near
Sumatra, was said by the Indians to be the site of Paradise
and to have footprints of Adam and a hill seven leagues
high, whence he ascended into heaven.   The natives had constructed a statue of Adam five or six fathoms high to fit the
footprints.   Heylyn himself, however, accepted the orthodox Mesopotamian site of Paradise.[50]   Kircher, who also

[45] Bruyn, Theatr. Urbium, quoted by Kircher, Mundus Subterraneus
(Amsterdam, 1664-5), t. i, p. 161.

[46] Milton, op. cit., Paradise Lost, bk. viii, ll. 300-305, bk. xi, ll. 118-120,
342-348, 829-838, bk. xii, ll. 639, 640, 649.

[47] Kirchmaier, De Diluvii Universalitate (Geneva, 1667), pp. 41, 83-99.

[48] For some reason he spoke of the meridian of Molucca as the location
for eastern Syria and Paradise.

[49] Postel, op. cit., pp. 34, 35, 40, 52-54, 61.

[50] Heylyn, Μικρόκοσμος (Oxford, 1633), p. 612; Heylyn, Cosmography
in Four Books (London, 1674), bk. iii, pp. 112, 226, who mentioned many
other suggestions on location.

located Eden in Mesopotamia,[51] declared that it still existed
on the summits of high and precipitous mountains near the
Caspian Sea, inaccessible to mortals, and placed Enoch and
Elias there. Thence the Tigris and the Euphrates left with
hidden wanderings; and thence, since the flood, the other two
rivers made their way by subterranean channels.[52] In the
Arca Noë he declared that Paradise was destroyed at the
flood. It was located at the junction of the Tigris and the
Euphrates, which later again parted into two rivers. Originally a subterranean channel led waters from the subterranean reservoirs or hydrophylacia in the Armenian mountains till they rose as a fountain in Paradise. After the fall
of man, God blocked this exit; the waters were poured out
from springs in the mountains near the reservoirs and flowed
on the surface.[53] Schott quoted the idea of many, with
which he agreed, that the garden retained its charm until
the flood and was then destroyed. It was probably not in
the mountains but was guarded during the antediluvian
epoch by cherubim.[54] De Luc's hypothesis was clear and
sensible. It declared that naturally the description of Moses
fitted no present locality for it applied to the antediluvian
continent, which became the bottom of the sea at the deluge.
Perhaps Paradise sank earlier than the rest of the continent,
soon after the fall, since it was probably destroyed immediately. As a temporary defense against incursion, the flaming sword mentioned by Moses was presumably the eruption of a volcano.[55] Few still believed that the Phison and

[51] Kircher, *Arca Noë* (Amsterdam, 1675), pp. 22, 25, 26, 197-203.

[52] Kircher, *Itinerarivm Exstaticvm* (Rome, 1656), pp. 46, 47.

[53] Kircher, *Arca Noë* (Amsterdam, 1675), pp. 22, 25, 26, 197-203.

[54] Schott, in Kircher, *Iter Extaticum Coeleste* (Würzburg, 1660) pp.
88, 89.

[55] De Luc, *op. cit.*, vol. v, pp. 667-669; De Luc, *Letters on the Physical
History of the Earth* (London, 1831), letter vi, pp. 262-264.

the Gihon were the Ganges and the Nile, though Hakewill listed the doctrine among current mistakes. He thought that Adam and Eve were in Paradise more than one day, that its perfection was then destroyed and that Enoch and Elias did not live there.[56] Le Clerc located Paradise in Syria on the Euphrates but apparently to the west of the mighty stream.[57] Bochart [58] and Huettius [59] endeavored to explain the four rivers of Paradise in some way that would fit the present state of the Tigris-Euphrates valley, and therefore declared that the two rivers met at the northern end of the garden, ran as one for some distance and then separated again into two. Beaumont modestly and vaguely located Paradise as merely east of Jerusalem, on the ground that God wished to conceal such details.[60] Buffon stated merely that it was in Asia.[61] Almost all other authorities placed it in the Tigris-Euphrates valley, generally between the rivers and near Babylon. Among such were Sir Walter Raleigh,[62] Sir Thomas Browne,[63] Milius, who thought that perhaps it

[56] Hakewill, *op. cit.*, pt. i, pp 2-4.

[57] Le Clerc, *op. cit.*, pp. 18-23, and as quoted by *An Universal History, from the Earliest Account of Time to the Present* (Dublin, 1744), vol. i, p. 55.

[58] Bochart, *op. cit.*, vol. i, *Geographia Sacra*, preface, map and *Dissertatio De Paradiso Terrestri*, by Stephen Morinus from Bochart's notes, pp. 9-28, and *Paradisi Terrestris Situs Juxta Sam. Bochartum*, pp. 29, 30.

[59] Huettius, *De Situ Paradisi Terrestris*, quoted and rejected by Le Clerc, *op. cit.*, pp. 18-23.

[60] Beaumont, *op. cit.*, pp. 137-142, 174. That had been Mersenne's solution of the difficulties with the site of Paradise and with the four rivers. Mersenne, *Qvaestiones Celeberrimae in Genesim* (Paris, 1623), cols. 1135-1144, 1171-1180.

[61] Buffon, *op. cit.*, vol. i, p. 238.

[62] Raleigh, *The History of the World* (Edinburgh, 1820), vol. i, pp. 71-140.

[63] Browne, *op. cit.*, vol. ii, p. 121.

extended far enough to include Judea,[64] Warren,[65] Woodward,[66] Whiston,[67] the *Universal History* [68] and Shuckford.[69] La Peyrère located it in Arabia Felix because it was bounded by the Tigris-Euphrates rivers.[70]

After the creation of man, a primary necessity was language. A few authors felt that speech was gradually developed as there was need, but almost all agreed that it was an innate gift of Adam or that he and Eve were taught by God or by some angel. The questions arose as to which tongue was the earliest and as to whether any survived the confusion of tongues at Babel. On the whole it was believed that Noah, if he was still alive, or Heber and Peleg, if their grandfather had died, were too righteous to have associated themselves with so impious a task as the construction of a tower that should reach to heaven. Therefore their language was unaltered. On this basis argued all except the few who thought that all memory of the original

[64] Milius, *De Origine Animalium, et Migratione Populorum* (Geneva, 1667), pp. 18, 19, 21, 22.

[65] Warren, *op. cit.*, pp. 130-137, 149-154; Warren, *Some Reflections upon the Short Consideration Of the Defence of the Exceptions against the Theory of the Earth* (London, 1692), p. 43; Warren, *Geologia* (London, 1690), pp. 262-268, 285-288.

[66] Woodward, *An Essay toward a Natural History of the Earth: and Terrestrial Bodies* (London, 1695), p. 266.

[67] Whiston, *A New Theory of the Earth* (Cambridge, 1708), pp. 118-121, 232, 334, 347, 348, though he thought that it was at the northern instead of the southern boundary of Assyria.

[68] *An Universal History, from the Earliest Account of Time to the Present* (Dublin, 1744), vol. i, pp. 56, 57, whereto was added an account of all the places assigned to Paradise by various authorities, *ibid.*, vol. i, pp. 53-57.

[69] Shuckford, *op. cit.*, vol. i, pp. 68-70; Shuckford, *The Creation and Fall of Man* (London, 1753), pp. 148-154.

[70] La Peyrère, *op. cit.*, *Systema Theologicvm, ex Praeadamitarvm Hypothesi*, p. 128.

language was lost. Throughout the seventeenth century and with less unanimity even to the end of the eighteenth, though gradually the problem fell into desuetude, the orthodox and overwhelmingly held opinion asserted that Hebrew was the primitive tongue.[71]   Raleigh, who himself accepted the tradition of Hebrew,[72] Kircher,[73] Hakewill,[74] Stillingfleet [75] and Shuckford [76] narrated the tradition of an attempt by an Egyptian king to solve the problem by scientific means.   He permitted two children to grow up fed by goats without hearing any human words.   Since after several

[71] Draper, *History of the Conflict between Religion and Science* (New York and London, 1928), p. 186; White (Andrew), *A History of the Warfare of Science with Theology in Christendom* (New York and London, 1910), vol. ii, pp. 182-187, 192, 193, who quoted the names, works and words of many theologians in support of Hebrew priority, including Stephen Guichard.   In 1606 Guichard attempted to derive the words of all other languages from the Hebrew.   His chief difficulty was in the transfer from Hebrew to the Aryan group; but he accomplished this finally by the free addition, subtraction or inversion of letters, which he claimed was justified by the fact that the Hebrews wrote from right to left while the Greeks and all others wrote from left to right.   Others who affirmed the priority of Hebrew were as follows : Mersenne, *op. cit.*, col. 1200; Bochart, *op. cit.*, vol. i, *Geographia Sacra*, cols. 38, 50-52; Gale, *The Covrt of the Gentiles* (Oxford and London, 1670-1677), vol. i, pt. i, bk. i, pp. 51-85, who throughout derived not merely language but all Gentile knowledge from the Hebrews; Kircher, *Turris Babel* (Amsterdam, 1679), especially pp. 11, 54, 107, 122, 123, 131, 132, 148-152, 164-171, 193-195, though he added that an imitation of letters by the Israelites from the Canaanites was much more probable than the reverse, *ibid.*, p. 186; and, when qualified by the addition of the word probably, Browne, *op. cit.*, vol. ii, pp. 91-95, vol. iii, pp. 223, 224; Hale, *op. cit.*, pp. 162, 163, who declared that some erroneously thought that the primitive tongue was Samaritan, Scythian or Chinese.

[72] Raleigh, *op. cit.*, vol. ii, pp. 120, 121, vol. iii, p. 428.

[73] Kircher, *op. cit.*, pp. 135, 136.

[74] Hakewill, *op. cit.*, pt. i, p. 6.

[75] Stillingfleet, *Origines Sacrae* (London, 1709), pt. i, p. 26.

[76] Shuckford, *The Sacred and Profane History of the World Connected* (Philadelphia, 1824), vol. i, p. 85.

years their vocabulary was found to consist of the term *Beccus,* which resembled the Phrygian word for bread, he decided that in that tribe he had found both the earliest tongue and the descendants of the first men. On the same basis Goropius Becanus reached a different conclusion and declared that low Dutch was the original tongue. Heylyn said that Becanus's assertion was in favor of high Dutch.[77] Webb, who wrote a book to prove that Chinese was the primitive language, denied the claims of both Hebrew and Dutch as mere patriotic tradition;[78] and Butler ridiculed the suggestion of Dutch.[79] The supposition that Chinese was the original tongue was based not only on the high civilization attributed to the race, on their great numbers, on their traditions of antiquity, but also on the hypothesis that after the flood Noah made his way to China, which had perhaps been his home before the catastrophe, and peopled it with his descendants.[80] Hale called this doctrine " a novel Conceit." [81] Naturally the later progeny of Noah retained their language, since they did not share in the sin or mistake at Babel; and their superior culture was due to the fact that they were instructed by the patriarch himself rather than by his sons. Shuckford thought the suggestion plausible, although he added that the primitive tongue might be Hebrew or Chaldean, which he called the same thing.[82] Later he denied that Hebrew was the primitive tongue.[83]

[77] Heylyn, *op. cit.,* bk. i, p. 28. Probably this is an adaptation of the story by Herodotus about Psammeticus. Herodotus, *History* (London and New York, 1921), bk. i, ch. ii.

[78] Webb, *op. cit.,* especially pp. 42, 43.

[79] Butler, *op. cit.,* pt. i, canto i, p. 13.

[80] Webb, *op. cit.* This thesis appealed to Whiston, *cf. supra,* pp. 111, 112.

[81] Hale, *op. cit.,* p. 163.

[82] Shuckford, *op. cit.,* vol. i, pp. 81, 82, 88-91.

[83] Shuckford, *The Creation and Fall of Man* (London, 1753), note p. 28.

Bishop Wilkins declared that the language, though Hebrew, was not the pure Hebrew of the Bible, which was not sufficiently versatile for ordinary converse.[84]   An important argument against Hebrew was presented by Heylyn [85] and by Le Clerc.[86]   With considerable Scriptural justification they asserted that Hebrew was a Canaanitish tongue acquired by Abraham after he had left home and dwelt in the land of Canaan.   The *Universal History* gave a long list of languages whose claim to priority had been suggested, including various Oriental ones, Armenian, Celtic, Coptic, Greek, Teutonic and Chinese, and ended with the wise conclusion that all claims were invalid and vain.[87]

The decision as to the date when writing was first invented was not so easily reached as that concerning the original tongue.   In the first place, there was a tradition that Seth had prepared two pillars, one of brick and one of stone, on which he had inscribed much knowledge, especially of astronomy, and the prophecy of the earth's future destruction by water and by fire.   Moreover, if Adam was created perfect and knew whatever was advantageous to man, he must have had knowledge of so important a matter infused into him at once by God or must have been taught it by some angel.   On the other hand, some argued that the writing by God on the tables of stone was the means of instructing mankind.   John Johnson, a vicar of some repute, thought that the forty days' retreat of Moses into Mt. Sinai could have no explanation except as an interval for his in-

---

[84] Wilkins, *op. cit.*, pt. iii, pp. 174, 175, 178, *Abstract of the Essay Towards a Real Character, and a Philosophical Language*, pt. i, chaps. i, iii, v.

[85] Heylyn, *op. cit.*, introduction, pp. 7, 15, bk. iii, p. 60.

[86] Le Clerc, *op. cit.*, Preliminary Dissertation *De Lingua Hebraica*.

[87] *An Universal History, from the Earliest Account of Time to the Present* (Dublin, 1744), vol. i, pp. 151-154.

struction in writing. Since, however, Moses before he
reached the mountain of the law was commanded to inscribe
in a book God's decree against Amalek, the vicar reconciled
the two facts by the declaration that the tables were already
written at the time when Moses was tending sheep in the
vicinity and that he had free access to them but was not
permitted to remove them from their place of concealment.[88]
Kircher was convinced that Adam was the author of letters,[89]
while Beattie, who probably agreed, called that the opinion
of some.[90] Wilkins declared that the agreement was general;
but he compromised by the declaration that the present
Hebrew alphabet was not original. All other letters were
derived from the ancient Hebrew.[91] Webb's reconciliation
was slightly different. Adam, because he was created perfect, must have known letters; but they were presumably
hieroglyphic. Moses received on the tables of stone the first
alphabetical letters.[92] Beattie's judgment as to the priority
of the two types of writing was the opposite of Webb's. He
asserted that, since hieroglyphics implied quaintness and
witticism and were less in accord with the primitive simplic-
ity and wisdom, they were a later development.[93] Camerarius seems to have agreed with him.[94] Gale [95] declared that a

[88] Johnson, quoted by White (Andrew), *op. cit.*, vol. ii, p. 197.

[89] Kircher, *op. cit.*, pp. 123, 162; Kircher, *Arca Noë* (Amsterdam, 1675), pp. 5, 204, 205.

[90] Beattie, *The Theory of Language* (London, 1788), especially p. 110.

[91] Wilkins, *op. cit.*, *An Abstract of the Essay Towards a Real Char-acter, and a Philosophical Language*, pt. i, chap. iii, secs. 1, 5, pp. 176, 177, chap. v, secs. 1, 2, p. 178.

[92] Webb, *op. cit.*, pp. 147-150.

[93] Beattie, *op. cit.*, especially pp. 110, 111.

[94] Camerarius, *Dissertationes Taurinenses* (?) (Tübingen, 1712), p. 304, quoted with disapproval by Woodward, *A Supplement & Continuation of The Essay towards a Natural History of the Earth* (London, 1726), pt. ii, p. 160.

[95] Gale, *op. cit.*, vol. i, pt. i, bk. i, pp. 55-58.

knowledge of letters came with the law of Moses, who as
Mercury or Theuth taught them to the Egyptians, but he
likewise quoted Horn [96] with apparent approval for the statement that the first mention of letters was on Seth's pillars.
Burnet was confident that they were known to Job or to his
compatriots, and therefore antedated Moses.[97]   Writing preceded the flood according to Shuckford,[98] Brouwer,[99] Beattie [100] and Raleigh,[101] the last of whom despairingly asserted
that it was invented " by Seth or Enos, or by whom else
God knows ".[102]   On the other hand, the *Universal History*
declared that the knowledge was probably not antediluvian; [103] and Woodward, that its discovery did not even occur immediately after the deluge.[104]

The question as to whether the earliest men ate flesh or
whether its use was forbidden before the flood, although
skins and wools were used for clothing and domestic animals
were sacrificed, was generally settled by the conclusion that
it was not allowed.   Shuckford declared that all agreed to
this,[105] and the *Universal History* thought that the prohibi-

[96] Gale, *op. cit.*, vol. i, pt. ii, bk. i, p. 8.

[97] Burnet, *Doctrina Antiqua de Rerum Originibus* (London, 1729, 1736),
Archaeologiae Philosophicae, pt. i, pp. 40, 43.

[98] Shuckford, *The Sacred and Profane History of the World Connected* (Philadelphia, 1824), vol. i, bk. iv, especially pp. 135, 141-143.

[99] Brouwer, *Dissertatio. Philologico-Theologica. Qua. Disquiritur. Unde.
Moses. Res. in. Libro. Geneseos. Descriptas. Didicerit.* (Leyden, 1753).

[100] Beattie, *op. cit.*, especially p. 110.

[101] Raleigh, *op. cit.*, vol. ii, pp. 491-493.

[102] *Ibid.*, vol. ii, p. 492.

[103] *An Universal History, from the Earliest Account of Time to the
Present* (Dublin, 1744), vol. i, p. 108.

[104] Woodward, *An Essay toward a Natural History of the Earth: and
Terrestrial Bodies* (London, 1695), p. 67.   Concerning the age of writing *cf.* also *supra*, p. 144.

[105] Shuckford, *op. cit.*, vol. i, pp. 72, 73, 77; Shuckford, *The Creation
and Fall of Man* (London, 1753), pp. cxviii-cxxiv, 282, 283.

tion was probable.[106] Jordan affirmed that although Lamech killed animals with his arrows for their skins he partook of neither flesh nor wine.[107] Grew said that meat was forbidden but that perhaps the law was broken by the descendants of Cain,[108] and Webb declared that at least the Sethians were vegetarians.[109] According to Burnet the antediluvian world was so fertile and the air and other conditions so favorable that the use of flesh was unnecessary. After the deluge the general deterioration compelled the removal of this restriction and greater latitude in diet.[110] Le Clerc, besides stating that meat was forbidden, declared that early man was probably vegetarian because the cooking of flesh would have been too difficult for him.[111] On the other hand, Hakewill before 1635 denied the illegality of meat before Noah's time,[112] while Kircher,[113] Catoir [114] and Duguet and d'Asfeld [115] declared that flesh was not forbidden and was eaten before and after the deluge. Nevertheless, the opinion in favor of the proposition that at least the Sethians refrained from meat before the flood was dominant.[116]

[106] *An Universal History, from the Earliest Account of Time to the Present* (Dublin, 1744), vol. i, pp. 108*, 114.

[107] Jordan, *op. cit.*, pp. 106-109.

[108] Grew, *Cosmologia Sacra* (London, 1701), pp. 227, 229, 231-233.

[109] Webb, *op. cit.*, p. 5.

[110] Burnet, *The Sacred Theory of the Earth* (London, 1722), vol. i, bk. ii.

[111] Le Clerc, *op. cit.*, pp. 15, 77, who quoted Grotius as another believer in the antediluvian prohibition of flesh food.

[112] Hakewill, *op. cit.*, pt. i, p. 2.

[113] Kircher, *op. cit.*, pp. 170-173.

[114] Catoir, *op. cit.*, sec. xiii.

[115] Duguet and d'Asfeld, *op. cit.*, pp. 252-256.

[116] It was accepted by the following in addition to those already named: Browne, *op. cit.*, vol. i, pp. 346-348; Bossuet, *Discours sur l'histoire universelle* (Paris, 1850), pp. 8, 130, 131; Warren, *op. cit.*, p. 282; Whiston, *op. cit.*, pp. 249, 250, 363; Cockburn, *op. cit.*, pp. 22-24, 116, 136, 143-158, 169-171. Draper, *op. cit.*, p. 185, spoke of it as the prevailing opinion.

This discussion has attempted to show the vast change in orientation from 1600 to 1800. New discoveries and observations transformed man's conception of the universe and its history. Not only had the heliocentric system superseded the gocentric, and the Newtonian theory of gravitation Descartes's vortices; but also the relation of the Bible to knowledge had been reinterpreted so that the view had come to be generally accepted that the Bible taught religious and moral truth rather than scientific. Both Catholics and Protestants affirmed this distinction. Most difficulties inherent in the Mosaic account of creation, when compared with the record inscribed in the earth itself, had been met by the simple device of lengthening the time involved in creation. The necessity for such readjustment was heightened by the altered attitude towards the method of creation. On the whole, the tendency in 1600 was to accept direct catastrophic action by an anthropomorphic God, while two hundred years later the idea of miraculous intervention in the production of the world and in its destruction had been largely discarded except for the preliminary production of matter, the creation of man and perhaps of other organic beings; instead of this idea, the search for appropriate secondary causes engaged the minds of theologians and of scientists. During the same period the Aristotelian doctrines, which, fostered by the universities, had lingered into the seventeenth century, and the marvellous tales of natural history collected by Pliny and other early scientists were discredited in the light of nature study assisted by the superior tools of the new age. The two centuries displayed the manner in which great additions have been incorporated into the sum of knowledge and in which the traditional, religious account has been brought into peaceful and harmonious relationship with the new, scientific doctrines.

BIBLIOGRAPHY

WORKS FIRST PRODUCED BEFORE 1600

Albertus Magnus: *Opera qvae hactenvs haberi potvervnt sub T. Turco, N. Rodulphio, J. B. de Marinis in lucem edita; studio et labore Petri Jammy* (Leyden, 1651), 21 vols.

Aristotle: *Works Translated into English under the Editorship of W. D. Ross* (Oxford), 11 vols.

——, *Physica, De Caelo, De Generatione et Corruptione,* vol. ii (1930).

——, *Meteorologica, De Mundo, De Anima, Parva Naturalia, De Spiritu,* vol. iii (1931).

Copernicus, Nicholas: *De Revolvtionibvs Orbivm Caelestivm Libri VI. Ex Avctoris Avtographo Recvdi Cvravit Societas Copernicana Thorvnensis. Accedit Georgii Ioachimi Rhetici De Libris Revolvtionvm Narratio Prima* (Thorn, 1873), xxx, 494 pp.

Herodotus: *History: With an English Translation by A. D. Godley* (London and New York, 1921).

Postel, William: *De Cosmographica Disciplina et Signorum coelestium vera configuratione Libri II* (Leyden, 1636), 2 parts, 172, 72 pp.; earlier ed., 1561.

——, *De Universitate Libri duo: In quibus Astronomiae, Doctrinaeve Coelestis Compendium . . . Terrae aptatum, & secundum Coelestis influxus ordinem, praecipuarumque Originum rationem totus orbis Terrae quatenus innotuit, cum Regnorum temporibus exponitur. Sed ante omneis alias orbis parteis Terra Sancta summo, hoc est, amplissimo compendio describitur. cui Gallia ob primarium orbis nomen, & ius substituitur, eo quod ambae toti orbi legem sunt daturae. Secundus liber Tabulas Ptolemaei explicat, quem Ptolemeolum vocat* (Leyden, 1635), 261 pp., 3d ed.; 2nd ed., 1563.

BOOKS AND PAMPHLETS 1600-1800

Adams, George: *Lectures on Natural and Experimental Philosophy, considered in it's present state of Improvement Describing, in a familiar and easy manner, the Principal Phenomena of Nature; and shewing, that they all co-operate in displaying the Goodness, Wisdom, and Power of God* (London, 1794), 5 vols., the last of which contains plates to illustrate the others. Vol. iv, 576 pp., discusses astronomy, electricity, magnetism and meteorology.

468   BIBLIOGRAPHY

Addison, *The Spectator* (London and New York, 1898), 8 vols.

Alsted, John Henry: *Cursus philosophici encyclopaedia libris xxvii complectens universae philosophiae methodum serie praeceptorum regularum* etc. (Herborn, 1620), 32 pp., 552 fols.

——, *Methodus Admirandorum Mathematicorum Novem libris exhibens universam Mathesin,* 3d ed. (Herborn, 1641), 456 pp. including a fifth book on Uranoscopia, pp. 169-248, and a sixth on Geography, pp. 249-315.

——, *Physica Harmonica, quattuor libellis methodice proponens I. Physicam Mosaicam. II. Physicam Hebraeorum. III. Physicam Peripateticam. IV. Physicam Chemicam.* Followed by *Physica Poetica Harmonica: hoc est, Consensus poëtarum & physicorum* (Herborn, 1642), 281 pp.

Bacon, Francis: *Works* (Boston, undated), ed. by James Spedding, Robert L. Ellis and Douglas Heath. 15 vols. Almost all first published between 1597 and 1625.

Beattie, James: *The Theory of Language. In Two Parts. Part I. Of the Origin and General Nature of Speech. Part II. Of Universal Grammar. A New Edition, enlarged and corrected* (London, 1788), 390 pp.

Beaumont, John, Jr.: *Considerations On a Book, Entituled The Theory of the Earth. Publisht some Years since by the Learned Dr. Burnet* (London, 1692-3), 187 pp.

Bentley, Richard: *The Folly and Unreasonableness of Atheism Demonstrated from The Advantage and Pleasure of a Religious Life, The Faculties of Humane Souls, The Structure of Animate Bodies, & The Origin and Frame of the World: In Eight Sermons Preached at the Lecture Founded by The Honourable Robert Boyle, Esquire; In the First Year, 1692* (London, 1699), 4th ed. corrected, 278 pp.

——, *Remarks Upon a late Discourse of Free-Thinking: in a Letter to F. H. D. D. by Phileleutherus Lipsiensis* (London, 1713), 2d ed., 2 parts, 85 and 82 pp. respectively. Pub. anon. in answer to the anon. discourse by Anthony Collins in 1713.

Blackmore, Sir Richard: *Creation; A Philosophical Poem. In Seven Books.* Pp. 75-251 of *The British Poets. Including Translations. In one hundred volumes.* Vol. xxviii, *Smith, Blackmore* (Chiswick, 1822). The same volume gives *Blackmore's Life by Samuel Johnson,* pp. 53-72.

Blancanus, Joseph: *Sphaera Mvndi, sev Cosmographia, Demonstratiua, ac facili Methodo tradita: in qva totivs mvndi fabrica, vna' cvm novis, Tychonis, Kepleri, Galilaei, aliorumq; Astronomorum Adinuentis continetur. Accessere I. Breuis introductio ad Geographiam. II. Apparatus ad Mathematicarum studium. III. Echometria, idest Geometrica traditio de Echo. Authore Iosepho Blancano Bononiensi è Societate Iesv, Mathematicarum in Gymnasio Parmensi professore. Ad Illustrissimum, ac Nobilissimum Petrvm Franciscvm Malaspinam aedificiorvm marchionem* (Bologna, 1620), 445 pp.

Bochart, Samuel: *Opera Omnia. Hoc est Phaleg, Chanaan, et Hierozoicon. Quibus accesserunt Dissertationes variae ad illustrationem sacri codicis aliorumque monumentorum veterum. Praemittitur vita auctoris à Stephano Morino descripta Et Paradisi terrestris delineatio ad mentem Bocharti. Indices denique accurati & mappae Geographicae suis locis insertae sunt. In quibus omnibus digerendis atque exornandis operam posuerunt Viri Clarissimi Johannes Leusden & Petrus de Villemandy* (Leyden, 1712), 4th ed., 3 vols., folio. Vol. i contains various short papers and the *Geographia Sacra, seu Phaleg et Chanaan,* 1st pub. Caen, 1646, 1651, 44 pages, followed by 1224 cols.; vols. ii and iii, *Hierozoicon, sive Bipartitum Opus de Animalibus S. Scripturae,* cols. 1094 and 888 with preface and indexes 133 pp., 1st ed., London, 1663.
Third edition of the preceding, apparently the same even to the pagination, Leyden, 1692.

Bossuet, Jacques Bénigne: *Discours sur l'histoire universelle. Édition conforme à celle de 1700, troisième et dernière édition revue par l'auteur* (Paris, 1850), 429 pp.; 1st ed. between 1670 and 1677, as a textbook for the son of Louis XIV.

Boyle, Robert: *Opera Omnia, Nunc primùm in unum Corpus redacta, ac tres in Tomos distributa: Accuratè recognita, & à mendis repurgata: Quorum Catalogum versa Pagina Exhibet. Cum Indicibus necessariis, multisque Figuris Aeneis* (Venice, 1697), 3 vols., 1030 pp., 903 pp., 845 pp., besides prefaces and indexes.

Brouwer, Peter: *Dissertatio. Philologico-Theologica. Qua. Disquiritur. Unde. Moses. Res. in. Libro. Geneseos. Descriptas. Didicerit. Quam. ...in Ill. Acad. Ludg. Bat. ...Publico. Examini. Submittit. Petrus Brouwer. ...Auctor. et. Defendens. March 7* (Leyden, 1753), 23 pp.

Browne, Sir Thomas: *Works* (London, 1888-1890), 3 vols., pp. lxxxii, 463, 563, 552. Vol. i contains the life of Browne by Dr. Johnson and the first four books of *Pseudodoxia Epidemica* or *Vulgar Errors*; vol. ii contains the last three books of the *Pseudodoxia Epidemica,* the *Religio Medici* and *The Garden of Cyrus.*

Buffon, George-Louis Leclerc, comte de: *Oeuvres Complètes* (Paris, 1831-2), 26 vols., chiefly the *Histoire naturelle.*

——, Premier Discours. *De la manière d'étudier et de traiter l'histoire naturelle,* vol. i, pp. 47-102.

——, Second Discours. *Histoire et théorie de la terre,* vol. i, pp. 103-167.

——, *Preuves de la théorie de la terre,* vol. i, p. 168–vol. iii, p. 71, followed by a discussion of the four elements, pp. 75-187.

——, *Recherches sur le refroidissement de la terre et des planètes*, vol. iv, pp. 236-380.

——, *Fondements des recherches précédentes sur la température des planètes*, vol. iv, pp. 380-425.

——, *Des époques de la nature*, vol. v; 1st pub., 1779.

Burnet, Thomas: *Doctrina Antiqua de Rerum Originibus: or, an Inquiry into the Doctrine of the Philosophers of all Nations, Concerning the Original of the World.... Made English from the Latin Original: By Mr. Mead* (Richard) *and Mr. Foxton* (Thomas) (London, 1729, 1736).

——, *Life of Dr. Burnet*, 39 pp.

——, *A Letter to Mr. E. Curll, Bookseller* (by C. B.—perhaps Charles Blount), xxi pp.

——, *An Essay On the Use of Reason in Religion*, pp. xxii-xxxii.

——, *Archaeologiae Philosophicae: or, the Philosophical Principles of Things*, pp. viii, 246, followed by *Remarks*, pp. 247-275.

——, *Dr. Burnet's Theory of the Visible World; By way of Commentary on his own Theory of the Earth. Being The Second Part of his Archaeologiae Philosophicae, faithfully Translated; With Remarks thereon. By Mr. Foxton.* 96 pp.

——, *Archaeologiae Philosophicae: or, the Ancient Doctrine Concerning the Originals of Things ... Part I. Being a Critique on the Mosaic Creation*, pp. 90, vi.

——, *An Appendix Concerning the Modern Brachmans in the Indies, Together with their generally received Opinions*, Burnet, 9 pp.

——, Appendix—*Letter by Blount* (on immortality), pp. 10-18.

——, *Remarks* (on *Archaeologiae Philosophicae*, by Foxton), pp. 19-104.

——, *M. De la Jonchere, The Immobility of the Earth Demonstrated. By Reasons Drawn from the Established Rules of Physics, Mechanics, and Geometry*, 32 pp.

——, *The Sacred Theory of the Earth: Containing an Account of the Original of the Earth, And of all the General Changes which it hath already undergone, or is to undergo, till the Consummation of all Things* (London, 1722), 2 vols., 456, 570 pp., 5th ed.; 1st English ed., 1684-1689.

——, *Telluris Theoria Sacra, Originem & Mutationes Generales Orbis Nostri, Quas aut jam subiit, aut olim subiturus est, complectens. Accedunt Archaeologiae Philosophicae, Sive Doctrina Antiqua de Rerum Originibus* (Amsterdam, 1694), 474 pp.

Burton, Robert: *The Anatomy of Melancholy* (London, 1920), 1st ed., Oxford, 1621, 3 vols.

Butler, Joseph (Bishop of Durham): *The Analogy of Religion Natural and Revealed to the Constitution and Course of Nature* (Oxford, 1897), ed. by W. E. Gladstone, 357 pp.; 1st ed., 1736.

Butler, Samuel: *Hudibras* (London and New York, 1886), 1st stolen ed.
of part i, 1662; 1st correct ed., 1663. Pt. ii, a forgery, 1663; by
Butler, 1664. Pt. iii, 1678. 286 pp.

Calmet, Dom Augustin: *Dissertations sur les apparitions des anges, des
démons & des esprits. Et sur les revenans et vampires. De Hongrie,
de Boheme, de Moravie & de Silesie* (Paris, 1746), xxxvi, 500 pp.

de Castelet: *Lettre de M. de Castelet à Monsieur Mallement de Messange
sur les deux nouveaux systhémes qu'ils ont inventez* (1679 ?), 8 pp.

Catcott, Alexander: *A Treatise on the Deluge, Containing I. Remarks
on the Lord Bishop of Clogher's Account of that Event. II. A full
Explanation of the Scripture History of it. III. A Collection of
all the Principal Heathen Accounts. IV. Natural Proofs of the
Deluge, deduced from a great Variety of Circumstances, on and in
the terraqueous Globe* (London, 1761), 296 pp.

Second ed., considerably enlarged (London, 1768), viii, 423 pp.

Catoir, John Nicolas: *Disputatio Theologica de Arca Noachi et Diluvio
quam . . . Publice ventilandam proponit Johannes Nicolaus Catoir*
(Gröningen, 1704), 50 sections.

Clayton, Robert (Bishop of Clogher): *A Vindication of the Histories
of the Old and New Testament in answer to the objections of the
late Lord Bolingbroke* (Dublin, 1752, 1754).

Cockburn, Patrick: *An Enquiry into the Truth and Certainty of the
Mosaic Deluge. Wherein The Arguments of the Learned Isaac
Vossius, and others, for a Topical Deluge are examined; and Some
Vulgar Errors, relating to that Grand Catastrophe, are discover'd*
(London, 1750), xvi, 355 pp.

Colbert, Jean Baptiste: *Regi Armis Omnia Expugnanti Architecturam
Militarem Sapientia Omnia Constituenti Totius Mundi Constitutionem
Belli Pacisque Arbitro Bellatricem Pacificamque Mathesin* (1668),
20 pp., of which pp. 3-13 are entitled *Positiones Mathematicae de
Mvndi Systemate*, and pp. 14-19 *Positiones Mathematicae ex Archi-
tectvra Militari.*

Collins, Anthony: *A Discourse of Free-thinking, Occasion'd by The Rise
and Growth of a Sect call'd Free-Thinkers* (London, 1713), vi, 178
pp. Anonymously published.

Comenius, John Amos: *Naturall Philosophie Reformed by Divine Light:
or, A Synopsis of Physicks: . . . Exposed To the censure of those
that are lovers of Learning, and desire to be taught of God. Being
a view of the World in generall, and of the particular Creatures
therein conteined; grounded upon Scripture Principles. With a briefe
Appendix touching the Diseases of the Body, Mind, and Soul; with
their generall Remedies* (London, 1651), 256 pp. preceded by a long
but unpaged preface.

Cowper, William: *The Poems* (New York, ?), 491 pp.

Cudworth, Ralph, D. D.: *The True Intellectual System of the Universe: The First Part; Wherein All the Reason and Philosophy of Atheism is Confuted, and Its Impossibility Demonstrated. With A Discourse concerning the True Notion of the Lord's Supper; and Two Sermons, on I John II. 3, 4. and I Cor. XV. 57.* (London, 1743), 2d ed., the 1st ed. having been pub. 1678. 2 vols., xl, 632, 633-899 pp.

Currie, William: *Disquisitio Philosophica Inauguralis, De vero Mundi Systemate* (Edinburgh, 1742), 15 pp.

Danforth, Samuel: *An Astronomical Description of the late Comet or Blazing Star As it appeared in New-England in the 9th, 10th, 11th, and in the beginning of the 12th Moneth, 1664. Together With a brief Theological Application thereof* (Cambridge, 1665), 22 pp.
An English reprint with the addition to the title page of the fact that the comet was the first of the three visible in Europe (London, 1666), preface and 28 pp.

De Luc, Jean André, F. R. S., Prof. of Philosophy and Geology at Göttingen: *Letters on the Physical History of the Earth, addressed to Professor Blumenbach: containing Geological and Historical Proofs of the Divine Mission of Moses. . . . To which are prefixed Introductory Remarks and Illustrations; together with a vindication of the author's claims to original views respecting fundamental points in geology. By the Rev. Henry de la Fite* (London, 1831), 138 pp. of introductory remarks, 6 letters, 271 pp., appendix pp. 273-284. 1st pub., 1793-1795.

——, *Lettres physiques et morales sur l'histoire de la terre et de l'homme. Adressées a la Reine de la Grande Bretagne, par J. A. de Luc citoyen de Geneve, Lecteur de Sa Majesté* (The Hague and Paris, 1779-1780), 5 vols.

Derham, William: *Astro-Theology Or a Demonstration of the Being and Attributes of God, from a Survey of the Heavens. Illustrated with Copper Plates* (London, 1721) (4th ed.), lvi, 246 pp.

——, *Physico-Theology: or, a Demonstration of the Being and Attributes of God, from his Works of Creation. Being the Substance of Sixteen Sermons Preached in St. Mary-le-Bow-Church, London; At the Honourable Mr. Boyle's Lectures, in the Years 1711, and 1712. With large Notes, & many curious Observations* (London, 1742) (10th ed.), 444 pp. (8th ed., London, 1727).

Descartes, René: *A Discourse on Method* (London and Toronto, 1929).

——, *A Discourse on Method*, pp. 1-62.

——, *Meditations on the First Philosophy*, pp. 65-143.

——, *Principles of Philosophy*, pp. 147-228, scientific part much cut. Appendix and notes, pp. 229-254.

——, *Oeuvres* (Paris, 1824). Vol. iii contains *Les principes de la philosophie*, 526 pp., 10 plates, each with several figures; 1st pub., Amsterdam, 1644.

Dickinson, Edmund, M. D.: *Physica Vetus et Vera: sive Tractatus de Naturali Veritate Hexaemeri Mosaici. Per quem probatur in historia Creationis, tum Generationis universae methodum atque modum, tum verae Philosophiae principia, strictim atque breviter à Mose tradi* (Rotterdam, 1703), 333 pp. followed by 4 plans or figures and index.

Donck, Adrian Hubert vander: *Disputatio Theologica, de Divina Creatione Coelorum et Terrae in Principio. Ad Genes. Cap. I. Vers. I. Prima, Secunda, & Tertia* (Leyden, 1713), 9 theses or sections and 6 corollaries, followed by 3 pp. of eulogistic poetry. Unpaged but really 28 pp.

Duguet, Jacques Joseph & Asfeld, Joseph Vincent Bidel d': *Explication de l'ouvrage des six jours nouvelle édition. Augmentée du second sens du Pseaume CIII, & d'une table des matières. Par Messieurs des Abbéz Duguet & d'Asfeld* (Paris, 1740), pp. vi, 527, the first 260 treating of the *Explication*.

Eberwein, George Philip: *Hassāthath hannāhāsh haḳḳadhmōni ... Sive, De Seductione Serpentis Antiqui, qui primum Parentem nostrum ex horto Eden exulare fecit, Dissertatio, Ad illustrandum locum Gen. III. I. & seqq.* (Jena, 1675), 2 caps. divided into sections, unpaged but 30 pp.

Essay d'un nouveau systeme du monde (Paris, 1691), 16 pp.

Fienus, Thomas: *De Cometa Anni 1618, Dissertationes. Ejusdem Thomae Fieni Epistolico quaestio, An Verum sit Coelum moveri, et Terram quiescere?* (London, 1655). The letter gives about six pages of proof, largely from reason, of the earth's immobility.

Fludd, Robert: *Utriusque Cosmi Maioris scilicet et Minoris Metaphysica, Physica atque Technica Historia In duo Volumina secundum Cosmi differentiam diuis [um?] ... Tomus Primus De Macrocosmi Historia in duos tractatus diuisa. Quorum Primus de Metaphysico Macrocosmi et Creaturarum illius ortu. Physico Macrocosmi in generatione & corruptione progressu. Secundus de Arte Naturae simia in Macrocosmo producta & in eo nutrita & multiplicata, cujus filias praecipuas hîc anatomiâ vivâ recensuimus, nempe Arithmeticam. Musicam. Geometriam. Perspectivam. Artem Pictoriam. Artem Militarem. Motus. Temporis Scientiam. Cosmographiam. Astrologiam. Geomantiam* (Oppenheim, 1617), 788 pp. The second part, bound with the first seems really to have been the 2d ed., Frankfurt, 1624.

Fontenelle, Bernard le Bovier de: *Conversations on the Plurality of Worlds* (London, 1809), *Life and Writings of Fontenelle by Voltaire*, pp. 5-10; then *Six Evenings*, pp. 1-146.

——, *Entretiens sur la pluralité des mondes, augmentés des dialogues des morts* (Paris, 1821), pp. xvi, 410, of which the *Entretiens* fills the first 158. 1st ed., 1686.

Gadbury, John: *Thesaurus Astrologiae: or, an Astrological Treasury, Containing The choicest Mysteries of that Curious, but Abstruse Learning, relating to Physick. Being the Collections and Experiments of a Learned Physitian and Astrologer deceased, whose Name is not known. But for its singular benefit to all the Sons of Physick and Astrology is commended to the World. Non Multa, sed Multum* (London, 1674), 272 pp.

Gadroys, C.: *Le systeme du monde, selon les trois hypotheses, où conformement aux loix de la mechanique l'on explique dans la supposition du mouvement de la terre les apparences des astres, la fabrique du monde, la formation des planetes, la lumiere, la pesanteur, &c. Et cela par de nouvelles demonstrations* (Paris, 1675), 457 pp., dedicated by permission to the members of the Royal Académie des Sciences. Anon.

Gale, Theophilus: *The Covrt of the Gentiles: or A Discourse touching the Original of Human Literature, both Philologie and Philosophie, From the Scriptures & Jewish Church* (Oxford and London, 1670-1677), 2d ed. revised and enlarged, 2 vols.

Galilei, Galileo: *Dialogo . . . Doue ne i congressi di quattro giornate si discorre sopra i due massimi sistemi del mondo tolemaico, e copernicano; proponendo indeterminatamente le ragioni filisofiche, e naturali tanto per l'vna, quanto per l'altra parte* (Florence, 1632), 458 pp.

——, *Nuncius Sidereus*, in the *Archives néerlandaises* (The Hague, 1903), ser. 2, vol. 8, pp. 115-189.

Gassendi, Pierre: *Institutio Astronomica Juxta Hypotheses tam Veterum quàm Copernici & Tychonis . . . Editio ultima paulò ante mortem Auctoris recognita aucta & emendata* (Amsterdam, 1680), 309 pp., followed by eulogies of the author and elegies over his death. The *Institutio* takes 160 pp.; the rest gives other speeches and papers on similar subjects.

Glanvill, Joseph: *Saducismus Triumphatus: or, Full and Plain Evidence Concerning Witches and Apparitions. In Two Parts, The First treating of their Possibility, The Second of their Real Existence* (London, 1681), pp. 180, 328.

——, *Scepsis Scientifica: or, Confest Ignorance, the way to Science; In an Essay of The Vanity of Dogmatizing, and Confident Opinion. With A Reply to the Exceptions of the Learned Thomas Albius* (London, 1665), 184 pp.

——, *Scir$\frac{e}{i}$-tuum nihil est: or, The Authors Defence of The Vanity of Dogmatizing; Against the Exceptions of The Learned Tho. Albius In his Late Sciri* (London, 1665), 92 pp.

Glaser, John Adam: *Dissertationem de Variis Philosophorum Circa Principia Corporum Naturalium, praesertim Viventium Placitis, . . . P. P. M. Daniel Ringmacher, . . . Respondente Joh. Adamo Glasero* (Leipzig, 1688?), 68 pp.

Grew, Nehemiah, Fellow of the College of Physicians and of the Royal Society: *Cosmologia Sacra: or a Discourse of the Universe As it is the Creature and Kingdom of God. Chiefly Written, To Demonstrate the Truth and Excellency of the Bible; which contains the Laws of his Kingdom in this Lower World. In Five Books* (London, 1701), pp. xviii, 372.

Hakewill, George, D. D.: *An Apologie or Declaration of the Power and Providence of God in the Gouernment of the World. Consisting in an Examination and Censvre of the Common Errovr Tovching Natvres Perpetuall and Universall Decay, Divided into Six Bookes. Whereof The first treates of this pretended decay in generall, together with some preparatives thereunto. The second of the pretended decay of the Heavens and Elements, together with that of the Elementary bodies, man onely excepted. The third of the pretended decay of mankinde in regard of age and duration, of strength and stature, of arts and wits. The fourth of this pretended decay in matter of manners, together with a large proofe of the future consummation of the World from the testimonie of the Gentiles, and the use which we are to draw from the consideration thereof. The fifth and sixth are spent in answering Objections made since the second impression. The third Edition revised, and in sundry passages and whole Sections augmented by the Authour; besides the addition of two entire bookes not formerly published* (Oxford, 1635), pp. 606, 378, since book five begins at page 1 again.

Hale, Sir Matthew, Late Chief Justice of the Court of the King's Bench: *The Primitive Origination of Mankind, Considered and Examined According to The Light of Nature* (London, 1677), 380 pp.

Halhed, Nathaniel Brassey: *A Calculation on the Commencement of The Millennium, and a short reply to Dr. Horne's Pamphlet entituled, "Sound Argument, Dictated by Common Sense." Together with Cursory Observations on the "Age of Credulity". To which is added, an original letter from Mr. Brothers, to Philip Stephens, Esq. with his Answer. A Paper is subjoined, pointing out those parts of Mr. Brothers's Prophecies that have been already fulfilled* (London, 1795), 40 pp.

Halley, Edmund: "On the Circulation of the watery Vapours of the Sea, and the Origin of Springs", Royal Society of London: *Philosophical Transactions* (London, 1665-1933), no. 192, art. 4, 1690, pp. 468 *et seq.*

——, " On the cause of the Change in the Variation of the Magnetic Needle; with an Hypothesis of the Structure of the Internal Parts of the Earth ", *ibid.*, no. 195, art. 3, 1692, pp. 563 *et seq.*

Harris, John: *Remarks On some Late Papers, Relating to the Universal Deluge: And to the Natural History of the Earth* (London, 1697), 270 pp.

Harris, Joseph: *The Description and Use of the Globes and the Orrery. To which is prefix'd, By Way of Introduction, A Brief Account of The Solar System* (London, 1740), 5th ed., viii, 190 pp., of which the first 34 are an introduction about the solar system and the stars.

Hempel, Alb. Ephraim: *Consilium Dei Circa Hominis Creationem, ex Gen. I, 26. deductum* (Wittenberg, 1704), 28 pp. Speech delivered at Wittenberg, 1697.

Hervey, James: *Meditations and Contemplations. In Two Volumes. Containing. Vol I. Meditations among the Tombs; And Reflections on a Flower-Garden. Vol. II. Contemplations on the Night; And Contemplations on the Starry Heavens.* Followed by *A Winter-piece, and a Descant on Creation.* 14th ed. (Dublin, 1767), xxiii, 169, 252 pp.; 1st ed., 1746?

Heylyn: *Cosmography in Four Books. Containing the Chorography and History of the Whole World, and all the Principal Kingdoms, Provinces, Seas, and Isles thereof. With an Accurate and an Approved Index of all the Kingdoms, Provinces, Countries, Inhabitants, People, Cities, Mountains, Rivers, Seas, Islands, Forts, Bays, Capes, Forests, &c. of any Remarque in the whole World* (London, 1674), 923 pp. in reality, though the pagination is irregular and returns twice to page 1 and once to page 139. Edition revised and corrected by the author and published posthumously. 1st ed. about 1648.

——, Μικρόκοσμος *a Little Description of the Great World* (Oxford, 1633), 808 pp., 6th ed.; 1st ed., 1621, preceded by lectures on cosmography at Oxford.

Heyn, John: *Specimen Cometologiae Sacrae, Dvabus Dissertationibvs propositvm, qvarvm altera De Dilvvio per Cometam Orbi Indvcto: Altera De Praelvdio Ivdicii Extremi Orbi per Cometas exhibendo agit.* By Balthasar Fridericus Kunstmann and John Gotthilf Werder (Leipzig, 1742), 64 pp.

——, *Versuch Einer Betrachtung über Die Cometen, die Sündflut und das Vorspiel des jüngsten Gerichts, Nach astronomischen Gründen und der heiligen Schrift angestellet* (Berlin and Leipzig, 1742), 328 pp.

Hobbes, Thomas: *Leviathan or the Matter, Forme & Power of a Commonwealth, Ecclesiasticall and Civill The Text edited by A. R. Waller* (Cambridge, 1904), xx, 532 pp. A reprint of the first edition (London, 1651).

Holbach, Paul Henri Thiry, Baron d': *The System of Nature or, Laws of the Moral and Physical World* (New York, 1835), x, 362 pp. Notes by Diderot. 1st ed., anon., 1770 or 1771.

Horn, George: *Arca Noae. Sive Historia Imperiorum et Regnorum à Condito orbe ad nostra Tempora* (Leyden, 1666), 548 pp.

Horrebow, Peter: *Clavis Astronomiae* in *Works* (1740), 1st ed., 1725.

Huettius, Peter Daniel: *Censvra Philosophiae Cartesianae* (Helmestadt, 1690), 128 pp.

Hutchinson, John: *Moses's Principia. Of the Invisible Parts of Matter; of Motion; of Visible Forms; and of their Dissolution, and Reformation* (London, 1724), 100 pp., anon.

Hutton, James: "Theory of the Earth; or, an Investigation of the Laws observable in the Composition, Dissolution, and Restoration of Land upon the globe", Royal Society of Edinburgh: *Transactions* (Edinburgh, 1788), vol. i, pp. 209-304.

——, *Theory of the Earth, with Proofs and Illustrations. In four parts* (Edinburgh? and London, 1795 and 1899), 3 vols.

Huygens, Christian: ΚΟΣΜΟΘΕΩΡΟΣ, *sive De Terris Coelestibus, earumque ornatu, conjecturae* (The Hague, 1698), 144 pp.

——, *Nouveau traité de la pluralité des mondes, où l'on prouve par des raisons philosophiques, que toutes les planètes sont habitées & cultivées comme notre terre* (Amsterdam, 1718), xxxvi, 276 pp.

Jordan, William: *The Creation of the World, with Noah's Flood* (London, 1827), viii, 186 pp., written in Cornish in 1611, with an English translation by John Keigwin.

Kant, Immanuel: *Allgemeine Naturgeschichte und Theorie des Himmels oder Versuch von der Verfassung und dem mechanischen Ursprunge des ganzen Weltgebäudes nach Newtonischen Grundsätzen abgehandelt* (Leipzig, 1890), 101 pp.; 1st ed., 1755.

——, *Examination of the Question proposed by the Royal Academy of Sciences at Berlin for the prize of the current year: Whether the Earth has undergone an Alteration of its Axial Rotation*, translated by Hastie (Glasgow, 1900), 11 pp.; 1st ed., 1754.

——, *Universal Natural History and Theory of the Heavens; or An Essay on the Constitution and Mechanical Origin of the Whole Universe Treated according to Newton's Principles*, translated by Hastie (Glasgow, 1900), pp. 15-167.

Keill, John: *An Examination of Dr. Burnet's Theory of the Earth. Together with some remarks on Mr. Whiston's New Theory of the Earth* (Oxford, 1698), 224 pp.

Kepler, Johann: *Epitome Astronomiae Copernicanae Vsitatâ formâ Quaestionum & Responsionum conscripta, inque VII. Libros digesta, quorum tres hi priores sunt De Doctrina Sphaerica. Habes, amice lector, hac prima parte, praeter physicam accuratam explicationem Motus Terrae diurni, ortusq; ex eo circulorum Sphaerae, totam doctrinam Sphaericam nova & concinniori Methodo, auctiorem, additis Exemplis omnis generis Computationum Astronomicarum & Geographicarum, quae integrarum praeceptionum vim sunt complexa* (Frankfurt, 1635), 932 pp.

Kircher, Athanasius, Soc. Jesu: *Arca Noë, in tres libros digesta, quorum I. De rebus quae ante Diluvium, II. De iis, quae ipso Diluvio ejusque duratione, III. De iis, quae post Diluvium à Noëmo gesta sunt, Quae omnia novâ Methodo, nec non Summa Argumentorum varietate, explicantur, & demonstrantur* (Amsterdam, 1675), 240 fols.

——, *Iter Extaticum Coeleste, Quo Mundi opificium, id est, Coelestris Expansi, siderumque tam errantium, quàm fixorum natura, vires, proprietates, singulorumque compositio & structura, ab infimo Telluris globo, usque ad ultima Mundi confinia, per ficti raptus integumentum explorata, novâ hypothesi exponitur ad veritatem, Interlocutoribus Cosmiele et Theodidacto: Hac secundâ editione Praelusionibus & Scholiis illustratum; ac schematismis necessariis, qui deerant, exornatum; nec non à mendis, quae in primam Romanam editionem irrepserant, expurgatum, ipso Auctore annuente, A. P. Gaspare Schotto Regiscuriano e Societate Jesu, ... Accessit ejusdem Auctoris Iter Exstaticum Terrestre, & Synopsis Mundi Subterranei* (Würzburg, 1660), 689 pp.

——, *Itinerarivm Exstaticvm qvo Mvndi Opificivm id est Coelestis expansi, siderumque tam errantium, quàm fixorum natura, vires, proprietates, singulorumque compositio & structura, ab infimo Telluris globo, vsque ad vltima Mundi confinia, per ficti raptus integumentum explorata, noua hypothesi exponitur ad veritatem Interlocvtoribvs Cosmiele et Theodidacto* (Rome, 1656), 462 pp.

——, *Mundus Subterraneus, In XII Libros digestus; Quo Divinum Subterrestris Mundi Opificium, mira Ergasteriorum Naturae in eo distributio, verbo* παντάμορφον *Protei Regnum, Universae denique Naturae Majestas & divitiae summa rerum varietate exponuntur. Abditorum effectuum causae acri indagine inquisitae demonstrantur; cognitae per Artis & Naturae conjugium ad humanae vitae necessarium usum vario experimentorum apparatu, necnon novo modo, & ratione applicantur* (Amsterdam, 1664, 1665), 2 tomes, 345 and 487 pp., the first dedicated to the Pope, the second to the Emperor. Tome II, published a year before tome I, has a new title page, saying in part, *In V. Libros digestus Quibus Mundi Subterranei fructus exponuntur, et quidquid tandem rarum, insolitum, et portentosum in foecundo Naturae utero continetur, ante oculos ponitur curiosi Lectoris.*

——, *Turris Babel, sive Archontologia qua Primo Priscorum post diluvium hominum vita, mores rerumque gestarum magnitudo, Secundo Turris fabrica civitatumque exstructio, confusio linguarum, & inde gentium transmigrationis, cum principalium inde enatorum idiomatum historia, multiplici eruditione describuntur & explicantur* (Amsterdam, 1679), 219 pp., 2d vol. never produced.

Kirchmaier, G. Gaspar: *De Dilvvii Universalitate Dissertatio Prolusoria* (Geneva, 1667) 109 pp.

Lambert, J. Heinrich: *Cosmologische Briefe über die Einrichtung des Weltbaues* (Augspurg [Augsburg?], 1761), xxviii, 318 pp.

La Peyrère, Isaac de: *Praeadamitae. Sive Exercitatio super Versibus duodecimo, decimo tertio, & decimoquarto, capitis quinti Epistolae D. Pauli ad Romanos. Qvibvs indvcvntvr Primi Homines ante Adamum conditi* (?, 1655), 70 pp., then *Systema Theologicvm, ex Praeadamitarvm Hypothesi. Pars Prima,* but no second part, then *Synagogis Ivdaeorvm Vniversis, Quotquot sunt per totum Terrarum orbem sparsae,* 7 pp. but unnumbered. All anon.

Laplace, Pierre Simon Marquis de: *Exposition du système du monde* (Paris, 1813), 4th ed., vii, 457 pp.; 1st ed., 1796.

Le Brun, Pierre: *Histoire critique des practiques superstitieuses, qui ont seduit les peuples, & embarassé les sçavans. Avec la methode et les principes pour discerner les effets naturels d'avec ceux qui ne le sont pas. Par un Prêtre de l'Oratoire* (Paris, 1702), 637 pp.

Le Clerc, Jean: *Mosis Prophetae Libri Quinque, ex translatione Joannis Clerici, cum ejusdem Paraphrasi Perpetua, Commentario Philologico, Dissertationibus Criticis Tabulisque Chronologicis et Geographicis. Editio tertia auctior et emendatior* (Amsterdam, 1735), xxxviii, 1057 pp.; 1st ed. of Genesis, 1693; whole Bible completed, 1731.

Lehmann, Johann Gottlob: *Versuch einer Geschichte von Flötz-Gebürgen* (Berlin, 1756), 240 pp.

Leibnitz, Gottfried Wilhelm: *Opera Omnia* (Geneva, 1768).

——, *Protogaca, sive de prima facie telluris et antiquissimae historiae vestigiis in ipsis naturae monumentis dissertatio, ex Schedis manuscriptis viri illustris in lucem edita a Christiano Ludovico Scheidio,* vol. ii, pp. 181-240; 1st pub., 1691?

——, *The Philosophical Works . . . Comprising The Monadology, New System of Nature, Principles of Nature and of Grace, Letters to Clarke, Refutation of Spinoza, and his other important philosophical opuscules, together with the Abridgment of the Theodicy and extracts from the New Essays on Human Understanding* (New Haven, 1890), 393 pp.

Lilly, William: *An Introduction to Astrology. With numerous emendations, adapted to the improved state of the science in the present day* (London, 1887), xiv, 346 pp., ed. by Zadkiel; 1st ed., 1647.

Mallement de Messange, C.: *Nouveau systheme du monde* (Paris, 1679?), 21 pp.

Mallet, Allain Manesson: *Description de l'univers, contenant les differents systêmes du monde, les cartes generales & particulieres de la geographie ancienne & moderne: les plans & les profils des principales villes & des autres lieux plus considerables de la terre; avec les portraits des souverains qui y commandent, leur blasons, titres & livrées: et les moeurs, religions, gouvernemens & divers habillemens de chaque nation. Dediée av Roy. Par Allain Manesson Mallet, Maistre de Mathematiques des pages de la petite Escurie de sa Majesté, cy-devant Ingenieur & Sergent Major d'Artillerie en Portugal* (Paris, 1683), 5 vols., 10 books, profusely illustrated.

Marsh, Ebenezer Grant: *An Oration, on the Truth of the Mosaic History of the Creation; Delivered at New-Haven, on the Public Commencement, September, A. D. 1798* (Hartford, 1798), 59 pp.

Maupertuis, Pierre Louis Moreau de: *Essay de cosmologie* (Paris or Amsterdam?, 1750), 173 pp.

Mentelle, Edme: *Cosmographie élémentaire, divisée en parties astronomique et géographique. Ouvrage dans lequel on a tâché de mettre les vérités les plus intéressantes de la physique céleste, à la portée de ceux même qui n'ont aucune notion de mathématiques* (Paris, 1781), xxiv, 429 pp.

Mersenne, Marin: *Cogitata physico-mathematica. In quibus tam naturae quàm artis effectus admirandi certissimis demonstrationibus explicantur* (Paris, 1644), pp. 370, 96, 140.

——, *Les mechaniqves de Galilée* (Paris, 1634), 88 pp.

——, *Novarvm Observationvm Physico-mathematicarvm Tomvs III. Qvibvs accessit Aristarchvs Samivs De Mvndi Systemate* (Paris, 1647), 235 pp.

——, *Les prelvdes de l'harmonie vniverselle, ov qvestions cvrievses. Vtiles aux predicateurs, aux theologiens, aux astrologues, aux medicins & aux philosophes* (Paris, 1634), 224 pp.

——, *Qvaestiones Celeberrimae in Genesim, cvm Accvrata Textvs Explicatione. In hoc Volvmine Athei, et Deistae impvgnantvr, & expugnantur, & Vvlgata editio ab haereticorum calumnijs vindicatur. Graecorum, & Hebraeorum Musica instauratur. Francisci Georgii Veneti Cabalistica Dogmata fvsè Refellvntvr, qvae passim in illivs problematibvs habentvr. Opvs Theologis, Philosophis, Medicis, Iurisconsultis, Mathematicis, Musicis verò, & Catoptricis praesertim vtile* (Paris, 1623), 1916, 440 cols.

——, *Les qvestions theologiqves, physiqves, morales, et mathematiqves. Où chacun trouuera du contentement, ou de l'exercice* (Paris, 1634), 240 pp.

——, *Vniversae Geometriae, Mixtaeqve Mathematicae Synopsis, et Bini Refractionvm Demonstratarvm Tractatvs* (Paris, 1644), 16, 589 pp., in which pp. 257-272 are entitled " Cosmographia Astronomica."

Milius, Abraham: *De Origine Animalium, et Migratione Populorum, . . . Ubi inquiritur, quomodo quaque via Homines caeteraque Animalia Terrestria provenerint; & post Diluvium in omnes Orbis terrarum partes & regiones: Asiam, Europam, Africam, utramque Americam, & Terram Australem, sive Magellanicam, pervenerint* (Geneva, 1667), 68 pp.

Milton, John: *The Poetical Works* (London, 1862), vii, 527 pp.; 1st ed. of *Paradise Lost*, 1667.

——, *Tractate on Education. A Facsimile Reprint from the Edition of 1673* (Cambridge, 1890), xxv, 43 pp.; 1st ed., 1644.

Mirabaud, M. de: *Le monde, son origine, et son antiquité. De l'ame, et de son immortalité. Essai sur la chronologie. Seconde édition, corrigée avec soin* (London, 1778), 2 parts, xiv, 134, 181 pp., anon.; 1st ed. during the author's lifetime in 1751.

Moncharville, Pierre Julien Brodeau de: *Preuves des existences, et nouveau systême de l'univers, ov idée d'une nouvelle philosophie* (Paris, 1702), 62 pp., anon.

Ozorio: *Theologie cvrievse. Contenant la naissance du monde. Auec douze questions belles & curieuses sur ce suiet. Traduittes du Docteur Ozorio, Portugais, par le Cheualier de Iant* (Dijon, 1666), 166 pp.

Petermann, Andreas: *Gründliche Beantwortung der Freymüthigen aber ungegründeten Bedancken welche Ein unbekandter Censor in seinem Aprill = Monate Von der Vindicatione Philosophiae Cartesianae Ohne gebührendem gnugsamen Bedacht geführet zu Besserer Nachricht auff Veranlassung einiger Warheit liebenden entworffen Von Jano Aristophilo*, pseudonym for Petermann. No date, place, or numbers to the fourteen pages.

——, *Philosophiae Cartesianae adversus Censuram Petri Danielis Huetii Vindicatio, In qva pleraqve intricatiora Cartesii loca clarè explanantur* (Leipzig, 1690), 60 pp.

Pfleumer, Johann: *Dissertatio Theologico-Critica, de Aqvis Svpracoelestibvs ad loc. Genes. Cap. I. Vers. 6. 7. 8. . . . . Qvam Praescitv et Consensv Maxime Reverendi Theologorvm Ordinis, . . . Pvblicae Lvstrationi Exponit M. Johannes Pfleumer . . . 1663* (Jena, 1733), 23 pp., 3d reprint to satisfy many.

Pike, Samuel: *Philosophia Sacra: or, the Principles of Natural Philosophy. Extracted from Divine Revelation* (London, 1753), 150 pp., followed by a copper plate with its explanation, pp. 1-8.

Planer, Andreas: *Cometa. Coeli Pars et Partus* (Tübingen, 1682), 18 pp.

Plot, Robert: *The Natural History of Oxfordshire, being an Essay toward the Natural History of England* (Oxford, 1677).

——, *The Natural History of Staffordshire* (Oxford?, 1686?).

——, *De Origine Fontium, Tentamen Philosophicum* (Oxford, 1685).

Potts, Thomas: *Discovery of Witches Reprinted from the original edition of 1613 With an Introduction and Notes by James Crossley For the Chetham Society* (Manchester, 1845), pages unnumbered except for the introduction and notes, lxxix, 51 pp.

Raleigh, Sir Walter: *The History of the World. In Five Books. Viz. Treating of the beginning and first ages of the same from the Creation unto Abraham. Of the birth of Abraham to the destruction of the Temple of Solomon. From the destruction of Jerusalem to the time of Philip of Macedon. From the reign of Philip of Macedon to the establishing of that kingdom in the race of Antigonus. From the settled rule of Alexander's successors in the East until the Romans (prevailing over all) made conquest of Asia and Macedon. A new Edition, revised and corrected. To which is added, Sir W. Raleigh's Voyages of Discovery to Guiana* (Edinburgh, 1820), 6 vols.; 1st ed., 1614.

Ray, John: *Three Physico-Theological Discourses, Concerning I. The Primitive Chaos, and Creation of the World. II. The General Deluge, its Causes and Effects. III. The Dissolution of the World, and Future Conflagration. Wherein Are largely Discussed the Production and Use of Mountains; the Original of Fountains, of Formed Stones, and Sea-Fishes Bones and Shells found in the Earth; the Effects of particular Floods and Inundations of the Sea; the Eruptions of Vulcano's; the Nature and Causes of Earthquakes: With an Historical Account of those Two late Remarkable Ones in Jamaica and England. With Practical Inferences* (London, 1693), 406 pp., 2d ed. very much enlarged, corrected and illustrated with copper plates which have disappeared. 1st ed., 1692; but the sermons which served as basis for the book were delivered before 1660.

——, *The Wisdom of God Manifested in the Works of the Creation. In Two Parts. Viz. The Heavenly Bodies, Elements, Meteors, Fossils, Vegetables, Animals (Beasts, Birds, Fishes, and Insects), more particularly in the Body of the Earth, its Figure, Motion, and Consistency; and in the admirable Structure of the Bodies of Man and other Animals; as also in their Generation, &c. With Answers to some Objections* (London, 1759), 405 pp., 12th ed.; 1st ed., 1691, based on sermons delivered before 1660.

Riccioli, Giovanni Baptista: *Almagestvm Novvm Astronomiam Veterem Novamqve Complectens. Observationibvs Aliorvm, et Propriis Nouisque Theorematibus, Problematibus, ac Tabulis promotam, in Tres Tomos Distribvtam* (Bologna, 1651), 2 vols., each containing one part of the first tome. Perhaps the other two were not printed. At least it said that this tome was printed "now". Pp. xlvii, 763, xviii, 675.

Rohault, Jacques: *Physica. Latinè vertit, recensuit, & Adnotationibus Ex Illustrissimi Isaaci Newtoni Philosophiâ maximam partem haustis, amplificavit & ornavit Samuel Clarke* (London, 1718), 495 pp., 4th ed.

——, Another edition of the same, asserted to be a translation from the French (London, 1682). Obviously this could not be annotated with references to Newton. 2 vols. in 1, 253, 289 pp.

——, *System of Natural Philosophy, Illustrated with Dr. Samuel Clarke's Notes Taken mostly out of Sir Isaac Newton's Philosophy. With Additions* (London, 1723), 2 vols. in 1, 4 parts, 285, 292 pp., translated by John Clarke.

Rothius, Vitus Eberhard: *Astrorum Influentias in Humana Corpora Dissertatione Astronomica-Physica . . . proponet Vitus Eberhardus Rothius* (Delivered, Ulm, 1703), 67 sections.

Royal Society of London: *Philosophical Transactions* (London, 1665-1933), 231 vols.

Scheiner, Christopher: *Rosa Vrsina, sive sol ex admirando facvlarvm & macularum suarum phoenomeno varivs, necnon circa centrum suum & axem fixum ab occasu in ortum annua, circaq. alium axem mobilem ab ortu in occasum conuersione quasi menstrua, super polos proprios, libris quatuor mobilis ostensus* (Bracciano, 1626-1630), 784 pp.

Schroeder, Caspar: *Aqvas Supracoelestes à multis hactenus Doctoribus Supra Coelum Sidereum locatas* (Kiel, 1671), unpaged but really 23 pp.

Shuckford, Samuel, D. D.: *The Creation and Fall of Man. A Supplemental Discourse to the Preface of the First Volume of the Sacred and Prophane History of the World connected* (London, 1753), cxxxii, 295 pp.

——, *The Sacred and Profane History of the World Connected, from the Creation of the World to the Dissolution of the Assyrian Empire at the Death of Sardanapalus, and to the Declension of the Kingdoms of Judah and Israel, under the Reigns of Ahaz and Pekah: Including the Dissertation on the Creation and Fall of Man. . . . Revised, Corrected, and Greatly Improved, By James Creighton* (Philadelphia, 1824), 1st American ed. from the 5th London ed., 4 vols. in 2, wherein each of the four recommences with page 1 and is preceded by a preface. Between vol. iii and vol. iv is inserted a brief article by Robert Clayton, *Strictures on Dr. Shuckford's Account of the Heathen Gods, and Egyptian Dynasties before Menes; Preceded by a Short Account of the Manner in which the Egyptians buried their Dead; whence originated the Grecian Fable of Charon, his Bark, and the Stygian Lake,* pp. 3-11.

Spencer, John: *A Discourse concerning Prodigies: Wherein The Vanity of Presages by them is reprehended, and their true and proper Ends asserted and vindicated. The Second Edition corrected and inlarged. To which is added a short Treatise concerning Vulgar Prophecies* (London, 1665), 408, 136 pp.

Steno, Nicholas: *The Prodromus of Nicolaus Steno's Dissertation concerning a Solid Body Enclosed by Process of Nature within a Solid* (New York and London, 1916), 283 pp., with an introduction and explanatory notes by John Garrett Winter and a foreword by William H. Hobbs.

Sticht, John Christopher: *Dissertatio Philologica de Urbe Hanochia, ... ad Genvinvm Capitis IV, 17. Geneseos Sensvm Investigandvm* (Jena, 1727), after 16 pp. the dissertation has been lost.

Stillingfleet, Edward, Bishop of Worcester: *Works* (London, 1709).

——, *Origines Sacrae: or, a Rational Account of the Grounds of Natural and Reveal'd Religion. The Eighth Edition. To which is now added Part of another Book upon the same Subject, Written A. D. 1697. Publish'd from the Author's Own Manuscript,* vol. ii, 386, 116 pp. followed by *A Letter to a Deist In Answer to several Objections against the Truth and Authority of the Scriptures,* pp. 117-146.

Suarez, Francesco: *De Renovatione Mundi in 3 partem Thomae,* from *Works* (1630), 6 pages of which were quoted by Hakewill in pt. ii, pp. 332-337.

Swedenborg, Emanuel: *The Heavenly Arcana contained in the Holy Scriptures, or Word of the Lord, Unfolded, beginning with the book of Genesis: together with Wonderful Things seen in the World of Spirits and in the Heaven of Angels* (London and Boston, 1839-1848), 12 vols.

——, *Miscellaneous Theological Works* (New York, 1863), 526 pp., containing on pp. 321-416 *The Earths in the Universe, and their inhabitants; also, their spirits and angels: from what has been heard and seen. . . . Being a translation of his work entitled "De Telluribus in Mundo Nostro Solari, quae vocantur Planetae: et de Telluribus in Coelo Astrifero: deque illarum Incolis; tum de Spiritibus et Angelis ibi: ex auditis et visis"* (London, 1758), 178 sections.

——, *Opera philosophica et mineralia* (1734), vol. i of which was entitled *Principia.*

Swinden, Tobias: *An Enquiry into the Nature and Place of Hell. Shewing I. The Reasonableness of a Future State. II. The Punishments of the next Life. III. The several Opinions concerning the Place of Hell. IV. That the Fire of Hell is not metaphorical, but real. V. The Improbability of that Fire's being in, or about the Center of the Earth. VI. The Probability of the Sun's being the*

Local Hell, with Reasons for this Conjecture; and the Objections from Atheism, Philosophy, and the Holy Scriptures, answered. . . . With a Supplement, wherein the Notions of Abp. Tillotson, Dr. Lupton, and Others, as to the Eternity of Hell Torments, are impartially represented. And the Rev. Mr. Wall's Sentiments of this learned Work (London, 1727), 472 pp.

Thomasius, Jacob: *Exercitatio de Stoica Mundi Exustione; Cui accesserunt Argumenti Varii, Sed inprimis ad historiam Stoicae Philosophiae facientes, Dissertationes XXI* (Leipzig, 1676), 255 pp.

An Universal History, from the Earliest Account of Time to the Present: Compiled from Original Authors; And Illustrated with Maps, Cuts, Notes, Chronological, and Other Tables (Dublin, 1744), 7 vols., of which vol. i, through Babylonian History, contains xlii, 1022 pp.

Vancouver, Charles: *A General Compendium; or, Abstract of Chemical, Experimental, & Natural Philosophy. To which is added, a Complete System of Commerce. The whole digested into the form of distinct Treatises, comprehending the History, Theory, & Practice of each, according to the latest Discoveries & Improvements: Selected from the best Authorities in several Languages, from the earliest Ages down to the present Times* (Philadelphia, 1785), 4 vols., of which only part of the first was apparently printed. It stops in the middle of a sentence after viii, 48 pp.

Van Helmont, John Baptista: *Opera Omnia. Additis his de novo Tractatibus Aliquot Posthumis Ejusdem Authoris, maximè curiosis pariter ac perutilissimis, antehac non in lucem editis; Una cum Indicibus Rerum ac Verborum ut Locupletissimis, ita et Accuratissimis* (Frankfurt, 1682), 2 parts, 765, 275 pp.

The Vulcano's: or, Burning and Fire-vomiting Mountains, Famous in the World: With their Remarkables. Collected for the most part out of Kircher's Subterraneous World; And expos'd to more general view in English, upon the Relation of the late Wonderful and Prodigious Eruption of Aetna. Thereby to occasion greater admirations of the Wonders of Nature (and of the God of Nature) in the mighty Element of Fire (London, 1669), 68, 30 pp., part of the second section being in the form of a letter to the king by the Earl of Winchilsea, late ambassador to Constantinople, who on his return journey to England was an eye-witness of the eruption.

Warren, Erasmus: *A Defence of the Discourse Concerning the Earth Before the Flood. Being A full Reply to a late Answer to Exceptions made against the Theory of the Earth: Wherein those Exceptions are Vindicated and Reinforced: And Objections against the New Hypothesis of the Deluge, Answered. Exceptions also are made against the Review of the Theory* (London, 1691), 232 pp.

——, *Geologia: or, a Discourse Concerning the Earth before the Deluge. Wherein The Form and Properties ascribed to it, In a Book intituled The Theory of the Earth, Are Excepted against: And it is made appear, That the Dissolution of that Earth was not the Cause of the Universal Flood. Also A New Explication of that Flood is attempted* (London, 1690), 359 pp.

——, *Some Reflections upon the Short Consideration Of the Defence of the Exceptions against the Theory of the Earth* (London, 1692), 53 pp.

Webb, John: *An Historical Essay Endeavoring a Probability That the Language Of the Empire of China is the Primitive Language* (London, 1669), 212 pp.

Werner, Abraham Gottlob: *Kurze Klassification und Beschreibung der verschiedener Gebirgsarten* (Dresden, 1787), 28 pp.

Wesley, John: *A Survey of the Wisdom of God in the Creation: or a Compendium of Natural Philosophy. In Three Volumes* (Bristol, 1770), 286, 256, 242 pp., 2d ed., anon., printed in 2 vols.

Whiston, William: *The Accomplishment of Scripture Prophecies. Being Eight Sermons Preach'd at the Cathedral Church of St. Paul, In the Year 1707. At the Lecture Founded by the Honourable Robert Boyle Esq; With an Appendix. To which is subjoin'd a Dissertation, to Prove that our Savior ascended into Heaven on the Evening after his Resurrection* (Cambridge, 1708), 300 pp.

——, *The Cause of the Deluge Demonstrated: Being an Appendix to the Second Edition of the New Theory of the Earth* (London, 1714), 14 pp.

——, *A New Theory of the Earth, From its Original, to the Consummation of all Things. Wherein The Creation of the World in Six Days, The Universal Deluge, And the General Conflagration, As laid down in the Holy Scriptures, Are shewn to be perfectly agreeable to Reason and Philosophy. With a large Introductory Discourse concerning the Genuine Nature, Stile, and Extent of the Mosaick History of the Creation. The Second Edition, with great Additions, Improvements and Corrections* (Cambridge, 1708), 4 books, 95, 453 pp., dedication to Sir Isaac Newton.
First Edition (London, 1696), 95, 388 pp.
Sixth Edition (London, 1755), 95, 478 pp., the last twenty of which give *An Appendix, containing a new Theory of the Deluge.*

——, *Nova Tellvris Theoria Das ist: Neue Betrachtung der Erde Nach ihren Ursprung und Fortgang biss zur Hervorbringung aller Dinge* (Frankfurt, 1713), 560 pp.

——, *A Second Defence of the New Theory of the Earth from the Exceptions of Mr. John Keill* (London, 1700), 22 pp.

——, *Six Dissertations. I. The Testimonies of Josephus concerning Jesus Christ, John the Baptist, and James the Just, vindicated. II. The Copy of the Old Testament made use of by Josephus proved to be that which was collected by Nehemiah. III. A Reply to Dr. Sykes's Defence of his Dissertation on the Eclipse mentioned by Phlegon. IV. The Chronology of the sacred Scriptures, and the Truth of their Predictions confirmed by Eclipses and Astronomical Observations. V. Remarks on Sir Isaac Newton's Observations upon the Prophecies of Daniel and the Apocalypse. VI. A Demonstration that our Saviour's Ministry continued at least Four Years, occasioned by a late Dissertation on that Subject* (London, 1734), 355 pp.

——, *A Vindication of the New Theory of the Earth from the Exceptions of Mr. Keill and Others, with An Historical Preface of the Occasions of the Discoveries therein contain'd: & some Corrections and Additions* (London, 1698), 52 pp.

White, Thomas: *Institutionum Peripateticarum Ad Mentem Summi Viri, Clarissimique Philosophi Kenelmi Equitis Digbaei, Pars Theorica. Item Appendix Theologica De Origine Mundi* (Frankfurt, 1664), 206 pp.

Wiethof, Johann Hildebrand: *Exercitatio Theologico-Philologica, de Polytheoteti...ante Diluviana Occasione loci inlust. Genes. IV. 26* (Bremen, 1716), 40 pp.

Wilkins, John, Late Bishop of Chester: *The Mathematical and Philosophical Works ... Containing, I. The Discovery of a New World: Or, a Discourse tending to prove, that 'tis probable there may be another Habitable World in the Moon. With a Discourse of the Possibility of a Passage thither. II. That 'tis probable our Earth is One of the Planets. III. Mercury: Or, The Secret and Swift Messenger. Shewing how a Man may with Privacy and Speed communicate his Thoughts to a Friend at any Distance. IV. Mathematical Magick: Or the Wonders that may be perform'd by Mechanical Geometry. V. An Abstract of his Essay towards a Real Character, and a Philosophical Language. To which is prefix'd the Author's Life, and an Account of his Works* (London, 1707, 1708), viii, 274, 90, 184 pp., 1st ed. of I in 1638, 1st ed. of V printed by order of the Royal Society in 1668. I and II were both anonymous until after the author's death.

Witty, John: *An Essay towards a Vindication of the Vulgar Exposition of the Mosaic History of the Creation of the World. In Several Letters* (London, 1705), 182 pp., 10 letters.

Wolf, Christian: *Cosmologia Generalis, Methodo Scientifica pertractata, qva ad solidam, inprimis Dei atqve Natvrae, Cognitionem Via sternitvr. ... Editio Nova Priori Emendatior* (Frankfurt and Leipzig, 1737), 447 pp.

Woodward, John: *An Essay toward a Natural History of the Earth: and Terrestrial Bodies, Especially Minerals: As also of the Sea, Rivers, and Springs. With an Account of the Universal Deluge: And of the Effects that it had upon the Earth* (London, 1695), 277 pp.

——, *Fossils Of all Kinds, Digested into a Method, Suitable to their mutual Relation and Affinity; with The Names by which they were known to the Antients, and those by which they are at this Day known: And Notes conducing to the setting forth the Natural History, and the main Uses, of some of the most considerable of them. As Also Several Papers tending to the further Advancement of the Knowledge of Minerals, of the Ores of Metalls, and of all other Subterraneous Productions* (London, 1728), xvi, 56, 182 pp.

——, *A Supplement & Continuation of The Essay towards a Natural History of the Earth. Written originally in Latin: And now first Translated by Benj. Holloway . . .To which is prefixed An Introduction, by the Translator, Wherein are set forth Physical Proofs of the Existence of God, his actual incessant Concurrence to the Support of the Universe, & of all Organical Bodyes, Vegetables, & Animals, particularly Man; with Several other Papers, transcribed out of Dr. Woodward's Larger Work, & never before printed* (London, 1726), 169, 163 pp. The title page of pt. ii adds that objections to the theory, particularly those lately published by Dr. Camerarius, are answered.

Wright, Thomas of Durham: *The Universe and the Stars, Being an Original theory on the visible Creation, founded on the laws of Nature. First American Edition, from the London Edition of 1750* (Philadelphia, 1837), 158 pp., 9 letters.

PUBLICATIONS AFTER 1800

Almagià, Roberto: "Il primo tentativo di misura del rapporto quantitativo fra le terre emerse e i mari", *Archivio di Storia della Scienza* (1921), vol. ii, pp. 51-64.

Arrhenius, Svante: *The Life of the Universe as conceived by man from the earliest ages to the present time* (London and New York, 1909), 2 vols., xv, 268 pp., translated by Dr. H. Borns.

Büchner, Ludwig: *Man in the Past, Present, and Future: a popular account of the Results of Recent Scientific Research regarding the Origin, Position and Prospects of Mankind. Translated from the German* (New York, 1894), 349 pp.

Busco, Pierre: *Les cosmogonies modernes et la théorie de la connaissance* (Paris, 1924), 435 pp.

Cajori, Florian: "History of determinations of the heights of mountains", *Isis* (Bruges, 1929), vol. xii, pp. 482-514.

Cartailhac, Emile: *L'age de pierre dans les souvenirs et superstitions populaires* (Paris, 1877), 103 pp.

Clerke, Agnes M.: *Modern Cosmogonies* (London, 1905), vi, 287 pp.

Dalyell, John Graham: *The Darker Superstitions of Scotland, Illustrated from History and Practice* (Edinburgh, Dublin and London, 1834), vii, 700 pp.

Delambre, J. Baptiste Jos.: *Histoire de l'astronomie au dix-huitième siècle* (Paris, 1827), lii, 796 pp.

Draper, John William: *History of the Conflict between Religion and Science* (New York and London, 1928), xxiii, 373 pp., 1st ed. about 1874.

——, *History of the Intellectual Development of Europe. Revised Edition in two volumes* (New York and London, 1900), 1st ed. about 1861.

Eggleston, Edward: *The Transit of Civilization from England to America in the Seventeenth Century* (New York, 1901), viii, 344 pp.

Elworthy, Frederick Thomas: *The Evil Eye an Account of this Ancient & Widespread Superstition* (London, 1895), xii, 471 pp.

Fahie, J. J.: *Galileo His Life and Work* (New York, 1903), xvi, 451 pp.

Faÿ, Bernard: *Franklin the Apostle of Modern Times* (Boston, 1929), xvi, 547 pp.

Faye, H.: *Sur l'origine du monde—théories cosmogoniques des anciens et des modernes* (Paris, 1884), 257 pp.

Geikie, Archibald: *The Founders of Geology* (London and New York, 1897), x, 297 pp.

Grant, Robert: *History of Physical Astronomy, from the Earliest Ages to the Middle of the Nineteenth Century. Comprehending a Detailed Account of the Theory of Gravitation by Newton, and its Developement by his Successors; with an Exposition of the Progress of Research on all the other subjects of Celestial Physics* (London, 1852?), xx, xiv, 637 pp.

Greenslet, Ferris: *Joseph Glanvill a Study in English Thought and Letters of the Seventeenth Century* (New York, 1900), 221 pp.

Hastie, W.: *Kant's Cosmogony as in his essay on the retardation of the rotation of the earth and his natural history and theory of the heavens With introduction, appendices, and a portrait of Thomas Wright of Durham Edited and translated by W. Hastie* (Glasgow, 1900), cix, 205 pp.

Jéhan (de Saint-Clavien), Louis François: *Dictionnaire de cosmogonie et de paléontologie. Examen critique des systèmes anciens et modernes sur l'origine du monde, vues sur la création de la terre et des corps célestes et appréciations des théories cosmogonico-bibliques, descrip-*

tion stratigraphique, géographique, zoologique et chronologique des terrains fossilifères et de leurs étages. Histoire de la géologie, ses application aux arts, etc. . . . pub. by l'Abbé Migne as volume 48 of the *Nouvelle encyclopédie théologique ou nouvelle série de dictionnaires sur toutes les parties de la science religieuse* (Paris, 1854), 79 pp., 1462 cols.

Joly, N.: *Man before Metals* (New York, 1883), vii, 365 pp.

Lecky, W. E. H.: *History of the Rise and Influence of the Spirit of Rationalism in Europe Revised edition* (New York and London, 1910), 2 vols.

Libby, Walter: *An Introduction to the History of Science* (Boston, New York, Chicago, 1917), xi, 288 pp.

Macpherson, Hector: *Modern Cosmologies A Historical Sketch of Researches and Theories concerning the Structure of the Universe* (London, 1929), 131 pp.

Maigron, Louis: "L'influence de Fontenelle", *Revue d'histoire littéraire de la France* (Paris, 1906), année 13, pp. 193-227.

Mayer, Joseph: *The Seven Seals of Science An account of the unfoldment of orderly knowledge & its influence on human affairs* (New York and London, 1927), xiv, 444 pp.

Olivier, Charles P.: *Comets* (Baltimore, 1930), x, 246 pp.

Pettigrew, Thomas Joseph: *On Superstitions connected with the History and Practice of Medicine and Surgery* (Philadelphia, 1844).

Playfair, John: *Illustrations of the Huttonian Theory of the Earth* (1802).

Stimson, Dorothy: *The Gradual Acceptance of the Copernican Theory of the Universe* (Hanover, N. H., 1917), 147 pp.

Thorndike, Lynn: "Measurement of mountain altitudes", *Isis* (Bruges, 1927), vol. ix, pp. 425, 426.

Warren, William Fairfield: *The Universe as Pictured in Milton's Paradise Lost An Illustrated Study for Personal and Class Use* (New York and Cincinnati, 1915), 69 pp.

Weld, Charles Richard: *A History of the Royal Society, with Memoirs of the Presidents. Compiled from Authentic Documents* (London, 1848), 2 vols.

White, Andrew Dickson: *A History of the Warfare of Science with Theology in Christendom* (New York and London, 1910), 2 vols.

White, William: *Life of Emanuel Swedenborg. Together with a Brief Synopsis of his Writings, both Philosophical and Theological* (Philadelphia, 1874), 272 pp., 1st American ed., preface dated 1856.

INDEX

Active and passive principles, 52, 58, 101, 186, 339, 359

Adams, 287-290, 306, 316, 340, 354, 355, 359, 375

Adam's intellectual endowments and divine instruction, 66, 107, 108, 142, 145, 146, 149, 158, 164, 172, 194, 197, 202, 203, 233, 263, 292, 356, 459, 462, 463

Addison, 20, 69, 126, 140, 141, 337

Almagià, 401

Alsted, 45, 46, 49, 302, 309, 315, 316, 326, 327, 329, 335, 340, 341, 344, 352, 355, 357, 360, 367

Analogy, 32, 50, 55, 90, 96, 329, 357, 382

Angels, 25, 31, 77, 78, 137, 145, 154, 164, 168, 202, 279, 280, 357, 358, 365, 367, 382, 383, 398, 419, 420, 444
    Creation, 26, 47, 70, 176, 199, 339
    Fall, 26, 135, 137, 139, 180, 199
    Government of stars and planets, 30, 51, 62, 137, 163, 316-318, 343
    Habitation of earth before Adam, 279

Animals, 63, 117, 118, 148, 197, 208, 209, 212, 213, 216, 217, 222
    Creation, 27, 31, 46, 49, 58, 61, 64, 75, 84, 92, 93, 95, 96, 107, 117, 118, 139, 162-164, 171, 176, 189, 201, 202, 207, 208, 210, 212, 213, 216, 221, 222, 224, 232, 241, 258, 272, 275, 294, 357, 423, 428-430, 433, 435, 454
    Number of each species created, 96, 201, 202, 216, 221, 232, 233, 428, 429
    Number of species, 94, 437, 438
    Destruction of species, 61, 66, 94, 213, 220-222, 233, 272, 275, 276, 279, 433, 437
    Evolution, 61, 217, 220-222, 276, 294, 437
    Frogs, etc. created in clouds, 50, 426

    In the ark, 61, 94, 197, 233, 240, 437, 438
    Naming by Adam, 64, 66, 108, 139, 146, 149, 172, 197, 198, 202, 233, 240, 450
    New species created, 61, 66, 94, 220-222, 233, 433, 437

Antediluvian earth, 72-78, 80, 81, 83-86, 89, 117-121, 124, 129, 130, 171, 197, 224, 231, 233, 278, 279, 366, 416, 430, 457, 465
    Perpetual equinox, 75, 78, 79, 86, 88, 129, 139, 233, 430, 449

Aristotle, 28, 31, 34, 35, 54, 55, 63, 68, 147, 149, 150, 158, 169, 299, 313, 339, 353, 360, 384, 401, 402, 421, 466

Arnold, 443

Arrhenius, 183, 184, 205, 246, 248, 249, 300, 307, 314, 317, 322, 324, 370

Astrology, 28, 29, 31, 46, 50-56, 58, 62, 89, 93, 139, 143, 146, 149, 153-155, 158-160, 162, 163, 185, 250, 311, 312, 316, 323, 325-337, 356, 361, 382, 383, 420-424, 432, 437, 444

Atlantis, 60, 208, 397

Augustine, Saint, 71, 139, 313, 452

Authorities, dependence on, 42, 44, 60, 68, 79, 117, 133, 158, 280

Bacon, 21, 22, 309, 326, 351, 353, 362, 377, 382, 397, 419, 423, 433, 434

Barometer, 129, 402, 403

Baumé, 410, 422, 423

Beattie, 286, 287, 463, 464

Beaumont, 71, 72, 81, 83-85, 89-91, 195, 328, 329, 353, 383, 400, 406, 407, 416, 442, 446, 450, 455, 458

Becanus, Goropius, 461

Bellonius, 453

Bentley, 85, 110, 117, 118, 332, 336, 374, 384, 429, 434, 435, 441, 445

Beringer, 443

Berry, 109, 248, 249, 259, 316, 318, 320

Blackmore, 141, 175, 378, 434

491